PRINCIPLES OF *Chemistry*

THE MACMILLAN COMPANY
NEW YORK · BOSTON · CHICAGO · DALLAS
ATLANTA · SAN FRANCISCO

MACMILLAN AND CO., LIMITED
LONDON · BOMBAY · CALCUTTA · MADRAS
MELBOURNE

THE MACMILLAN COMPANY
OF CANADA, LIMITED
TORONTO

PRINCIPLES OF *Chemistry*

JOEL H. HILDEBRAND, PH.D., SC.D.

PROFESSOR OF CHEMISTRY IN THE UNIVERSITY OF CALIFORNIA

FIFTH EDITION

NEW YORK 1947 *THE MACMILLAN COMPANY*

PREFACE

This fifth edition, like its predecessors, has been written in a continuing faith in perfection as a goal but not as an achievement. This has necessitated repeated revisions; indeed, the present volume would hardly recognize its progenitor of thirty years ago. The changes have been, in part, of a pedagogical kind. In this I have profited, as heretofore, from criticisms by our own staff, whose members, senior as well as junior, have always willingly cooperated by taking quiz sections, but this time, particularly from suggestions gathered by the publisher at my request from users of the book in other institutions. I wish here to express my gratitude for the pains several of these teachers have taken. I have made most of the changes indicated by their friendly criticisms.

But changes and additions in subject matter have also been called for by the constant growth of the science itself. One who merely dips facts from a stagnant reservoir is hardly teaching science; rather, he owes it to his students to give them the impression of an onflowing stream. Chemistry is in such a fluid state that it lends itself readily to this purpose. Indeed, the young chemist needs the recent discoveries in atomic structure to illuminate physical and chemical properties. Conventional instruction in physics postpones this for a couple of years, but we can set this exciting story before him in the freshman year. We can escape the restrictions of what I have called, on page 80, the "chronological" order of presentation, according to which all the oldest knowledge must be learned first.

Of course, the intellectual appetites and digestive powers of different students vary enormously, far beyond the range between the traditional 60 and 100 per cent. Teachers should both teach and grade with the Gaussian curve in mind, and try to stimulate their best students to achieve not merely a fraction above but several times the average.

It seems worthwhile here to repeat an explanation of our practice in the University of California to allow for this wide spread. I have heard our plan of instruction questioned as too difficult for average students, but I believe we treat them with due consideration. Although we deliberately set before all students a far richer fare than most of them can assimilate, we do not expect everyone to tackle every item. One device is to distinguish the entrees from the hors d'oeuvres, as in this volume by the use of different kinds of type, and asterisks for the difficult exercises at the end of chapters. One of our weekly quizzes will contain decreasing credit, as in the following sample of a quiz given near the close of the first term:

1. Divide the following substances into three groups according as dilute aqueous solutions made from them are acid, alkaline, or neutral:

(1) KCl   (2) NH_4NO_3 (3) $BaCl_2$ (4) SrO   (5) $BaAc_2$
(6) $KHSO_4$ (7) NH_4Ac (8) $Al_2(SO_4)_3$ (9) NH_3 (10) Na_2CO_3.

Credit 30

2. State what you can about the concentration of H^+ in each of the following:

(1) 0.05 M-H_2SO_4 (5) 1 M-KAc   (9) 0.05 M-$KHSO_4$
(2) 0.2 N-H_2SO_4 (6) 0.1 M-$BaCl_2$ and 0.02M-HCl in
(3) 1 M-NH_4Cl (7) 1 M-NH_3 the same solution.
(4) 0.5 M-K_2CO_3 (8) 0.01 M-NH_4Ac (10) 0.01 M-HAc.

Credit 20

3. If a soluble base, MOH, is 0.4 per cent ionized in 0.2 molal solution, what are the concentrations of M^+, OH^-, and MOH?

Credit 10

4. What is the ionization constant of the MOH in the above case?

Credit 5

5. Set up the four equations from which you could calculate the concentration of OH^- in 0.1 molal MNO_3 solution.

Credit 5

Such an arrangement permits the ordinary student to get enough points for a "C" grade from two easier questions to prevent discouragement, but the student who earns an "A" grade must answer the difficult third, fourth, and fifth questions.

New chapters or paragraphs have been added on systems of acids and bases, polymers, trans-uranium elements, structure of inorganic compounds, silicones, and carbonic acid and its ions. The last of these offers excellent drill, both qualitative and quantitative, in the principles of equilibrium as applied to substances of great significance in biology, geology, industry, and the home.

I have given, in Chapter XXII entitled "Systems of Acids and Bases," a careful explanation of the "Brönsted Theory," along with the others. I fully appreciate the usefulness of this system for the purposes for which it is appropriate, but I have not used it throughout the rest of the book for two reasons: first, I regard it as better pedagogy to begin with the ordinary water system, extending to the proton-donor-acceptor system later for the special purposes of organic chemistry; and, second, because the other systems are equally "right" and so much more useful for certain purposes that the Brönsted viewpoint should not be allowed to usurp the field. I have stated the criteria in paragraph 18 of the chapter. A teacher in another institution has stated his experience regarding the pedagogic difficulties as follows: "At our institution I have been required to present the Brönsted definitions as *the* definitions of acids and bases. To avoid confusion and doubts, the students are not supposed to be made aware of the existence of other points of view. The students have great difficulty with the Brönsted concept. We make the presentation as simple as possible, then conclude that the students haven't grasped it, so we go over it again, and again. We spend an inordinate amount of time on it—and then recognize that the students have digested very little of it, so we ask practically nothing about it in the examinations. For the sake of simplicity we practically ignore the Brönsted con-

cepts in the remainder of the course. All in all, the result is a
mess. I believe the majority of our freshman staff agrees with
me in this conclusion, and I believe the Brönsted theory is
ignored completely in the analytical courses that follow. I am
decidedly *not* in favor of 'going Brönsted' in the freshman
courses."

Many new exercises have been added, and the answers
have been transferred to an appendix to combat the temptation to estimate them instead of working them out by analysis.

I wish, finally, to express my gratitude to my colleague,
Professor Kenneth S. Pitzer, and to my former colleague,
Professor James Arthur Campbell, now of Oberlin College,
for specific contributions, to Dr. Ralph R. Hultgren, Professor of Physical Metallurgy, for the prints for Figs. 3–6 in
Chapter I, and to my colleague, Professor Glenn T. Seaborg,
for criticism of the material on the trans-uranium elements.

JOEL H. HILDEBRAND

Berkeley, California

TABLE OF CONTENTS

PRINCIPLES OF *Chemistry*

CHAPTER I

KINDS OF MATTER

1. What Is Chemistry? The answer to this question, appropriate at the beginning of a book or a course, might be attempted in various ways. One would be to give a definition, which students could commit to memory and recite whenever called upon; a process which, from time immemorial, has been a prominent feature of education. The weakness of this method lies in the fact that definitions are often mere words, giving only the illusion of understanding to those who repeat them. Big subjects cannot be expressed at all adequately in sentence definitions. Dictionaries must give definitions but the full meaning of, say "friendship," requires an essay, a book, or still better, long experience. The scope of chemistry, similarly, is but dimly conveyed by its definition in the dictionary, and will be found by the inquiring student to be a continually enlarging and interesting subject. This chapter is intended to give only a partial exposition of the scope of chemistry, to be expanded throughout the entire book and through firsthand contact in the laboratory.

2. This distrust of definitions may seem inconsistent with calls for definitions that will be found in the exercises at the end of this and other chapters. The intention is not that the student should ransack his memory, but that he should endeavor, solely as an exercise, to put into clear concise English whatever degree of comprehension he may have attained at the time. A clear concept can be put into words, but words are no guarantee that the concept is clear.

Not all definitions are subject to the above difficulties. The units of length, volume, mass, time, and so on, are clearly defined, also properties such as density, specific heat, solubility, viscosity. It may be interesting, as we proceed, to

1

notice which terms are capable of rigid definitions and which are not. (Cf. Exercise 5 at the end of this chapter.)

3. Many teachers of chemistry have felt it necessary to define chemistry as distinct from physics. Such a distinction is arbitrary, unnecessary, and undesirable, as is clearly shown by the existence of a large common domain known as "physical chemistry." There is published a *Journal of Physical Chemistry* and also a *Journal of Chemical Physics*. This does not imply that there is no difference between chemistry and physics, but only that the differences lie in emphasis or in point of view, or sometimes only in the label on the laboratory in which a piece of work has been done. Our language is full of similar contrasting terms: bright and dull, rich and poor, blonde and brunette, fast and slow. These are useful enough, but the lines between them are either hazy or arbitrary. To a student no better illustration of this is needed than the grading practices of at least some of his professors.

We may now return to our question, What is chemistry? with the understanding that it is to be answered by no single sentence, propounded on the authority of the author to be memorized and recited by the student, but rather by a sort of aerial reconnaissance to get at least a preliminary and partial view of what is contained in the domain of chemistry. If we find that chemistry and physics, like the oceans, are separated by no recognizable line of demarkation, or if the line is purely arbitrary, like the Arctic Circle, we shall not expect to have to jump across it.

4. Substances and Their Properties. Chemistry is, first of all, concerned with substances, materials, or kinds of matter, such as wood, glass, iron, copper, clay, sugar, each recognizable by its inherent properties, such as color, taste, odor, hardness, density, etc. The names of substances must not be confused with the names of objects or articles, such as log, bottle, coin, brick, which are made of certain substances. Again, the forms which may be artificially imposed upon matter are not properties. It is a natural property of glass to become plastic at elevated temperatures, which permits it to be shaped into a variety of useful articles, but the glass does not assume these shapes of itself, hence they are not properties of glass. The only forms which are inherent, serving to identify materials, are the crystal forms which most of them are able to assume on separating as solids from the liquid or gaseous states.[1]

We use the more obvious qualitative properties of matter to identify the substances encountered in daily life: the color of copper, the luster of silver, the taste of sugar or salt, the

Properties (Partial List)

Absorption spectrum	Heat ot
+Boiling point	+combustion
+Coefficient of expansion	dissociation
Color	expansion
Compressibility	+formation
Conductivity for heat	fusion
Conductivity for electricity	ionization
Critical pressure	reaction
Critical temperature	+vaporization
Critical volume	Ignition temperature
Crystal form	Index of refraction
+Density	Luster
Dielectric constant	Magnetic susceptibility
Elastic limit	+Melting point
Elasticity	Odor
Emission spectrum	Reflectivity
Emissivity	Solubility
Entropy	Surface tension
Fluidity	Tensile strength
Free energy	+Vapor pressure
Hardness	Viscosity

hardness and transparency of glass, the melting of ice, the low density of aluminum. We readily distinguish solids, liquids, and gases. There are, however, many properties which are not evident to our unaided senses but which can be measured, often with great accuracy, by the aid of suitable instruments, such as electrical conductivity, refractive index, coefficient of expansion. Since chemists, physicists, and en-

[1] Cf. Latimer and Hildebrand, *Reference Book of Inorganic Chemistry*, New York, The Macmillan Company, 1940, Appendix V.

gineers have several hundred thousand different substances to identify and utilize, it is important to be able to measure all the properties with the requisite degree of accuracy. The table on p. 3 is an incomplete list of properties. The student would do well to be able to define or explain or describe a method for measuring as many of these properties as possible, particularly those marked by +. Use may be made of the Glossary in *Reference Book of Inorganic Chemistry*, p. 461, by Latimer and Hildebrand.

5. Chemical Reactions. Substances may change into other substances by processes called chemical reactions. Among the countless examples may be mentioned the rusting of iron, the burning of fuel, the fermentation of sugar, the explosion of gunpowder, the digestion of food, and the solution of silver in nitric acid. The ability of a substance to undergo a given chemical change is one of its chemical properties, aiding in its identification. Thus starch and talc may be distinguished by the fact that the former will burn in air but the latter will not. Silver will dissolve in nitric acid, tin reacts with the same acid to give a white insoluble powder, platinum will not react with it at all.

6. The quantities involved are often important to know. What weights of iron ore and coke are necessary to produce a ton of iron? What proportions of baking soda and cream of tartar should be used for a baking powder? It is part of chemistry to be able to answer such questions.

7. Or again, we may be chiefly interested not in the nature of the substances involved but in **the amount of energy** liberated in the form of light, heat, or mechanical power. We purchase flashlight cells for the electrical energy liberated by the chemical reaction that goes on in the cells while in use. In the manufacture of substances by electrochemical processes, such as chlorine, caustic soda, aluminum, and magnesium, the cost of the electrical energy that must be supplied is as important as the cost of the raw materials that must be used.

8. We may summarize our view of the field of chemistry up to this point by saying that **chemistry is concerned with**

substances and their properties; with the changes or reactions whereby other substances are formed; with the conditions necessary for bringing about or preventing these reactions; and with the relative amounts of matter and energy involved.

9. Various motives may lead one to study chemistry. More or less knowledge of the subject is essential for agriculture, engineering in all its branches, medicine, the biological sciences, and most manufacturing industries. Again, all persons whose minds are active feel lively curiosity concerning their environment. This environment is physical and chemical as well as social and economic. Again, chemistry if studied properly as a science gives unsurpassed training in the **scientific method,** one of the major intellectual achievements of mankind. Chemistry, first of all, has progressed much farther than certain other sciences beyond the era of mere description and classification; second, it shares with physics and astronomy a good deal of mathematical rigor, while presenting at the same time phenomena too complicated, as yet, for mathematical treatment and which must be dealt with by more qualitative methods such as are largely characteristic of biology. The scientific method, like chemistry itself, is not subject to brief, precise definition but it includes the search for pertinent facts, the planning and performing of experiments carefully designed to reveal new facts and relationships; the use of the imagination to form hypotheses, along with scrupulous care and honesty in subjecting them to the tests both of facts and logic. Such training has both moral and intellectual value and although it is difficult for man to transfer the lessons he learns from one realm to another, nevertheless the problems presented in other fields, particularly the social, political, and economic, are so pressing and complicated that both the desire and ability to attack them scientifically is of the utmost importance. It is the hope of the author that the students of this book will find not only that they have learned about substances and their transformations but will find themselves more inclined as well as able to treat scientifically, all problems, whether chemistry or not, which are appropriate for scientific treatment.

10. **Heterogeneous Mixtures.** As we attempt to apply our tests to distinguish substances, we notice that some

materials give a rather ambiguous answer. How shall we state the color, density, or hardness of a piece of granite? On close examination we find it composed of several kinds of minerals, having different degrees of hardness, different colors, and different properties in general. Although we might determine the density of a given piece of granite, it would be folly to regard this as the density of all samples of granite, because the components of granite are present in different proportion in different samples. Granite is obviously a mixture and not a pure substance, and its properties change abruptly at each boundary from one small region to another. **All of the regions of the same kind together constitute a phase.** In the case of granite there are three phases: quartz, mica, and feldspar. The freezing mixture used in making ice cream consists of three phases: all of the pieces of ice together constitute one phase, the crystals of salt another, and the salt solution the third. Some alloys, such as solder, appear quite uniform to the eye, as if they contained but one phase, whereas, by careful etching with acid and using a microscope with reflected light, it is evident that the alloy is heterogeneous, more than one phase being present. **A mixture containing more than one phase is called heterogeneous.**

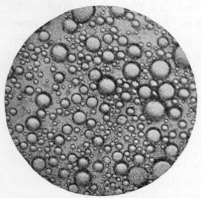

Fig. 1. Photograph taken through a microscope of a familiar heterogeneous system, oil emulsified in water by the aid of soap.

Evidently, then, the first step in our examination and classification of matter is to separate heterogeneous mixtures into their component homogeneous phases. This may be accomplished by purely mechanical means, which may vary with the nature of the separation. A suspended solid may be removed from a liquid by filtration. A fog (liquid particles) or a smoke (solid particles) may be removed from a gas by the same means. Two solids might be picked apart, though such a process would often be impracticable. Where two kinds of solid particles have different densities it is sometimes possible to employ a liquid whose density is such that one solid will rise to the surface while the other stays on the bottom, as would be the case if a mixture of sand and sawdust were thrown into water. Two liquids which do not mix, such as kerosene and water, are easily separated by skimming or some equivalent process. Where one is emulsified in the other, the highly dispersed globules of the one may often be made to coalesce prior to a separation, as when butter is obtained from cream.

11. Solutions. Having separated heterogeneous mixtures into single phases, our next step is the examination of these phases. We will find that a phase may consist of one pure substance, or of two or more substances, in which case it is called a **solution.** For example, we may mix sugar and water, two pure substances, getting a solution, uniform throughout in its properties, in which the sugar can neither be seen with a microscope nor filtered out. It is not distinguishable from a pure substance in appearance. It can be distinguished, however, by the fact that its properties depend on the relative amounts of its component pure substances. The properties of a pure substance are always the same at the same temperature and pressure. All samples of pure water have the same density, provided that the pressure and temperature at which the density is measured are kept the same. Ice always melts to water at the same temperature unless a different pressure is applied to it, and even then for every pressure there is a definite melting point. Similarly the boiling point of water depends only upon the barometric pressure. The properties of solutions, on the other hand, depend on the composition, as well as on the temperature and pressure. The properties of a sugar solution are not completely defined by the temperature and pressure alone, as is the case with pure sugar or pure water. In order to predict the density or sweetness of such a solution, or the temperature at which it would freeze or boil, we would have to know its composition, i.e., how much sugar there is in a given amount of water. In general, then, **the properties of a solution depend not only upon the temperature and pressure, but upon the composition as well.**

12. The experimental distinction between a pure substance and a solution is quite simple when the solute (the dissolved substance) is not volatile so that it is left behind when the solvent is evaporated. However, when both are volatile the matter is not quite so simple and it is necessary to find out whether any change in composition and hence in properties occurs during a change in state. By changes in state we understand any change between solid, liquid, and gas, such as freezing, boiling, condensation, sublimation, solution, or crystallization.

Suppose, for example, we wish to determine whether air is a pure substance or a solution. One method would be to

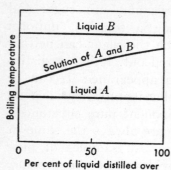

Fig. 2. Experimental distinction between pure liquids and liquid solutions.

liquefy a certain amount and then observe what happens to it as it slowly evaporates. As the evaporation proceeds one may observe that (*a*) the light blue color gradually becomes deeper; (*b*) the temperature of the liquid slowly rises (cf. Fig. 2); (*c*) the densities of both liquid and gas change; there is a gradually increasing attraction of the liquid by a magnet; (*d*) different samples of the gas given off show increasing power to support combustion. Any one of these as well as other possible observations show that air must contain two or more components whose relative amounts change during the evaporation, causing the observed changes in properties due to differences between the components in color, volatility, density, magnetic susceptibility, chemical behavior. Still other properties might have been used.

13. Solid Solutions. The term solution is not restricted to liquid solutions, although they furnish the most familiar examples. All gases are completely miscible with each other, forming but one phase, so that every mixture of gases is a solution. Alloys of silver and gold, no matter what the relative amounts of the two metals, contain but one kind of crystal, the properties of which, such as density, color, electrical conductivity, melting point, change continuously with the composition. This is a **solid solution,** and may be contrasted with alloys of copper and silver, which contain two kinds of crystals through a certain range of composition. This could be shown, first, by the microscope; second, by the fact that alloys of these latter metals, though of different composition, would all begin to melt at the same temperature. This is true because a change in the proportion of the metals produces no change in the nature of the two crystals but simply in their relative amount, and the melting and boiling points of substances never depend upon how much of the substance is used.

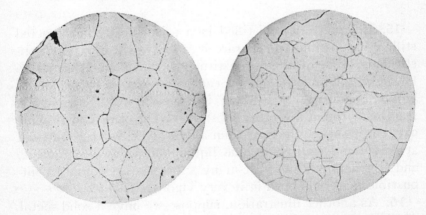

Fig. 3.   Hardened steel; a solid   *Fig. 4.*   Wrought (pure) iron.
         solution.

14. Hardened steel is a solid solution, for though it contains carbon it shows but one kind of crystal under the microscope, as shown in Fig. 3, just as does wrought iron, Fig. 4, which is nearly pure iron. Gray cast iron, however,

contains graphite crystals, as shown in Fig. 5, and is obviously heterogeneous, as is annealed steel, Fig. 6, which consists of an intimate mixture of pure iron, of the kind shown in Fig. 4, with an iron carbide.

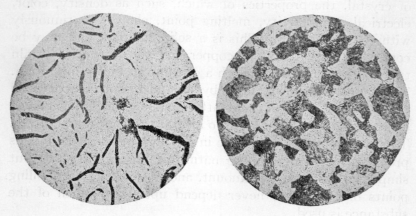

Fig. 5.   Grey cast iron.   *Fig. 6.*   Annealed steel.

15. If liquid air is distilled in a scientifically constructed still, it is possible to separate it into two nearly pure constituents. One of these constituents, **nitrogen,** is found to be slightly lighter than air; it can be condensed to a colorless liquid boiling at − 194° C.; it is very inert chemically, reacting with but few other substances. The other constituent, **oxygen,** is slightly heavier than air; it gives, when condensed at low temperatures, a blue liquid boiling at − 182.5° C., and it reacts readily with many substances. Ordinary combustible materials burn in it very vigorously.

16. As another illustration, suppose we have a solid metal which appears perfectly homogeneous under the microscope. We could determine whether it is a solution or a pure substance by melting it, dipping into the melt a suitable thermometer and letting it cool slowly, taking temperature readings at regular intervals, and plotting temperature against time. If the metal is a pure substance we would get a curve like a, Fig. 7, but if the metal consists of two components the curve would be like b, for the solid which freezes out would, in general, have a composition different from that of the liquid and the freezing temperature would alter with the composition.

The term "mixture" is applied loosely to the result of any mixing process in which no obvious chemical reaction occurs. A housewife may mix flour, baking powder, sugar, salt, and lard for biscuit batter while her husband mixes a cocktail. Both the batter and the cocktail are "mixtures," but their son, who is studying freshman chemistry, should be able to designate the former as a heterogenous mixture, and the latter, at least before an olive or cherry is added, as a homogeneous mixture, or solution.

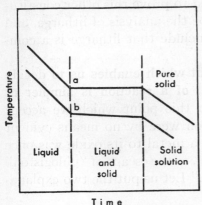

Fig. 7. Experimental distinction between pure solids and solid solutions.

17. Compounds and Elements. Having found out how to separate mixtures into their pure components, let us consider what further we may learn about the composition of pure substances. This question may be answered by means of appropriate chemical reactions. They may consist in producing the substance in question by direct combination of other substances, a process called **synthesis,** meaning putting together; or we may separate the substance into simpler constituent substances, a process called **analysis,** meaning taking apart. If molten lead is exposed to the air, it becomes coated with a scum, and if this is constantly removed, the lead entirely changes into another substance, called litharge, with a considerable increase in weight, indicating that something has been absorbed from the air. This would be the synthesis of litharge. Of the two main constitutents of the air only one, the oxygen, will transform the lead in this way. We would conclude from these facts that the litharge is composed of lead and oxygen, or, as chemists would say, is a **compound** of lead and oxygen.

18. On the other hand, we could put litharge into a crucible, heat it to a red heat, pass over it some illuminating gas, when we would find that it changed into lead, with a loss in weight. Evidently litharge contains lead plus some other constituent which has been removed by the illuminating gas. Further experiments might be performed to prove this other constituent to be oxygen. This would be the analysis of litharge, and from it, likewise, we would conclude that litharge is a compound of lead and oxygen.

19. **It is the change in weight which enables us to decide definitely whether the product of a reaction is simpler or more complex.** Conclusions on this point which we accept today with little or no question were by no means evident for a long time. The change of a metal to its oxide was once explained in a very different way, as the escape of "phlogiston" from the metal, leaving a "calx." Let us put the two explanations side by side as follows:

(a) Metal reacts to give calx + phlogiston,
(b) Metal + oxygen react to give calx + heat.

Some metals, including aluminum (powdered) and magnesium give off much heat, or even light, in changing to calx, and it is easy to see how this could be regarded as the escape of phlogiston at a time when there were no very clear distinctions between matter and energy. We may recall that the ancients considered earth, air, fire, and water to be the elements. Even Priestley, who discovered oxygen by forming mercuric oxide by heating mercury in air and then decomposing it in vacuum at higher temperatures, was so obsessed by the phlogiston theory that he explained what he had done in terms of phlogiston. It remained for the French chemist, Lavoisier, to weigh the metal and the calx and to point out that since the calx is heavier it could be more elementary only on the absurd assumption that phlogiston has negative weight.

20. If we pass an electric current through water, using platinum or gold electrodes to introduce the current into the water, we find that gases are given off at the electrodes and water is used up. If we collect the gas given off at the negative electrode, we find that it is very light, that soap bubbles filled with it rise like balloons, and that it will burn in air with a faintly luminous, very hot flame. This gas is **hydrogen.** The other gas is slightly heavier than air, will not burn in air, but burning substances thrust into it will continue to burn with greatly increased vigor and brilliancy. This gas is oxygen, also one of the constituents of air. From this analysis of water we may conclude that water is a compound of hydrogen and oxygen. The analysis might be made in many other ways. We might also synthesize water by allowing hydrogen and oxygen to combine, which they do very readily.

Now it has never been possible to resolve lead, oxygen, and hydrogen into simpler substances. These substances, and all others which have never by ordinary chemical reactions [1] been resolved into simpler substances, are called **elements.** Ninety-two are known at the present time. They can form almost endless combinations with each other; considerably over one hundred thousand are known and new ones are constantly being prepared.

Table 1 contains a list of the chemical elements. Many of them are well-known substances; many are rare, occurring in but small quantities.

21. Symbols. Along with each element in the table is also a symbol used as an abbreviation of its name. It consists of the initial letter of the name, followed, where necessary to distinguish between several elements having the same initial, by a second appropriate letter. In many cases the symbol follows the Latin name of the element rather than the English name, allowing the symbols to be practically the same in all the principal languages. Thus, the symbol for iron is Fe, from

---

[1] Certain elements decompose into others by a different type of change called radioactive, to be treated in Chapter XVII.

the Latin *ferrum*; that for gold is Au, from the Latin *aurum*, etc.

These symbols stand, also, for the smallest particle of each element called an **atom,** each having an exceedingly small but definite weight, called its **atomic weight.** The numerical values of these atomic weights depend upon the units chosen. The values in the table are in terms of the arbitrary number of 16.000 given to the weight of an atom of oxygen.

22. Formulas of Compounds. Symbols are combined in formulas to denote the elementary atoms present in compounds. For example, NaCl, is the formula of sodium chloride, common salt, and shows that it is made by combining sodium atoms, Na, and chlorine atoms, Cl, in equal numbers. Again, Fe_2O_3 is the formula of ferric oxide, familiar as the ore, hematite, the pigment, Venetian red, and the pigment or polishing material, rouge, and shows that it contains iron (ferrum) and oxygen in the proportion of two atoms of iron to three of oxygen. By using the atomic weights in Table 1, we can calculate, further, the ratio of weights, as shown in the following scheme.

Formula	Ratio of atoms	Ratio of weights
NaCl	$\dfrac{\text{1 atom of sodium}}{\text{1 atom of chlorine}}$	$\dfrac{23.00 \text{ parts by weight of sodium}}{35.46 \text{ parts by weight of chlorine}}$
Fe_2O_3	$\dfrac{\text{2 atoms of iron}}{\text{3 atoms of oxygen}}$	$\dfrac{2 \times 55.84 \text{ parts by weight of iron}}{3 \times 16.00 \text{ parts by weight of oxygen}}$

These matters are explained in detail in Chapters II, III, and IV.

23. Molecules. If a substance is a gas, or can be vaporized, or can be dissolved in an appropriate solvent without undergoing a chemical change, it is possible to determine, by experiments and deductions explained in Chapter IV, the groups of atoms, or molecules, which are capable of independent existence. One striking result is that the molecules of many elements do not consist of single atoms, but of various numbers, as illustrated by:

Helium	He	Oxygen	O_2
Neon	Ne	Ozone	O_3
Hydrogen	H_2	Phosphorus (active form)	P_4
Nitrogen	N_2	Sulfur (in	
Iodine	I_2	solution)	S_8

24. Molecular Weights. Molecules of compounds often are multiples of the simple numbers of atoms that weight ratios alone would indicate, e.g., H_2O_2 hydrogen peroxide; C_2H_2 acetylene; C_6H_6 benzene. The last two contain the same ratio of carbon to hydrogen but differ in molecular weight.

	Ratio of weights	Molecular weight
H_2O water	$\dfrac{H}{O} = \dfrac{2 \times 1.008}{16.00}$	18.016
H_2O_2 hydrogen peroxide	$\dfrac{H}{O} = \dfrac{2 \times 1.008}{2 \times 16.00}$	34.016
C_2H_2 acetylene	$\dfrac{C}{H} = \dfrac{12.01}{1.008}$	26.036
C_6H_6 benzene	$\dfrac{C}{H} = \dfrac{12.01}{1.008}$	78.108

25. Kinds of Matter: Experimental Distinctions. We may summarize the classification of materials presented in this chapter by the following scheme. It is not important to memorize it, but it is desirable to review the experimental distinctions that have been made in order to be sure that they have been clearly understood.

Kinds of Matter:
    Heterogeneous. Separable by mechanical means into
    Homogeneous.
        Solutions. Separable by changes of state into
        Pure Substances.
            Compounds. Separable by chemical reactions into
            Elements.

TABLE 1
The Chemical Elements

Element	Symbol	Atomic weight	Element	Symbol	Atomic weight
Aluminum	Al	26.97	Mercury		
Americium	Am		(Hydrargyrum)	Hg	200.61
Antimony (Stibium)	Sb	121.76	Molybdenum	Mo	95.95
Argon	A	39.94	Neodymium	Nd	144.27
Arsenic	As	74.91	Neptunium	Np	239
Astatine	At		Neon	Ne	20.183
Barium	Ba	137.36	Nickel	Ni	58.69
Beryllium	Be	9.02	Nitrogen	N	14.008
Bismuth	Bi	209.00	Osmium	Os	190.2
Boron	B	10.82	Oxygen	O	16.000
Bromine	Br	79.916	Palladium	Pd	106.7
Cadmium	Cd	112.41	Phosphorus	P	31.02
Calcium	Ca	40.08	Platinum	Pt	195.23
Carbon	C	12.010	Plutonium	Pu	239
Cerium	Ce	140.13	Potassium(Kalium)	K	39.10
Cesium	Cs	132.91	Praseodymium	Pr	140.92
Chlorine	Cl	35.457	Protoactinium	Pa	231
Chromium	Cr	52.01	Radium	Ra	226.05
Cobalt	Co	58.94	Radon	Rn	222
Columbium	Cb	92.91	Rhenium	Re	186.31
Copper (Cuprum)	Cu	63.57	Rhodium	Rh	102.91
Curium	Cm		Rubidium	Rb	85.48
Deuterium	D	2.014	Ruthenium	Ru	101.7
Dysprosium	Dy	162.46	Samarium	Sm	150.43
Erbium	Er	167.2	Scandium	Sc	45.10
Europium	Eu	152.0	Selenium	Se	78.96
Fluorine	F	19.00	Silicon	Si	28.06
Francium	Fr		Silver (Argentum)	Ag	107.880
Gadolinium	Gd	156.9	Sodium (Natrium)	Na	22.997
Gallium	Ga	69.72	Strontium	Sr	87.63
Germanium	Ge	72.60	Sulfur	S	32.06
Gold (Aurum)	Au	197.2	Tantalum	Ta	180.88
Hafnium	Hf	178.6	Technetium	Tc	
Helium	He	4.003	Tellurium	Te	127.61
Holmium	Ho	163.5	Terbium	Tb	159.2
Hydrogen	H	1.0081	Thallium	Tl	204.39
Indium	In	114.8	Thorium	Th	232.12
Iodine	I	126.92	Thulium	Tm	169.4
Iridium	Ir	193.1	Tin (Stannum)	Sn	118.70
Iron (Ferrum)	Fe	55.84	Titanium	Ti	47.90
Krypton	Kr	83.7	Tungsten(Wolfram)	W	183.92
Lanthanum	La	138.90	Uranium	U	238.07
Lead (Plumbum)	Pb	207.22	Vanadium	V	50.95
Lithium	Li	6.940	Xenon	Xe	131.3
Lutecium	Lu	175.0	Ytterbium	Yb	173.04
Magnesium	Mg	24.32	Yttrium	Y	88.92
Manganese	Mn	54.93	Zinc	Zn	65.38
Masurium	Ma	?	Zirconium	Zr	91.22

26. Classification of the Elements. The elements may be classified in various ways, any of which might be useful for certain purposes. Some of them are solids, some liquids, and some gases, at ordinary temperature and pressure. This is, however, not a very fundamental distinction, as each element may be made to exist in any of these states by suitable alterations in temperature and pressure. The most useful classification is that furnished by the Periodic System, whereby the elements are arranged in families or groups which show similar properties. This arrangement will be used very extensively later, after we have explained the basis upon which it is made.

One of the most useful divisions is that into metals and nonmetals. Several characteristics of metals and nonmetals are familiar to all. Metals are characterized by an appearance called metallic luster, by malleability and ductility, and by relatively high conductivity for heat and electricity. These physical differences are accompanied by fundamental differences in chemical behavior to be discussed later.

27. Kinds of Matter: Theoretical Distinctions. There is a second way of stating the above distinctions, one which seeks to account for them in terms of the atomic-molecular structure of matter. Although the statements of this structure in paragraphs 21–24 above are only very partial and preliminary, intended only to prepare the way for chapters that follow, most readers have already sufficient acquaintance with these things to make it worth while to restate the preceding scheme in these terms. Here again we have something to understand, structures to visualize, not simply a form to memorize.

Kinds of Matter:
   Heterogeneous. Different kinds of visible regions separated by sharp boundaries.
   Homogeneous. Visually uniform throughout.
   Solutions. Different molecular species irregularly mixed.

Pure Substances. Molecules all of one species.[1]

Compounds. Different atomic species within the molecules.

Elements. Atoms and molecules each of one species.

Exercises

1. Make as large a list as you can of the properties which serve to identify and distinguish substances.

2. What experimental evidence would serve to distinguish (a) a gaseous element from a gaseous compound; (b) a solid solution from a pure substance; (c) whether kerosene is a pure substance?

3. Many years ago the process of combustion was explained as the escape of "phlogiston." Thus metallic magnesium was supposed to give a white ash or "calx," with loss of phlogiston. What evidence could there be to contradict this theory?

4. Classify the following substances according to the above table, giving reasons; where you are not sure of the classification devise an experiment which would enable you to decide: concrete, air, tobacco smoke, well water, paint, glass, fog, salt, copper.

5. Define each of the following terms: phase, element, symbol, metal, substance, solution, property, compound, density, melting point, boiling point, chemical reaction, volatility, crystalline form.

6. Criticize the following definition: "Chemistry is the science which deals with the deep-seated permanent changes in matter."

---

[1] A substance containing molecules of different species will also survive a partial change of state without separation of these separate species if they are in rapid equilibrium with each other. Sulfur, for example, is usually regarded as a pure substance, in spite of the fact that in the neighborhood of 200° C. liquid sulfur contains both octagonal molecules of S_8 and chain molecules of varying lengths.

CHAPTER II

WEIGHT RELATIONS IN CHEMICAL REACTIONS—ATOMS AND MOLECULES

1. An examination of the amounts of material involved is fundamental to an understanding of chemical reactions. The practical importance of this has been referred to already in Chapter I, but we shall soon see that further consideration of these relations gives rise to theories and laws which lie at the very foundations of modern chemical science.

It is possible to approach this, like most scientific problems, in either of two ways. One may begin as a theorist, giving free rein to his imagination, as did the Greek philosopher Democritus (460–360 B.C.) and postulate that matter is composed ultimately of discrete atoms. The theorist may then deduce consequences of such a hypothesis and, if he is a scientist as well as a philosopher, test them by the most searching experiments he can devise. Or, one may start with experiments, his own and those of others, and work up to any general rules, called scientific laws, that can be perceived and ultimately devise a theory or picture which fits them. The former method is called deduction, the latter induction. The distinction is interesting, but a scientist is seldom conscious of the particular method he is using. Indeed, theory and experiment are usually a sort of double team, both members of which join in doing the work, although first one, then the other may momentarily pull most of the load.

Certain statements about atoms and molecules were made in Chapter I from which, after some further elaboration, many useful conclusions can be drawn, particularly about weight relations in chemical reactions. Every serious student of chemistry must practice calculations of weight relations till he has gained reasonable facility, whether or not he is altogether clear regarding the logical foundations of atomic and molecular theory. The matter essential to this task is set in ordinary and boldface type in this chapter and the two succeeding. The more inquiring students, however, are likely to desire not merely to use atomic theory for practical purposes but also to understand it. The portions in fine print are for them.

2. Law of the Conservation of Mass. Everyday experience teaches us that many changes in matter take place without any change in weight of the materials involved (weight being the usual measure of mass). Thus 100 lb. of ice, on melting, give 100 lb. of water; 1 lb. of salt dissolved in 10 lb. of water gives 11 lb. of solution; the weight of slaked lime equals the weight of quicklime from which it is made plus the weight of the water added in slaking. It is true that there is a loss in weight when quicklime is made from limestone, but that is because a gas, carbon dioxide, is given off, and if this were caught, compressed into a cylinder, as is often done, and weighed, its weight would be found exactly equal to the loss in weight when the limestone changed into quicklime. Similarly, although, when something burns, it may seem to disappear, that is only because gases are formed which escape notice. If a candle is allowed to burn in a closed vessel, no change in weight of the vessel and its contents can be detected.

As a result of vast scientific experience it may be asserted with great confidence that **in every chemical reaction the sum of the masses of the products is the same as that of the substances taken.** This is known as the Law of the Conservation of Mass, or sometimes as the Indestructibility of Matter. It has been tested with considerable accuracy in millions of cases, and with extreme accuracy in a number of them, so that there is hardly another scientific law in which we have such confidence.

A good balance can easily detect a difference of 0.1 milligram in 100 grams, or 1 part in 1,000,000. Few quantities can be measured with anything like this accuracy.

3. The Law of Conservation of Mass is violated appreciably only in reactions in which new atoms are formed, involving enormous quantities of energy, in which cases it is the sum of the mass and the energy that is unchanged. However, it takes enormous energy changes to have a detectable influence on mass, for 1 g. is equivalent to 9×10^{20} ergs. Another way of stating this is that 1 pound of mass is equivalent to 11,000,000,000 kilowatt hours. To make this relationship more real we may note that if 50 liters of hydrogen measured at 1 atmosphere and room temperature weighing 4.032 grams, were converted entirely into helium, the loss in mass would be 0.03 gram and the energy evolved would be 700,000,000 kilogram calories, enough heat to raise 7000 tons of water from freezing to boiling temperature. This heat is 5,000,000 times the amount that would be liberated in burning this same amount of hydrogen. Conversely, the heat lost in burning hydrogen, which is large as chemical reactions go, corresponds to a change far too small to detect on the most delicate balance.

4. The Law of Definite Proportions. It was pointed out in Chapter I that although there are many pairs of substances which can be "combined" to form solutions in continuously varying proportions, all solutions can be resolved into their pure components of constant composition by submitting them to fractional changes of state, including distillation, crystallization, and sublimation.

The existence of vast numbers of pure substances, compounds as well as elements, is a striking fact which can hardly be explained except on the assumption of atoms combining in some simple, definite pattern. If matter were continuous, as it appears to the eye, it would be hard to see why elements could not be combined in continuously variable proportions.

5. The varying ways in which the "law of definite proportions" is stated indicate some confusion with respect to it. Here is one: "A chemical compound always consists of the same elements in the same proportions by weight. This statement can be reversed to give a clear definition of a chemical compound: a substance which has a definite composition by weight is a chemical compound." Now a critical student may well object to defining two things in terms of each other as merely going around in a circle. Also, he might ask, will not a particular sample of sea water "always" show the same composition, year after year, if portions of it are drawn off and analyzed? The answer is, of course, yes. The composition of any particular solution is quite "definite." Another statement of the law is: "The composition of a pure compound never varies." The joker in these statements lies in the words "always" and "never." It is necessary to realize that something must have happened during the interval of time implied in these words, namely, one or more of the purification processes, natural or artificial, afforded by changes of state. The significant fact about the law of definite proportions is the existence of immense numbers of pure compounds whose properties, including composition, are identical for all samples from different sources.

6. The Law of Simple Multiple Proportions. There are many cases in which the same elements combine in different weight ratios to form different compounds. The following compounds of oxygen may be considered as examples:

TABLE 1

	Other element	Per cent oxygen	$\dfrac{Wt.\ oxygen}{Wt.\ other\ element}$	
Water ⎫ Hydrogen ⎬ peroxide ⎭	Hydrogen	79.9 94.1	7.94 = 1 × 7.94 15.88 = 2 × 7.94	
Rouge ⎫ Lodestone ⎬	Iron	30.06 27.64	.4298 = 9 × 0.04775 .3820 = 8 × 0.04775	
Litharge ⎫ Lead dioxide ⎬ Red lead ⎭	Lead	7.167 13.375 9.264	0.0772 = 1 × 0.0772 = 3 × 0.0257 0.1544 = 2 × 0.0772 = 4 × 0.0257 0.1021 = $\frac{4}{3}$ × 0.0772 = 6 × 0.0257	

The ratios of the weight of oxygen to the weight of the other element are in each case simple multiples of each other, that is, one can be obtained from another by multiplying it by a small integer or by a fraction containing only small integers. The compounds of carbon with hydrogen are so numerous that larger numbers have to be used, but they too are always integers. The above are no isolated cases, for all experience shows that in all cases in which two or more compounds of the same elements exist, the amount of one element combined with a fixed weight of the other in the different compounds can stand to each other in ratios of whole numbers, usually small.

The picture of matter as composed of elementary atoms furnishes a complete explanation of the laws of definite and multiple proportions, and is, indeed, the only reasonable one ever offered. We can feel as sure of the existence of atoms as if we could see them with the naked eye, for if the above table is not enough to convince a sceptic there is still more evidence available, as will be set forth in Chapters XVI and XVIII. We would expect certain simple combinations of unlike atoms to be the stable ones, giving "definite," reproducible proportions, and, if additional combinations are possible, they too should be simple, and hence simple multiples of the first. The water molecule was for a long time thought to have the formula HO, but we now know, for reasons to be explained later, that it is H_2O. If hydrogen peroxide is HO or H_2O_2, it explains the figures in Table 1. (The true formula is H_2O_2, as we shall see in Chapter IV.) Litharge is PbO, lead dioxide is PbO_2, and red lead is Pb_3O_4. (There is also a Pb_2O and Pb_2O_3.) Rouge is Fe_2O_3 and lodestone is Fe_3O_4. The weight ratios given in Table 1 all agree with these formulas when combined with the atomic weights, Chapter I, Table 1. Thus,

$$\frac{Fe_2O_3}{}$$

$$\frac{Fe_3O_4}{}$$

$$\frac{\text{Wt. oxygen}}{\text{Wt. iron}} \quad \frac{3 \times 16.00}{2 \times 55.84} = 0.4298 \qquad \frac{4 \times 16.00}{3 \times 55.8} = 0.3820$$

We have not yet proved that the above formulas are the correct ones and give them only to show that simple atomic formulas can yield the simple multiple relations observed.

7. The smallest group of atoms that can exist isolated from other like groups, as in a gas or in solution, is called a molecule. The molecule of a compound contains more than

one kind of atom. **The molecule of an element consists of one or more like atoms.** The atoms of the elements are designated by the symbols given in the table on page 16. For example, H denotes an atom of hydrogen. In hydrogen gas, a pair of atoms forms a molecule, designated H_2. Similarly the oxygen atom is O and the molecule is O_2. A molecule of water is designated by the **formula,** H_2O, indicating that it contains two atoms of hydrogen and one atom of oxygen. The evidence for these formulas will be presented later, our purpose at present being merely to explain the significance of chemical symbols and formulas.

8. Numerical Values of Atomic Weights. The actual weights of the atoms are exceedingly small, expressed in ordinary units, such as grams, and it is far more convenient to select a much smaller weight as unit, such as the weight of one of the atoms themselves. It is purely arbitrary which atom we choose and what number we assign to it, so long as we select corresponding values for the other atoms. Thus, knowing that the molecule of water contains 7.94 times as much oxygen as hydrogen, and granting that H_2O is the correct formula for it, we might call O = 100, when H would be 6.375, or again, if we let O = 1, then H = 0.063,75, etc.

The choice appeared a very simple one to most early chemists, who, finding that the atom of hydrogen is lighter than that of any other known element, decided to call its weight 1, corresponding to atomic weights greater than one for all other elements. Later it was found that the ratio of weights of the atoms of hydrogen and oxygen is not exactly 1 to 16, but 1 to 15.88, and that if we take O = 16.00 as our unit, making H = 1.008, the atomic weights of most of the other elements come out much nearer whole numbers than if we let H = 1 and O = 15.88. This is illustrated by the following sets of values based on the two assumptions.

Hydrogen	1.008	1.000
Oxygen	16.00	15.88
Calcium	40.08	39.67
Carbon	12.01	11.91
Lithium	6.94	6.89

Magnesium	24.32	24.13
Nitrogen	14.01	13.90
Phosphorus	31.02	30.82
Potassium	39.10	38.80
Sodium	23.00	22.83
Sulfur	32.06	31.82

An additional reason for the choice of O = 16.00 lies in the fact that but few of the elements form compounds with hydrogen, while nearly all form compounds with oxygen, and hence the atomic weight ratio between an element and oxygen can be determined directly, while the atomic weight ratio between the element and hydrogen could only be determined indirectly, and would therefore be subject to greater error.

9. The numerical values of the atomic weights permit us to extend the meanings of chemical formulas to include the ratios of weights of the elements contained in compounds. For example, the formula, CO_2, indicates not only a molecule of carbon dioxide, composed of one atom of carbon and two atoms of oxygen, but since an atom of carbon weighs 12, if the weight of an atom of oxygen is called 16, the molecule weighs 44 and contains 12 parts by weight of carbon and 32 parts by weight of oxygen. Furthermore, since this proportion, $\dfrac{\text{wt. carbon}}{\text{wt. oxygen}} = \dfrac{12}{32}$, applies to any molecule of CO_2, it applies to any number of molecules and to any units of weight. Hence we can write for CO_2,

$$\frac{\text{Wt. carbon}}{\text{Wt. oxygen}} = \frac{12 \text{ atomic wt. units}}{32 \text{ atomic wt. units}} = \frac{12 \text{ g.}}{32 \text{ g.}} = \frac{12 \text{ lb.}}{32 \text{ lb.}}$$

$$= \frac{12 \text{ oz.}}{32 \text{ oz.}} = \frac{1.000 \text{ g.}}{2.667 \text{ g.}}, \text{ etc.}$$

10. It is convenient to let the symbol of an element stand not only for one atom, but, alternatively, for one gram-atom, which is that quantity of the element whose weight in grams is numerically equal to the atomic weight. Since atoms are so small as to be invisible through the most powerful microscope, it is evident that the number of atoms in a gram-atom must be an extremely large number. There are, fortunately, several independent methods for determining it, all of which agree within their own limits of error. The best value at present is that **it takes 6.023×10^{23} atoms to have the weight of 1 gram-atom. This number is called the Avogadro Number,** in honor of the Italian physicist who discovered the principle that bears his name (cf. Chapter III, paragraph 20) and dispelled the confusion that once existed regarding atomic weights and formulas. The relation between atoms and gram-atoms is illustrated in Table 2.

TABLE 2

| | Weight of 1 atom | | Weight of 1 gram-atom, |
	In atomic weight units	*In grams**	*or 6.023×10^{23} atoms*
Oxygen	16.00	2.66×10^{-23}	16.00 grams
Hydrogen	1.008	0.168×10^{-23}	1.008 "
Copper	63.57	10.6×10^{-23}	63.57 "
Gold	197.2	32.8×10^{-23}	197.2 "

* The student who has forgotten the significance of the use of exponents for expressing very large and very small numbers would do well to get it clear, as we shall make frequent use of it. The following relations should help:
$$10^3 = 10 \times 10 \times 10 = 1000, \qquad 10^{-3} = 1/10^3 = 1/1000 = 0.001,$$
$$5 \times 10^4 = 50,000, \qquad 3 \times 10^{-4} = 0.0003, \qquad 100 = 1,$$
$$2 \times 10^{-23} = 0.000,000,000,000,000,000,000,02, \cdot \text{ etc.}$$

11. In like manner, **the formula of a molecule can stand, alternatively, for 6.023×10^{23} molecules, called a gram-molecule or mole, whose weight in grams is numerically equal to its molecular weight.** For example, the formula, CO_2, in addition to standing for 1 molecule, whose molecular weight is 44 atomic weight units, can also stand for 44 grams of it, which quantity contains 6.023×10^{23} molecules.

12. There are several ways of determining the Avogadro Number, the easiest to comprehend probably being the following. It is possible to measure the electric charge of a single atom or particle of negative electricity, called an electron, in the following way, devised and carried out with great accuracy by Dr. Robert A. Millikan, who received a Nobel Prize for his work. The method consists in holding a minute drop of oil, charged negatively by having acquired one or several electrons, suspended in an electric field just sufficient to neutralize the effect of gravity. The apparatus is shown in simplified form in Fig. 1. Oil drops are blown into the upper chamber by an atomizer and one has fallen through the hole in the bottom into the space between the two metal plates where it can be observed by a microscope. Electrons are produced by letting X-rays enter the chamber. When the oil drop has picked up an electron it can be kept from further falling by applying the

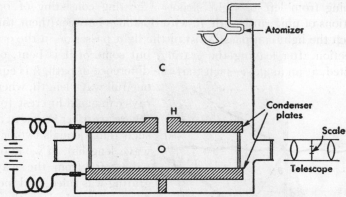

Fig. 1. Apparatus for determining the elementary charge.

proper charge to the electric plates, the upper one made positive. In order to determine the weight of the drop, which just balances the electric force, the charge on the plates is removed and the velocity observed as the drop falls. An equation, known as Stokes' Law, permits the calculation of the radius of the drop, therefore its weight, from the velocity of fall and the density of the oil. The gravitational force on the drop gives, in turn, the electrical force which balances it, and from the known electrical charge on the plates the charge on the drop is calculated. It turns out to be 1.6020×10^{-20} coulombs or some integral multiple thereof. This furnishes the most convincing proof of the atomic nature of electricity. It makes it possible, also, to calculate Avogadro's Number, for it takes 96,500 coulombs of electricity to deposit enough hydrogen atoms to give 1.008 grams of hydrogen, which is 1 gram-atom of it, and $96,500 \div 1.6020 \times 10^{-20}$ gives 6.023×10^{23}.

13. The most accurate method of determining the Avogadro Number is to compare the angle of diffraction of X-rays of definite wave length by a grating whose lines are a known distance apart with the diffraction of the same X-rays by the atoms in a certain crystal. A comparison of the two angles of diffraction permits the calculation of the number of atoms per centimeter along the edge of the crystal, and knowing the volume of a mole of the crystal substance by the aid of its density, it is possible to calculate the number of atoms it contains.

Figure 2 should make this clear to the reader unfamiliar with the diffraction grating. Parallel light of single wave length—X-rays— coming from left to right strikes a grating consisting of opaque portions of uniform length, d, with openings between them through which the light can pass. Most of the light passes on in the original direction after leaving the grating, but some of it is bent, or diffracted, at an angle, θ, such that the difference in path, l, is equal to one full wave length, where the rays can again fit crest to crest (there are other beams at angles such that l equals two or more wave lengths). If we know the value of d from the way the grating was ruled, and measure θ, we can calculate the wave length of the X-rays l from the relation $\sin \theta = l/d$. If we now substitute a crystal, where d' is the distance apart of the atoms,

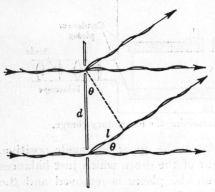

Fig. 2. Diffraction of light or X-rays; relation between angle of diffraction, wave length, and grating distance.

and measure a new angle, θ', since we know l for the X-rays being used we can calculate d'. The number of atoms per cm. is then l/d'. If the crystal is simple cubic, e.g., rock salt, NaCl, molal weight 58.46 g. and density 2.163, a mole cube would have a volume of 27.00 cc. with 3.0 cm. on each edge. The number of atoms (ions) along each edge would be $3.0/d'$ and the number in the cube would be $(3.0/d')^3$ which would be twice the Avogadro Number.

14. Weight Relations from Formulas. Let us at this point consider a sample calculation of the sort that we now have the basis for making. Suppose that we wish to calculate the amount of lead required to make 100 grams of red lead,

Pb_3O_4. We will assume that some process can be found whereby all the lead taken can be turned into Pb_3O_4, hence we can write the following series of logical steps.

3 atoms of Pb are required to produce 1 molecule of Pb_3O_4.

3 gram-atoms of Pb are required to produce 1 gram-molecule of Pb_3O_4.

3×207 grams of Pb are required to produce $(3 \times 207) + (4 \times 16)$ grams of Pb_3O_4.

621 grams of Pb are required to produce 685 grams of Pb_3O_4.

$\dfrac{621}{685}$ grams of Pb are required to produce 1 gram of Pb_3O_4.

$100 \times \dfrac{621}{685} =$ grams of Pb required to produce 100 grams of Pb_3O_4.

90.7 grams of Pb required to produce 100 grams of Pb_3O_4.

An alternative and briefer method of expressing the solution would be to state explicitly the idea of the proportionality of 3 Pb to Pb_3O_4 regardless of the amounts of the units used, as follows:

$$\frac{\text{Wt. lead}}{\text{Wt. } Pb_3O_4} = \frac{3 \times 207 \text{ g.}}{685 \text{ g.}} = \frac{x \text{ g.}}{100 \text{ g.}},$$

whence

$$x = \frac{100 \times 621}{685} = 90.7 \text{ g.}$$

15. A third form is much used in books on chemistry, $685 : 621 : : 100 : x$. This too readily becomes a purely formal procedure, the basis for which is often not understood by the student; there is nothing in it as written to show why it should not be $685 : 621 : : x : 100$; and it is likely to be worked by a rule divorced from ordinary algebraic procedure. It is highly desirable to be freed as much as possible from mere rules, blindly accepted. A person may be trained to rival a computing machine in carrying out operations by some sort of formal procedure that he does not understand, but if he is to be educated he must learn how to anlayze problems for himself, starting from the pertinent data given and at his command; obtaining a clear view of the answer desired, which is the objective; and proceeding towards it by a series of logical steps, like a man crossing a stream by a series of stepping stones. The first method given above is a sample of such a series of steps, chosen to require very small logical jumps; many persons could take bigger ones. But this, like the second, and logically equivalent one, indicates the reasoning involved, simple as it is. The steps can be easily checked and the units are shown.

16. Chemical Equations. When a chemical reaction takes place there is a rearrangement of atoms into new groups, or molecules, forming new substances. This is indicated by a chemical equation, in which the rearrangement is shown by the regrouping of the atomic symbols to represent the new molecular species formed. For example, the formation of iron and carbon dioxide, CO_2, from the ore Fe_2O_3 by the action of carbon monoxide, CO, is represented by the equation

$$Fe_2O_3 + 3CO = 2Fe + 3CO_2.$$

The following facts may be noted about such an equation:

First, an equation states nothing about the conditions necessary for carrying out the reaction, and the mere writing of an equation does not imply that the reaction it represents can actually be realized.

Second, it must represent the fact that no matter disappears, by showing the same number of atoms of each element on both sides of the equation, though they are arranged in different molecules.

Third, it represents the relative number of molecules of each substance taking part in the reaction.

Fourth, it represents the relative weights of each substance, which can be readily computed with the aid of the table of atomic weights.

The above equation, then, may be read as follows: 1 molecule of ferric oxide reacts with 3 molecules of carbon monoxide to yield 2 molecules (or atoms) of iron and 3 molecules of carbon dioxide; also, $2 \times 56 + 3 \times 16$ **parts (by weight)** of iron oxide react with $3(12 + 16)$ parts of carbon monoxide to give 2×56 parts of iron and $3(12 + 32)$ parts of carbon dioxide. These parts by weight may be in any kind of weight unit, pounds, tons, ounces, grams, etc. In accordance with our double usage of the symbols and formulas to represent not only single atoms and molecules, but also gram-atoms and gram-molecules, or moles, as explained on page 26, we often read an equation in terms of grams; hence, 160 g. of iron oxide, when reacting with 84 g. of carbon monoxide, give 112 g. of iron and 132 g. of carbon dioxide, which quantities represent 1 mole, 3 moles, 2 moles, and 3 moles respectively.

This may be summarized briefly by writing under each formula in the equation its complete meaning in both of the above senses.

	Fe_2O_3	+ 3CO	= 2Fe	+ $3CO_2$
(1) Number of molecules	1	3	2	3
Weight, in terms of one-sixteenth the weight of an oxygen atom	160	84	112	132
(2) Number of moles	1	3	2	3
Weight	160 g.	84 g.	112 g.	132 g.

17. Calculation of Weight Relations. The meaning thus attached to chemical formulas and equations makes it possible to calculate the weights of all the other substances involved in a chemical reaction from the weight given for any one of them. Suppose, for example, that it is required to find the weight of iron that should be obtained from 100 lb. of the oxide of iron considered above. From the weights implied by the formulas, as explained above, we may write the following:

160 g. of Fe_2O_3 gives 112 g. of Fe.

160 lb. of Fe_2O_3 gives 112 lb. of Fe.

1 lb. of Fe_2O_3 gives $\dfrac{112}{160}$ lb. of Fe.

100 lb. of Fe_2O_3 gives $\dfrac{100 \times 112}{160} = 70$ lb. of **Fe.**

Again, suppose we wish to find the amount of coke, containing 80 per cent carbon, the rest being ash, that is required to reduce to iron the above amount of ore. From the weights implied in the equation, we can say that

1 mole Fe_2O_3 requires 3 moles CO, which requires
3 gram-atoms of C.

160 lb. Fe_2O_3 requires 36 lb. C.

100 lb. Fe_2O_3 requires $\dfrac{100}{160} \times 36 = 22.5$ lb. C.

22.5 lb. C is 80 per cent or $\dfrac{80}{100}$ of the coke required, which

is $\dfrac{100}{80} \times 22.5$ lb. $= 28.1$ lb.

This connection between atomic weights, formulas, and relative weights of substances may be used not only to calculate the relative weights from the formulas and atomic weights, as above, but also to calculate the atomic weights when the formulas and suitable weight relations are known, or again, to determine formulas when the other two factors are known.

18. Calculation of Atomic Weights. As an example of the calculation of atomic weights let us suppose that we know the formula of a certain oxide of copper to be Cu_2O and find on analysis that 0.5120 g. of it contains 0.4548 g. of copper, and wish to calculate the atomic weight of copper, provisionally called x. We may arrange the steps in the reasoning as follows:

Given by formula	Cu_2O contains	2 Cu and	1 O
Given weights, by analysis	0.512 g. —	0.4548 g. =	0.0572 g.
Given relative no. gram-atoms from formula		2	1
Wts. in 1 mole of Cu_2O from formula		$2x$ g.	16 g.
Wts. in 1 mole of Cu_2O from analysis		$\dfrac{16}{0.0572} \times 0.4548$ g.	16 g.

Comparing the last two figures in the column for copper both represent the copper combined with 16 g. of oxygen, hence they are equal, and

$$2x = \frac{16}{0.0572} \times 0.4548 \text{ g., or } x = 63.6 \text{ g.,}$$

hence the atomic weight of copper is 63.6.

19. Calculation of Formulas. The third case consists in calculating the formula when the other two factors, atomic weight and composition, are known. Suppose that we find on analysis that a certain chloride of arsenic contains 58.68 per cent of chlorine, and know the atomic weight of arsenic, As = 74.91, and chlorine, Cl = 35.46, and wish to determine the formula of the compound. Now the formula indicates the number of atoms, or of gram-atoms, in the molecule, or mole, repectively, so that we may proceed to determine the number of gram-atoms of one element combined with 1 gram-atom of the other.

Given, 58.68 g. Cl combine with 41.32 g. As to yield 100.0 g. of compound, then

$$35.46 \text{ g. Cl combine with } \frac{35.46}{58.68} \times 41.32 = 24.970 \text{ g. As,}$$

or 1 gram-atom Cl, combine with $\frac{24.97}{74.91} = 0.3334$ or almost

exactly $\frac{1}{3}$ gram-atom As (analyses are, of course, subject to small errors), or 3 gram-atoms Cl combine with 1 gram-atom As, and 3 atoms Cl combine with 1 atom As; therefore the simplest possible formula is $AsCl_3$.

The above weight relations would, however, be equally satisfied by the formulas As_2Cl_6, As_3Cl_9, etc., and before deciding upon $AsCl_3$ we shall have to determine the weight of 1 mole, for 1 mole of $AsCl_3$ would weight 181.23 g., while 1 mole of As_2Cl_6 would weigh twice as much. (Chapter IV deals with the problem of molecular weights.)

The simplest formula that fits the figures obtained from analysis is often called the **empirical formula,** the word "empirical" meaning based on experiment or experience rather than upon theory, or full scientific knowledge. In this case, however, the experiment is incomplete, calling for further experiment to determine molecular weight.

Exercises

See Appendix 2 for answers.

1. What do you understand by the law of simple multiple proportions?

2. How does the atomic theory explain this law?

3. Write out in words all that the following formulas mean to you: H_2O; H_2O_2; $Ca(OH)_2$; $FeSO_4$.

4. Define symbol, formula, chemical reaction, chemical equation, mole, molecule, atom.

5. How many atoms of oxygen are in 1 molecule of $Ca(OH)_2$?

6. How many gram-atoms of lead (Pb) are in 2 moles of Pb_3O_4?

7. How many gram-atoms of oxygen would be used up in converting 1 gram-atom of lead into Pb_3O_4?

8. PbO_2 can be made from Pb_3O_4 by the reaction:

$$Pb_3O_4 + 4H^+ = PbO_2 + 2H_2O + 2Pb^{++}.$$

How many pounds of PbO_2 could be obtained from 100 lb. of Pb_3O_4?

9. How many gram-atoms of sulfur are there in 196 g. of sulfuric acid, H_2SO_4?

10. What weight of water could be obtained from 1.00 g. of Cu_2O?

11. How much water would be required to convert 100 g. of phosphorus pentoxide, P_2O_5, into phosphoric acid, the equation being: $3H_2O + P_2O_5 = 2H_3PO_4$?

12. What per cent of Al_2O_3 is aluminum?

13. What weight of aluminum, Al, must be used per kilogram of iron oxide, Fe_3O_4, to carry out the reaction: $8Al + 3Fe_3O_4 = 4Al_2O_3 + 9Fe$?

14. When treated with hydrochloric acid, barium peroxide yields hydrogen peroxide according to the following equation: $BaO_2 + 2HCl = H_2O_2 + BaCl_2$. How much BaO_2 is required to make 10 lb. of a 5 per cent solution of H_2O_2?

15. What weight of aluminum could be dissolved by 196 g. of sulfuric acid, H_2SO_4? The equation is: $2Al + 3H_2SO_4 = Al_2(SO_4)_3 + 3H_2$.

16. What weight of Fe_2O_3 would result upon burning 10 kilograms of FeS_2? The equation for the reaction is: $4FeS_2 + 11O_2 = 2Fe_2O_3 + 8SO_2$.

17. A certain compound of sulfur and oxygen only was found by analysis to contain 2.00 g. of sulfur and 3.00 g. of oxygen. (*a*) How many grams of oxygen, (*b*) how many gram-atoms of oxygen would be combined with one gram-atom of sulfur in this compound?

18. Since engineers use the avoirdupois units, including pounds, more often than metric units, it is possible to use pound-atoms and pound-molecules. Define them, give their relation to gram-atoms and gram-molecules, and calculate the number of atoms in a pound-atom. (1 lb. = 453.6 g.)

CHAPTER III

THE KINETIC THEORY

1. Common Properties of Gases. While we are discussing the general properties of substances it will be profitable to consider certain properties of gases, on account of the existence of important uniformities in their behavior from which we can learn much about molecules. When solids and liquids are heated, they expand, in nearly all cases, but the rate of expansion with the temperature is a specific property of each substance. The same holds true for the compressibility of solids and liquids. With gases, however, the effect upon the volume of changing temperature or pressure is nearly independent of the particular gas used. This is illustrated by the accompanying table.

TABLE 1
Increase in Volume When 1 Cubic Centimeter of Material at 0° C. Is Heated to 1° C.

Gases		Liquids	
Acetylene	0.003,77	Alcohol	0.001,05
Ammonia	.003,75	Chloroform	.001,21
Argon	.003,68	Ether	.001,56
Carbon monoxide	.003,67	Mercury	.000,18
Chlorine	.003,90	Water	.000,06
Helium	.003,66	*Solids*	
Hydrogen	.003,66	Common salt	.000,032
Methane	.003,68	Copper	.000,017
Oxygen	.003,66	Diamond	.000,000,27

Similar regularity with gases is evident on examining the compressibility, i.e., the relative decrease in volume on applying pressure.

A further distinction between gases, on one hand, and liquids and solids, on the other, is their tendency to expand indefinitely, so as to fill completely any space at their disposal, always exerting pressure on the walls of the containing vessel.

Again, the rate of diffusion of one gas through another is vastly more rapid than diffusion through a liquid or through a solid, in which case, indeed, measurable diffusion is very rare, as illustrated by sharp boundaries in rocks between minerals which have been in contact for millions of years.

2. Now these characteristics of gases are such as to excite the curiosity of persons having the scientific attitude as to *why* gases behave as they do. We may also wish to be in a position to predict more accurately than we can from the above meager information *how* they behave. The former question is theoretical, the latter immediately practical. We may choose to begin by speculating regarding the answer to the former, or by performing a series of careful experiments to reveal the latter. The former course should yield a theory, the latter the "gas laws." Science advances by using either avenue of approach, now the one, now the other, or both together.

3. The student might, at this point, go into the laboratory and work out by well-controlled experiments the relations between pressure, volume, temperature, mass, and molecular weight of one gas; satisfy himself that the formulas obtained are applicable to a number of gases and hence, probably, to all gases. This is the inductive approach already referred to in Chapter II; it starts with particular cases and leads up to general laws which are essentially descriptions of behavior. The other approach is to construct some theory, model, or picture, of the possible structure of gases in this case, from which the behavior of individual gases could be inferred by deduction. All the various consequences of the theory should, of course, be tested by experiment before it should be given any great scientific standing.

4. In the present case, the latter approach will be emphasized because the resulting theory is a powerful tool for dealing with other more complicated matters, such as the control of chemical reactions. If it were merely a question

of gas behavior, we might leave the whole matter to the physicists, but the theory is of such value to chemists, and so illuminating, indeed, to anyone interested in his physical environment that practice in working it into one's active imagination is rather sure to be rewarding. It is, at least, a labor saver, for it leads so obviously to the correct arithmetical treatment of gas problems as to make it unnecessary to commit to memory formulas almost certain to be misapplied or forgotten.

5. Let us ask the question. What sort of structure must gases possess in order to account for their general properties? The most satisfactory picture is that furnished by the **Kinetic Theory,** which assumes that a gas is composed of particles called **molecules,** whose size is very small compared with the distance between them, and that each molecule is in rapid motion, colliding with other molecules and with the walls of the containing vessel.[1] It is these impacts which produce the observed pressure, a rapid series of impacts obviously having the effect of a steady pressure. The further assumption is made that the average velocity of the molecules, and hence the pressure produced upon the walls of the vessel, depends upon the temperature, increasing as the latter increases. The molecules are in such rapid motion, and are most of the time so far apart, relatively, that their mutual attractions have very little effect.

This picture of the condition of gases has proved to be of such immense service in explaining and predicting their properties that it is hardly questioned by scientists at the present time.

6. **Relation between Quantity and Pressure When Volume and Temperature Are Constant.** Let us see first, how, on the basis of the theory just given, we should expect changes in

---

[1] An idea of the actual values calculated may be obtained from the following figures for oxygen. At one atmosphere pressure and 0° C., one cubic centimeter of oxygen contains 27×10^{18} molecules, moving with an average velocity of 0.46 kilometer per second (about ⅓ mile per second). Each molecule travels on an average about 1000 times its own diameter before colliding with another molecule.

the amount of a gas to be related numerically to changes in pressure. Imagine a gas inclosed in a vessel provided with a cock, as represented in Fig. 1*a*. The vessel is supposed to be immersed in a bath to preserve constant temperature. Let us have very few molecules in the vessel, and visualize them by the dots in the figure. These molecules will all be in rapid rectilinear motion, some moving faster, some more slowly, between impacts, but with a certain average velocity depending on the temperature, producing a definite pressure on the vessel walls as they rebound from them. Suppose, now, that we introduce an equal number of the same kind of molecules through the valve, producing the condition illustrated in Fig. 1*b*. It is obvious that since the volume of the vessel remains the same, and the average speed of the molecules

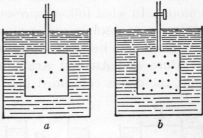

Fig. 1

is kept the same by the action of the bath in maintaining constant temperature, the only effect of the doubling of the amount of gas is merely to double the number of impacts in a given time per unit of area of the vessel walls, and hence to double the pressure. Evidently we would expect any change in the number of molecules in the vessel to produce a proportional change in the pressure, and since the number of molecules depends on the amount of the gas, we can make the general deduction that **when temperature and volume are kept constant the pressure of a gas is proportional to the quantity present.**

As an example of how this may be applied let us consider a tank, with an attached pressure gauge, containing any gas. Allow the gas to escape until the pressure falls from 100 lb. per square inch to 30 lb. It is evident, since the pressure has fallen to 0.3 of its initial value, that there remains in the tank only 0.3 of the gas originally present. Many pressure gauges give, not the absolute pressure, upon which this discussion is based, but only the excess over atmospheric pressure. A familiar example is a tire pressure gauge, reading zero, not when the pressure is zero but when it is the same as the outside atmospheric pressure, which is 14.7 lb. per square inch. If the pressure given in the above problem was not the absolute pressure but the differential pressure, as read on such a gauge, then the true pressures inside the tank were 114.7 lb. per square inch before release and 47.7 lb. per square inch after release, and the amount of gas remaining in the tank after release was 47.7/114.7 or 0.416 of the original amount. In what follows, pressure always is intended to mean the true, or absolute pressure, not the net pressure.

7. Relation between Pressure and Volume When Temperature and Amount Are Constant. Let us imagine, next, that the gas is contained in a cylinder like that of a steam

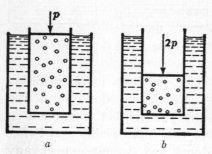

engine, with a movable piston, as in Fig. 2, so that the volume of the inclosed gas may be altered without changing the amount. If, now, the piston is pushed down from the position represented by *a*, in the figure, to that represented by *b*, where the volume is half as great, the number of impacts on a given area of the walls in a given time will be doubled.

Fig. 2. Relation between pressure and volume of a fixed quantity of gas at constant temperature.

While the piston is being pushed down, the molecules striking it will rebound a little faster than before, causing a slight increase in temperature,[1] so that we must wait a moment till this temperature has been lowered to that of the bath surrounding the cylinder, when the average speed of the molecules will be the same as before the piston was pushed down. Since the number of impacts on a given area of the walls has been doubled, the pressure is likewise twice what

[1] This effect may be noticed in the heating of the pump when a bicycle or automobile tire is pumped up.

it was before the piston was moved. Evidently, if the volume were made one third as great as at first, the pressure would become three times as great, etc., so that we may conclude in general that **when the temperature and amount of gas are constant the pressure is inversely proportional to the volume.** This is usually called Boyle's Law.

As an example, let us calculate the final volume when 10 l. of gas at a pressure of 76 cm. of mercury is subjected to a pressure of 19 cm. Since the pressure is **decreased** in the ratio 19/76, the volume will be **increased** in the same ratio, becoming seventy-six nineteenths of 10 l., the original volume, or 40 l.

8. Relation between Pressure and Concentration When Temperature Is Constant. The ratio of the amount of material to the volume in which it is contained, or the amount in unit volume, is called its **concentration.** Evidently it is the concentration which determines the number of impacts, and hence the pressure, so long as the speed of the molecules is unaltered. If, for example, 2 g. of a certain gas in 5 l. exerted a pressure of 2 atmospheres, then 1 g. of the same gas at the same temperature in a volume of 10 l. would be only one fourth as concentrated, and would exert only one fourth of the pressure, which would be one half atmosphere. In general, we may say that **the pressure of a gas is proportional to its concentration when the temperature is constant.**

9. Relation between the Pressure, Mass, and Speed of the Molecules. Although, as has been said, the pressure exerted by a gas depends upon the velocity of its molecules, it is not directly proportional to the speed, for if the speed is doubled, not only does each molecule hit the vessel walls twice as often, but also twice as hard, for the momentum of each molecule is doubled by doubling the speed. The pressure is thus proportional to the square of the average velocity of the molecules. Moreover, the change of momentum at each impact is proportional to the mass of the molecules. A heavy molecule would exert more pressure than would a light one moving at the same speed; hence, the contribution of a single molecule to the pressure of the gas is proportional both to its mass, which we will call m, and to the square of its velocity, which we will call u, that is, to mu^2. Now $\frac{1}{2} mu^2$ is kinetic energy, so we can say that the contribution of a single molecule to the pressure of a quantity of gas depends upon its kinetic energy. In a mixture of gases, the different species of molecules must have the same average kinetic energy, since they tend to equalize kinetic energies by collisions. It is evident, therefore, that light molecules, like those of hydrogen, must move much faster than heavier ones, like those of oxygen (cf. paragraph 23).

10. Effect of Temperature, When Amount Is Constant. Let us next see how a fixed quantity of a gas would be affected by a change in the temperature. It will be simplest, first, to consider the effect of this change upon the pressure and volume separately, keeping one constant while the other is allowed to vary. We will imagine a constant weight on the

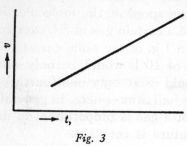

Fig. 3

piston of the cylinder containing the gas, so that the volume may vary while the pressure remains the same. We may now vary the temperature by altering that of the bath in which the cylinder is immersed. If the temperature of the gas is increased, we would expect, in terms of our theory, that the molecules would gain in kinetic energy, moving faster and hitting the vessel walls and the piston both harder and more frequently, forcing the latter upwards until the reduction in the number of impacts in a given time compensates for the greater force of each impact. It is found by experiment that this increase in volume is uniform, as expressed by the plot in Fig. 3.

11. Absolute Zero of Temperature. Similarly, if the piston is not permitted to move, so that the volume remains constant, an increase in temperature would be expected to increase the kinetic energy of the molecules, resulting in harder and more frequent impacts, and hence an increase in pressure. The pressure of a gas at any temperature depends upon the amount of gas and its volume, i.e., its concentration, but for any given concentration the pressure increases uniformly with temperature, as shown in Fig. 4 for three concentrations. By careful measurements the increase is found to amount to $\frac{1}{273}$ of the value of the pressure at 0° C. for each degree rise in temperature. We are led naturally to inquire the effect of

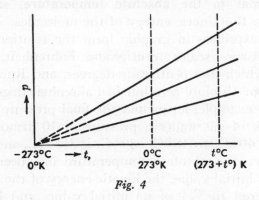

Fig. 4

a continued **decrease** in temperature. Diminishing the pressure $\frac{1}{273}$ of its value at 0° C. for every degree the temperature is lowered would give no pressure at all at − 273° C. (more exactly, − 273.15° C.) if the gas did not condense to a liquid somewhere along the line.

What does this mean in terms of the kinetic theory? Since we have attributed gas pressure to the impacts of gas molecules moving with an energy depending on the temperature, when the pressure becomes zero we must conclude that the molecules are no longer in motion, and that we have reached the **Absolute Zero** of temperature. A lower temperature is inconceivable in terms of our theory. This remarkable conclusion is confirmed by the behavior of other properties, many of which approach either zero or infinity, as the temperature approaches − 273° C.

It is both logical, therefore, and for many scientific purposes more convenient, to reckon temperature from the absolute zero, which is 273° below the centigrade zero. We denote absolute temperature by K for Lord Kelvin. On this scale the melting point of ice, 0° C., is + 273° K.; 17° C. is 273 + 17, or 290° K., and in general, letting T and t stand for temperature on the absolute and centigrade scales respectively, $T = t + 273$. The most convenient way of expressing the effect of temperature on the pressure is to say that **when the amount and volume of a gas are kept constant, the pressure is proportional to the absolute temperature,** since both depend upon the kinetic energy of the molecules.

Figure 5 expresses in graphic form the relation between four temperature scales: centigrade, Fahrenheit, absolute or Kelvin, which uses centigrade degrees, and Rankine, also counting from absolute zero but in Fahrenheit degrees.

12. As an example, let us find the final pressure produced when a tank of gas under a pressure of 10 atmospheres is cooled from 40° C. to 18° C. 40° C. is 313° K., and 18° C. is 291° K. Since the absolute temperature has been lowered to $\frac{291}{313}$ of its initial value, the kinetic energy of the molecules will be lowered to $\frac{291}{313}$ of its initial value, and hence the pressure will be lowered to the same fraction of its initial value, which is $\frac{291}{313}$ of 10 atmospheres, or 9.3 atmospheres.

When the amount of gas and the pressure are kept constant, any change in the absolute temperature, with its proportionate change in the kinetic energy of the molecules, must be compensated by a proportionate change in volume.

Suppose, for example, that we have 250 cc. of gas at 27° C., and wish to determine at what temperature the volume will become 200 cc. The new volume will be $\frac{200}{250}$, or 0.8 of the old volume; hence the **absolute** temperature will be reduced to 0.8 of its initial value, or from 300° K. to 240° K., which is − 33° C.

13. Effect of Changing Both Temperature and Pressure, When Amount of Gas Is Constant. When any two of the factors pressure, temperature, and volume are changed, the effect on the third can be calculated by separating the process into two steps similar to the above. For example, suppose

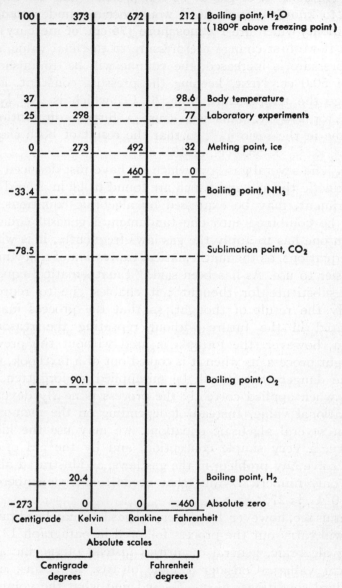

100	373	672	212	Boiling point, H_2O (180°F above freezing point)
37			98.6	Body temperature
25	298		77	Laboratory experiments
0	273	492	32	Melting point, ice
		460	0	
−33.4				Boiling point, NH_3
−78.5				Sublimation point, CO_2
90.1				Boiling point, O_2
20.4				Boiling point, H_2
−273	0	0	−460	Absolute zero
Centigrade	Kelvin	Rankine	Fahrenheit	

Absolute scales

Centigrade degrees   Fahrenheit degrees

Fig. 5. Temperature scales.

we have 50.0 cc. of gas at 74 cm. pressure and 20° C., and wish to know the volume it would occupy under **standard conditions,** which are **1 atmosphere (76 cm. of mercury) and 0° C.** If we first change the pressure to the final value, since the pressure is increased, the volume will be diminished to $\frac{74}{76}$ of 50.0 cc. Next, keeping the pressure constant, let us change the temperature from 20° C., which is 293° K., to 0° C., or 273° K. This will cause a further diminution in volume in the ratio $\frac{273}{293}$, so that the result of both changes is $\frac{273}{293} \times \frac{74}{76} \times 50.0$ cc., or 45.3 cc.

14. The several gas laws which we have just deduced from the kinetic theory, and which are found to be in accord with experiment, may be expressed by algebraic equations, and may be combined into one fundamental general equation. When one has to apply the gas laws frequently, it is wise to use equations, as the mathematical expression of a law makes it easier to use. As has been said, "a mathematical equation is a substitute for thought"; it enables one to represent briefly the result of thought, so that the process may be repeated in the future without repeating the reasoning. When, however, the formula is used without the previous thought process, as when it is copied out of a textbook, there is the danger that it will be misapplied or forgotten, and even when applied correctly the process is nearly devoid of educational value. Instead of depending on the memory to retain several algebraic equations, we may use the kinetic theory, a very simple conception, and by the aid of easy logic solve any problem in the gas laws, as illustrated above. The only numerical value that needs to be remembered is that 0° C. is 273° K.

Let us see, however, how a general gas law may be obtained. We will carry out the process followed in paragraph 13, but using algebraic, general quantities instead of specific arithmetical values. Consider 1 mole of gas, M grams, under standard conditions, p_0, v_0, T_0, and find what the volume of M grams will be, v, at some other pressure, p, and temperature, T. Changing p_0 to p while keeping T_0 the same changes the volume to $v_0 p_0/p$, and then changing to T while keeping p the same changes this volume to T/T_0 of its former value giving $v_0 p_0 T/p T_0$. If, finally, we use w grams of gas instead of M grams, $v = w v_0 p_0 T/M p T_0$. We may rearrange this, writing the more striking form,

$$\frac{pv}{T} = \frac{w}{M} \cdot \frac{p_0 v_0}{T_0}$$

Now p_0, v_0, and T_0 are fixed values, so we follow the universal practice of setting $p_0 v_0/T_0 = R$, a constant, called the "gas constant." Its numerical value depends, of course, upon the units chosen for expressing p_0, v_0, and T_0. Using atmospheres, liters, and Kelvin degrees, $R = 1 \times 22.4/273 = 0.0821$ (cf. Chapter IV for the value of v_0.) Using cm. of mercury and cc., $R = 76 \times 22,400/273 = 6240$. The general gas equation can then be written

$$pv = \frac{w}{M} RT \tag{1}$$

for w grams of gas or

$$pv = RT \tag{2}$$

for 1 mole of any gas. We may solve these equations for any one of the quantities which may be unknown in a particular case. We must be careful, however, to express R in the units used for p, v, and T. Suppose, for example, we wish to calculate the weight of oxygen, in grams, which will exert a pressure of 100 mm. of mercury at 27° C. in a vessel having a capacity of 600 cc. If we happen to remember R only in liter-atmospheres, 0.0821, then we must express p in atmospheres, $\frac{100}{760}$, and v in liters, 0.600, and since we want w in grams we write $M = 32.0$ grams. Accordingly,

$$w = \frac{pvM}{RT} = \frac{100 \times 0.600 \times 32.0}{760 \times 0.0821 \times 300} = 0.1025 \text{ grams}$$

15. The following somewhat oversimplified derivation of the relation between pressure, p, number of molecules, n, mass per molecule (molecular weight), m, volume, v, and average molecular velocity, u, may prove helpful to some. Imagine a cubic box, l cm. on a side; a single molecule moving back and forth between opposite walls with velocity x would hit x/l times per second, with a force of $2mx$ (the change of momentum) at each impact. The pressure exerted on these two walls is thus $2mx^2/l$. The velocity in the x-direction is, however, only one component of the total velocity, u, the relation being $u^2 = x^2 + z^2$, where y and z are the component velocities in the two other directions. The total pressure exerted by 1 molecule on all six walls, is $2mu^2/l$. Since the area is $6l^2$, the pressure per sq. cm., p, is $\frac{1}{3}mu^2/l^3$. But $l^3 = v$, the volume of the box, so that, for 1 molecule, $p = \frac{1}{3}mu^2/v$, and, for n molecules,

$$p = \tfrac{1}{3}nmu^2/v \tag{3}$$

Now, $\frac{1}{2}mu^2$ is the average kinetic energy per molecule, which is, by the theory, assumed proportional to the temperature, provided that temperature is reckoned, not from 0° C., but from the point where molecular velocity ceases, the real "absolute zero." Writing $\frac{1}{3}mu^2 = kT$, where T is the temperature on the new scale and k the universal "Boltzmann constant" of proportionality, we have,

$$pv = nkT \tag{4}$$

It is evident that nk in equation 4 is identical with R in equation (2).

In the derivation given above it has been assumed that all the molecules have the same velocity. Actually, of course, this cannot be true, for a molecule may move after a collision either faster or slower than before. The distribution of velocities and its change with temperature are shown in Fig. 2, p. 174.

16. In drawing the various conclusions given above concerning the relations between pressure, volume, amount and temperature, we must remember that we have assumed that when the gases are sufficiently expanded the volume occupied by the molecules themselves is negligible compared with the volume of the vessel, also that they are so far apart and moving with such high velocity that their mutual attractions can be neglected. The higher the temperature and the lower the concentration, the more nearly do these assumptions correspond to the truth. On the other hand, as the temperature is lowered and as the concentration is increased, increasing deviations are to be expected from the behavior previously deduced, becoming more and more marked until the attractive forces become sufficient to cause the molecules to condense to the liquid state. The conditions under which this condensation takes place obviously depend upon the kind of molecules involved. With the gas helium, at a pressure of one atmosphere, the temperature must be lowered to 4.5° before liquifaction takes place.

The deviations actually found from the ideal gas laws are illustrated in Fig. 6 for H_2, O_2, and CO_2, where the experimental values of pv are plotted against p. The quantity of gas and the units used have been arbitrarily selected so as to make $pv = 1$ at low pressures.

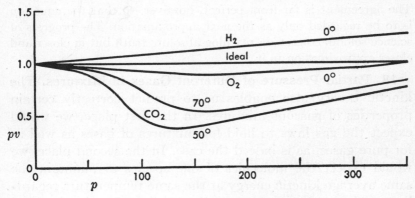

Fig. 6. Deviations from Boyle's Law.

In the case of hydrogen, pv increases right from the start. This can be explained as due to the fact that molecules themselves take up part of the space of the container, which is v, causing the molecules to strike the walls more frequently than they otherwise would, and also to the weakness of the attractive forces between hydrogen molecules, as could be inferred from the very low temperature necessary to liquefy it. Oxygen molecules attract each other more strongly, making p smaller at first, and CO_2 molecules attract each other still more strongly, causing pv to dip to 0.5 at 100 atmospheres; in other words, the actual volume of the gas at this pressure would be only 0.5 of what it would be if CO_2 were an ideal gas.

17. van der Waals' Equation. The Dutch physicist, van der Waals, designated the actual volume of the molecules in 1 mole of gas as b, so that the free space in the vessel becomes $v - b$, and he expressed the attraction between the molecules as a/v^2, where a is another constant. Since the pressure of a real gas is made smaller than the pressure of an ideal gas by reason of this attraction, we correct it by *adding* a/v^2. The ideal gas equation, equation (2), is transformed in this manner into

$$\left(p + \frac{a}{v^2}\right)(v - b) = RT. \tag{5}$$

This agrees much better with the behavior of highly compressed gases than does the simple $pv = RT$, and values for a and b can be chosen which will permit the van der Waals' equation to agree approximately with the actual values such as those in Fig. 5. The agreement is far from perfect, however, so that the equation is to be regarded only as the next approximation. The progress of science seldom consists in reaching absolute truth but in closer and closer approximation to it.

18. Partial Pressure of Different Gases in Mixtures. The kinetic theory also enables us to predict correctly certain properties of gaseous mixtures. In the first place, we would expect the gas laws to hold for mixtures of gases as well as for pure gases, as is indeed the case. In the second place, we would expect the molecules of one species to maintain the same average kinetic energy at the same temperature regardless of the presence of any other species of molecules, and therefore **the part of the pressure which is due to the impacts on the vessel walls of one species, called the partial pressure of that gas, would be the same no matter what other gases are present.** This law is usually known as Dalton's Law. By way of illustration, let us suppose a closed vessel containing water and carbon dioxide gas maintained at a constant temperature. Some of the carbon dioxide will dissolve in the water. Suppose now that some other gas, say nitrogen, is injected into the same vessel. How would this affect the amount of carbon dioxide dissolved in the water? Without the aid of the kinetic theory one might suppose that more carbon dioxide would be forced into the water, but from the molecular-kinetic standpoint we see that the number and momentum of the carbon dioxide molecules striking the water surface, upon which alone the solubility of the gas depends, are practically unaltered by the presence of the nitrogen molecules.

The form in which Dalton announced the law known by his name was not identical with the statement here given. His studies antedated the kinetic theory, a fact which makes this and other discoveries of his the more remarkable. In one place[1] he says, ". . . the elastic or repulsive power of each particle is confined to those of his own kind; and consequently the force of such a fluid, retained in a given vessel, or gravitating, is the same in a separate as in a mixed state, depending on its proper density and temperature." With reference to the solubility of a single constituent of a mixture of gases he said, "If a quantity of water free from air be agitated with a mixture of two or more gases (such as atmospheric air) the water will absorb portions of each gas the same as if they were presented to it separately in their proper density."

Again, suppose we consider two vessels of equal size, one evacuated and the other containing oxygen, both kept at the same temperature. If water is introduced into the first one, a little of it will vaporize, since the molecules of the liquid are in rapid motion with a velocity depending on the temperature, and certain molecules at the surface which have unusually high velocities may be able to escape the attraction of the liquid and go into the vapor phase. As the number of molecules in the vapor phase increases, there is a constantly increasing chance that some of them, moving more slowly than usual, will be caught into the liquid again, instead of rebounding at the surface. The concentration of molecules in the vapor state thus tends to become adjusted, so that there is an equilibrium or balance between the two phases such that the number of molecules of liquid vaporizing in a given time just equals the number of molecules of water condensing in the same time. The pressure of vapor necessary for this equilibrium depends on the nature of the liquid and on the temperature, increasing as indicated by the curves

[1] Alembic Club Reprints, "Foundations of the Atomic Theory," No. 2, p. 1, published by William F. Clay, Edinburgh, 1893. This reprint, together with No. 4, which quotes brief papers by Dalton, Wollaston, Thomson, Gay-Lussac, and Avogadro, gives the steps, experimental and logical, by which the conclusions presented in Chapters I to IV in this book were reached. It might comfort a reader who finds these matters a bit difficult to learn that the able men who worked them out did not find them easy.

in Fig. 7. It is obvious that this pressure will not depend on the extent of the liquid surface, as an increase in surface has the same effect on the number of molecules vaporizing as it has on the number condensing, so that the net effect is zero.

Suppose, now, we admit water to the second vessel, containing oxygen. Evidently the tendency of molecules of

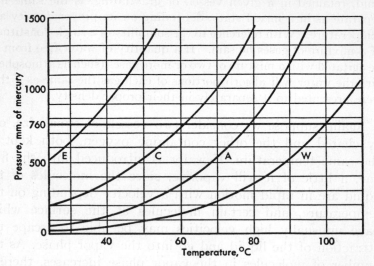

Fig. 7. Vapor pressure and temperature of liquids. A, ethyl alcohol; C, chloroform; E, ethyl ether; W, water.

liquid to escape will be the same as before, but the vaporized molecules will be unable to distribute themselves so rapidly throughout the vessel, since they must diffuse through oxygen molecules which collide with them and retard their progress. Hence the liquid will evaporate more slowly than in the previous case, where oxygen was absent, but eventually the molecules of water vapor will be distributed throughout the vessel just as if the oxygen were absent, and the partial pressure of the water vapor will be independent of the other gas (or gases) present.

19. Relation between the Pressure of a Gas and Its Solubility in a Liquid. When a gas is placed over the surface of a liquid, it dissolves to an extent dependent on the nature of the gas, the nature of the liquid, the temperature and the pressure of the gas. When no more gas will dissolve in the liquid, we have a state of equilibrium, in which the number of molecules of gas being caught into the liquid in a given time is the same as the number escaping.

Suppose, now, that more of the same gas is introduced into the space above the liquid. If the temperature is kept the same, the momentum of the molecules striking the surface of the liquid is unaltered, but the number so striking is increased, so that more of them enter the liquid than escape from it, and the added number of dissolved molecules finally increases the number escaping until it again equals the number entering. An increase, therefore, in the pressure of the gas above the liquid causes an increase in the amount of gas dissolved by it. We would naturally expect this amount dissolved to be proportional to the pressure, which is approximately true for gases which are not too soluble and do not react chemically with the solvent. This is known as **Henry's Law.**

20. Avogadro's Rule. One more consequence of the kinetic theory should be given at this time, as it will play a very important part in the reasoning in Chapter IV.

When two different gases are at the same temperature, the average kinetic energy of the two different kinds of molecules is the same. We conclude that this is true from the fact that when two different gases at the same temperature are mixed the total resulting pressure is the sum of the partial pressures each gas would have if the other were absent; hence the kinetic energy of neither is altered by the mixing, which can be the case only when they have the same kinetic energy before mixing. Let us then take, in two vessels of equal volume, such amounts of two different gases at the same temperature that their pressures will be the same. Now we have seen that the pressure of a gas depends upon the number of molecules, their kinetic energy, and the volume they occupy, and upon no other factors. Since, therefore, we have chosen equal pressures, volumes, and temperatures (and hence kinetic energies) the only other factor, the number of molecules in the two quantities of gas, must likewise be the same. In other words, **equal volumes of all gases, at the same temperature and pressure, contain the same number of molecules.** This was first announced by an Italian physicist, Avogadro, in 1811, and is usually called **Avogadro's Rule** or **Law.** We will use it presently to measure the relative numbers of molecules involved in chemical reactions.

21. The conclusion just drawn can be more concisely expressed in algebraic terms, by aid of the equation, $pv = nkT$, derived in paragraph 15. Letting the subscripts 1 and 2 stand for two different gases, we write $p_1v_1 = n_1kT_1$ and $p_2v_2 = n_2kT_2$. Let us take two vessels of equal size, so that $v_1 = v_2$, and hold them at the same temperature, so that $T_1 = T_2$, and adjust the quantities of the two gases so that $p_1 = p_2$, then it follows that $n_1 = n_2$.

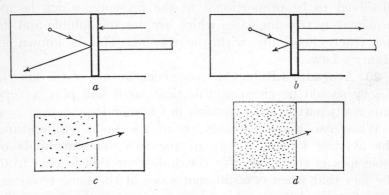

Fig. 8. Effect on temperature of a gas of a, compression; b, expansion while doing work; c, expansion of a dilute gas into a vacuum; d, expansion of a compressed gas into a vacuum.

22. Other consequences of the kinetic theory may readily be drawn. For example, the molecules of a gas striking a compressing piston rebound with increased velocity just as is the case with a baseball struck by a batter; hence they are hotter and the process of compressing heats the gas, cf. Fig. 8a. The reverse is of course true, and a gas expanding by doing work on a retreating piston is cooled, cf. Fig. 8b. This occurs both in steam engines and gasoline motors. On the other hand, a molecule leaking through a fine hole into

a vacuum is not cooled, any more than a ball is retarded by passing through an open window, cf. Fig. 8c. However, if the gas is highly compressed, then, on expansion through an orifice the mutual attractions of its molecules may be enough to cause retardation as they move apart, just as a ball is retarded when rising against the earth's gravitational attraction, cf. Fig. 8d. This effect is used in the liquefaction of air. The air is highly compressed, cleaned of moisture and carbon dioxide, cooled to remove the heat of compression, first by water, then, in certain plants at least, by liquid ammonia, then by air that has already expanded and cooled itself. Part of this strongly cooled air then liquefies on expansion through an orifice.

23. Molecular Velocities and Diffusion. Since the molecules of different gases must have equal kinetic energies at the same temperature, we can write $\frac{1}{2} m_1 u_1^2 = \frac{1}{2} m_2 u_2^2$ (cf. paragraph 15) where the subscripts refer to the two species, whence $u_1/u_2 = \sqrt{m_2/m_1}$. If the first gas is hydrogen, H_2, for which $m_1 = 2$, and the second is oxygen, O_2, for which $m_2 = 32$, then $u_1 = 4\, u_2$, that is, hydrogen molecules move on the average four times as fast as oxygen molecules at the same temperature. We may conclude from this that hydrogen could diffuse through a small hole or down through another gas four times as fast as oxygen.

The actual mean velocities can be calculated from equation 3. We will obtain u in centimeters per second if we use the molal weight, $nm = M$, in grams, and p in dynes. Let us take 1 mole of gas in 22,400 cc. at 0° C. and 1 atm., then, since 1 atm. = 76 cm. of Hg = 76×13.6 grams = $76 \times 13.6 \times 980$ dynes = 1.013×10^6 dynes, we obtain

$$u = \frac{\sqrt{3\, pv}}{M} = \frac{2.6 \times 10^5}{\sqrt{M}} \text{ cm./sec.}$$

M for hydrogen is 2, giving $u = 1.85 \times 10^5$ cm./sec. or 1.85 kilometers per second (1.15 miles per second). The corresponding figure for oxygen, where $M = 32$, is 0.46 km./sec. or 0.29 mile/sec.

24. Heat Capacity of Gases. If a monatomic gas, such as helium, He, neon, Ne, argon, A, or mercury vapor, Hg, is heated in a vessel of fixed volume, all of the energy absorbed goes into increasing the kinetic energy of the molecules. We can calculate this by the aid of equation 1, $3\, pv = nmu^2$. The mean kinetic energy of the molecules is $\frac{1}{2} nmu^2 = \frac{3}{2} pv$, and this is equal (paragraph 14) to $\frac{3}{2} RT$. At a temperature one degree higher, $T + 1$, the kinetic energy is greater by an amount equal to $\frac{3}{2} R$. It is convenient for this purpose to take the value of R not in liter-atmospheres per degree per mole, as in paragraph 14, but in calories per degree per mole, 1.987. The heat required to raise the temperature of 1 mole of monatomic gas 1° C. is $\frac{3}{2} \times 1.987$ or 2.96 calories when the volume is kept constant. This heat capacity is usually designated C_v.

If the pressure is kept the same during the heating, work has to be done against the external pressure and a larger amount of heat

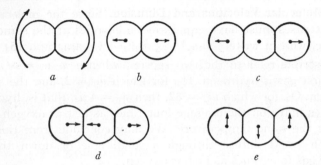

Fig. 9. Internal energies of molecules. *a*, rotation; *b*, vibration of diatomic molecule; *c*, *d*, *e*, modes of vibration of linear triatomic molecule, e.g., OCO.

is required to raise the temperature of the gas 1° C. Writing $pv = RT$ and $pv' = R(T + 1)$ for the gas before and after heating 1° C., respectively, the work done against the external pressure is equal to the pressure times the increase in volume, $p(v' - v) = R(T + 1) - RT = R = 1.987$ cals. The heat capacity at constant pressure, designated C_p, exceeds C_v by R calories per degree, i.e., $C_p - C_v = R$.

On heating a gas whose molecules contain more than one atom, the kinetic energy is increased by $\frac{3}{2} R$, as with monatomic molecules, but additional energy can be absorbed by rotations and internal vibrations of the molecules, as illustrated in Fig. 9. These will vary in magnitude depending on the constitution of the molecules. Of course $C_p - C_v = R$, as with monatomic molecules. Table 2 gives illustrative values for gases whose molecules have varying complexity.

TABLE 2

Approximate Values for Heat Capacities at 15°C.

	He, A, *etc.*	H$_2$	N$_2$	O$_2$	CO$_2$	NH$_3$	C$_2$H$_6$
C_p	5.0	6.8	6.9	7.0	8.8	8.9	11.6
C_v	3.0	4.8	4.9	5.0	6.8	6.9	9.6
$C_p - C_v$	2.0	2.0	2.0	2.0	2.0	2.0	2.0
C_p/C_v	1.67	1.41	1.40	1.40	1.30	1.31	1.22

The ratios, C_p/C_v, given in the bottom row, have been calculated from the velocity of sound in the gas, which depends on this ratio.

25. Solids and Liquids. As the temperature of a gas is lowered, the kinetic energy of the molecules decreases until a point is reached where the attractive force between the molecules, a/v^2 in the van der Waals equation, equation 5, together with the external pressure, causes the molecules to condense to liquid. The higher the external pressure the higher the temperature at which condensation can occur. Our picture of a liquid is one in which the molecules are in vigorous motion, with sufficient space in which to change their positions continually, but without sufficient kinetic energy to enable any but the fastest among them to escape into a vapor space above the liquid. Molecules in the vapor phase close to the liquid surface which happen to be moving slowly as a result of the most recent collision may be caught into the liquid. A liquid and its vapor in contact at constant temperature quickly reach a state of balance or equilibrium in which the number of molecules which escape from the liquid to the vapor in any interval of time is the same as the number of those which reenter the liquid, and their concentration or pressure in the vapor phase has a fixed value, called the vapor pressure at that temperature. Lowering the temperature diminishes the vapor pressure because it decreases the speed of the molecules, allowing them to be more easily captured by the liquid, and also because it allows the liquid molecules to crowd more closely together so that they escape less easily into the vapor. (Intermolecular attraction often varies inversely with the seventh power of the distance.) A lower pressure then suffices to restore the equilibrium.

Figure 7 shows the form of vapor pressure curves for several familiar substances, ether, chloroform, alcohol, and water. These and all other vapor pressure curves can be expressed with little error by the **Clausius-Clapeyron equation,**

$$\log_{10} p = \frac{-L}{4.575\,T} + C \qquad (6)$$

where p stands for the vapor pressure, L the heat absorbed in the vaporization of 1 mole of the liquid, T the absolute temperature, and C a constant chosen to fit the data. This equation suggests plotting log p against $1/T$, which gives a straight line which most vapor pressures fit with close approximation.

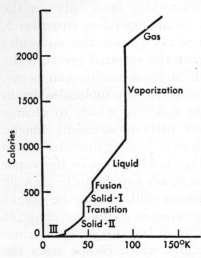

Fig. 10. Heat absorbed by oxygen, starting at absolute zero.

On lowering the temperature of a liquid, the thermal agitation of the molecules diminishes, the liquid contracts, the molecules attract each other more strongly due to the smaller distances separating them, and a point is finally reached where they can no longer wander about in the liquid, exchanging places, and they become fixed in a regular array in a solid crystal lattice. Fig. 5, p. 417, shows the arrangement of atoms in crystals of a number of metals, including aluminum, nickel, lead, copper, and silver. This is known as the face-centered cubic lattice. Here they are still free to oscillate in their places, or "cages," but only occasionally, if at all, can a pair exchange places. Melting is the reverse of this process. Many solids show one or more further transitions as the temperature is further lowered. Changes in the amount of vibrations within the molecule, changes in its rotation, etc., can favor one type of crystal lattice over another. Iron is stable at high temperatures in the face-centered cubic structure, but below about 900° C. it changes to the body-centered cubic lattice[1] shown in Fig. 4, p. 417.

These changes all involve the addition or subtraction of heat and in Fig. 10 is shown the amount of heat that must be added to oxygen starting at absolute zero to bring it to its stable form at any particular temperature.

Exercises

See Appendix II for answers.

It is recommended that the student remember that the purpose of the following exercises is not simply to get the correct answers, which might be achieved simply by substituting unintelligently in the formulas found in a high school text, but rather to stimulate the exercise of the imagination. Exercises 18 and 19 are particularly good tests of this ability.

1. What properties serve to distinguish solids, liquids, and gases? State the distinctions in terms of the kinetic theory.

2. If a certain quantity of gas occupies 100 cc. at 3 atm., at what pressure will it occupy 60 cc. if the temperature remains unchanged?

3. If 16 g. of oxygen is required to inflate a rubber balloon to a certain size at 0° C., what weight of oxygen must be used to inflate it to the same size at 20° C.?

4. Some gas occupies 100 cc. at 127° C. and 50 cm. pressure. To what temperature would it have to be cooled in order that a simultaneous decrease in volume to 60 cc. would produce no change in pressure?

5. If an automobile tire is inflated to a pressure of 30 lb. per sq. in. gauge pressure at 15° C., what will the gauge pressure become if the tire is heated to 50° by running?

6. What proportion by weight of the air in an automobile tire must be allowed to escape in order to reduce its gauge pressure from 70 lb. to 60 lb. per sq. in., the temperature remaining the same?

7. A quantity of gas occupies a volume of 40 cc. at 127° C. At what temperature will its volume become 22 cc., the pressure remaining the same?

[1] See Latimer and Hildebrand, *Reference Book of Inorganic Chemistry* Appendix V, for types of crystal lattice.

8. At what temperature will a flask contain 3.30 g. of carbon dioxide gas at 1 atm. if it contains 2.00 g. at 57° C. and 1 atm.?

9. To what temperature must an open flask be heated in order that one fifth of the gas which it contains at 7° C. shall escape?

10. If a balloon has a capacity of 480 cubic meters, how many tanks of hydrogen must be used so fill it if each tank has a volume of 0.300 cubic meters and contains hydrogen at a pressure of 40 atm.?

11. If 1 liter of a certain gas, measured at 76 cm. and 0° C., weighs 1.25 g., what would be the weight of 1 liter of the same gas at 60 cm. and 47° C.?

12. A tank contains 150 g. of hydrogen at 15 atm. and 17° C. What weight of hydrogen would escape if the tank were heated to 100° C. and the cock opened?

13. If the concentration of chlorine gas in a flask is 3.16 g. per liter at 0° C. and 1 atm., what will it be at 47° C., if the pressure is 0.8 atm.?

14. A flask contained enough oxygen molecules to exert a pressure of 0.5 atm. upon the walls. If twice as many nitrogen molecules and three times as many helium molecules are introduced, what will be the pressure upon the walls?

15. If water is introduced into an evacuated vessel at 20° C. the pressure inside the vessel becomes 17 mm. of mercury. If some air which has been standing over water at 20° C. is put into a flask to a pressure of 756 mm., a piece of quicklime introduced and the flask closed, what will the pressure become when the quicklime has absorbed all of the water vapor from the air?

16. According to the kinetic theory how will the temperature of a gas be affected by expansion into a vacuum? Explain briefly.

17. Explain, in terms of the kinetic theory, why an automobile pump gets hot while pumping air into a tire.

18. State the effect, quantitatively where you can, of each of the following changes upon (a) the number of molecular impacts per second per square centimeter upon the containing walls and (b) the force of each impact.

(1) Gas in a cylinder with a movable piston, immersed in a large water bath, is expanded from 2 liters to 3 liters.

(2) The air pressure in an automobile tire is slowly pumped up from a gauge pressure of 20 lb. per sq. in. to 30 lb. per sq. in.

(3) H_2S gas is kept in a closed vessel at constant temperature until it has all decomposed into H_2 and liquid sulfur.

19. Consider the following quantities for two gases, designated 1 and 2, respectively: pressure, p; volume, v; temperature, T; molecular weight, m; mean molecular speed, s; number of molecules, n. If you are given the following relations between certain of these pairs of variables, you can draw conclusions regarding others. Indicate this conclusion in each of the following cases by writing in the sign, $>$, when the first is greater than the second (e.g., $p_1 > p_2$ means p_1 is greater than p_2), the sign, $<$, when it is less, and the sign, $=$, when it is equal to the second. If no conclusions can be drawn, write a question mark (?).

Conclusions from the Kinetic Theory. Indicate by writing in the appropriate sign, $>$, $<$, $=$ or ?

(a) $m_1 > m_2$, equal p, v, T; s_1 . . . . s_2

(b) $m_1 > m_2$, equal p, v, T; n_1 . . . . n_2

(c) $p_1 > p_2$, $m_1 > m_2$, equal T, n; v_1 . . . . v_2

(d) $n_1 > n_2$, equal p, v; T_1 . . . . T_2

(e) Equal v, n, s; p_1 . . . . p_2.

*20. Divers can operate at greater depths if they breathe an atmosphere of helium and oxygen instead of compressed air because helium is less soluble than nitrogen in the body fluids, and therefore has less tendency to form bubbles when the diver comes to the surface, releasing the pressure. This "effervescence" produces the serious and painful "caisson disease," or "bends." It is much harder, however, to keep warm in this helium atmosphere, and electrically heated clothing has been found necessary. Explain.

*21. Which gas, in each of the following pairs, would you expect to conduct heat faster from a hot body: (a) H_2 or N_2, (b) A or CO_2 (nearly equal molecular weights), (c) dry air or water vapor at the same pressure?

22. What difference would you infer from the kinetic theory between (a) He and Ne, and (b) Ne and O_2, in the amounts of heat energy necessary to raise the temperature of 1 mole of the gas 1° C.?

*23. Helium atoms have an average speed of 1150 meters per second. The "mean free path" (i.e., average distance between collisions) is 25×10^{-6} cm. How many collisions does a helium atom undergo per second?

*24. Compare the rise in temperature for (a) A and Ne and (b) A and CO_2 when the volume of each is suddenly diminished

---

* Questions of greater difficulty, that should not be attacked until the others have been mastered.

to one half its former value; the initial pressures and temperatures being the same.

*25. A MacLeod gauge, shown in Fig. 11, is used to measure low pressures. A represents the vessel containing the gas at low pressure. When the mercury in the reservoir, C, is forced upwards by pressure

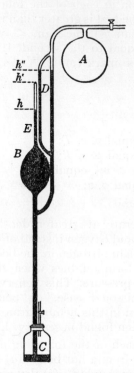

Fig. 11.   MacLeod gauge.

in C into the capillary D to a height, h'', the gas in B, previously at the same pressure as the gas in A, is trapped and forced into the capillary, E, the mercury rising to a height, h. If the volume of B is 200 cc., and the diameter of the capillary is 0.8 mm., h' − h = 100 mm., and h'' − h = 125 mm. What is the pressure of the gas in A?

CHAPTER IV

MOLECULAR WEIGHTS

1. Fixing Formulas and Atomic Weights. In the preceding chapters a number of molecular formulas have been used without explaining how we know them to be the correct ones. The law of simple multiple proportions considered by itself merely allows us to say, for example, that if the formula of water is H_2O, as stated in Chapter II, paragraph 6, then that of hydrogen peroxide could be H_2O_2 or HO, since the ratio of the weights of oxygen to hydrogen is, by analysis, 7.94 in the former and 15.88 in the latter. These formulas are consistent with the accepted values of the atomic weights of oxygen, 16.00, and hydrogen, 1.008, since

$$\frac{\text{Wt. of oxygen}}{\text{Wt. of hydrogen}} = \frac{16.00}{2 \times 1.008} = 7.94 \text{ in } H_2O,$$

and is

$$\frac{2 \times 16.00}{2 \times 1.008} = 15.88 \text{ in } H_2O_2.$$

But the formula of water was long considered by many, among them Dalton himself, to be HO, which would be consistent with the analytical weight ratio of 7.94 if the atomic weight of oxygen were set at 8.00. Hydrogen peroxide would then have to be HO_2, or some multiple thereof, to agree with the analytical weight ratio of 15.88. How do we now know that water is H_2O and not HO?

The decision resulted, historically, from the discovery that molecules of elements are not identical with their atoms. Dalton had spoken, in 1808, of "an atom of water or steam, composed of 1 of oxygen and 1 of hydrogen, retained in contact by a strong affinity, and supposed to be surrounded by a common atmosphere of heat; its relative weight = 8." Gay-Lussac, later in the same year, announced the law now called by his name. It is interesting to read this in his own words. "Thus it appears evident to me that gases always combine in the simplest proportions when they act on one another; and we have seen in reality in all the preceding examples that the ratio of combination is 1 to 1, 1 to 2, or 1 to 3. It is very important to observe that in considering weights there is no simple and finite relation between the elements of any one compound; it is only when there is a second compound between the same elements that the new proportion of the element that has been added is a multiple of the first quantity. Gases, on the contrary, in whatever proportions they may combine, always give rise to compounds whose elements by volume are multiples of each other.

"Not only, however, do gases combine in very simple proportions, as we have just seen, but the apparent contraction of volume which they experience on combination has also a simple relation to the volume of the gases, or at least to that of one of them."

We must understand, of course, that these volumes are all measured at the same pressure and temperature. Avogadro, in 1811, seized upon this discovery to draw the conclusion now known as Avogadro's Law, which we saw in Chapter III, paragraph 15, to be also a direct consequence of the kinetic theory. He wrote, "It must then be admitted that very simple relations also exist between the volumes of gaseous substances and the numbers of simple or compound molecules which form them. The first hypothesis to present itself in this connection, and apparently even the only admissible one, is the supposition that the number of integral molecules in any gas is always the same for equal volumes, or always proportional to the volumes." Avogadro proceeded to explain how this principle, applied to the volumes of gases taking part in reactions, leads to a consistent set of formulas and atomic weights. His work of clarification was not generally understood or appreciated, unfortunately, and the formula of water continued to be written H_2O by some chemists and HO by others until Cannizzaro revived it in 1858. Let us state the case in the language of today.

2. If hydrogen and oxygen are made to combine at a temperature and pressure at which the resulting water is steam, the volumes involved are in the proportion indicated below.

$$\text{Hydrogen} + \text{Oxygen} \longrightarrow \text{Steam}$$

Relative volumes   2   1   2

It follows from Avogadro's Law that the molecules are involved in the reaction in the same proportion. Let us note particularly that 1 volume of oxygen suffices to produce 2 volumes of steam and therefore that 1 molecule of oxygen has enough atoms in it, at least two, to give 2 molecules of steam. Its formula must be O_2, or O_4, etc. But no reactions are known in which 1 molecule of oxygen gives more than 2 molecules of another compound containing oxygen, hence the formula, O_2, explains all the known facts.

The ratio of the volumes of hydrogen and steam in the above reaction tells us only that the number of hydrogen atoms in both molecules is the same. It could be one atom per molecule so far as this particular reaction is concerned; however, there are many other reactions known in which 1 molecule of hydrogen gives 2 molecules of some other gas; never more. Such a reaction is

$$\text{Hydrogen} + \text{Chlorine} \longrightarrow \text{Hydrogen chloride}$$

Relative
volumes   1   1   2

The molecule of hydrogen, therefore, must be H_2. The molecule of chlorine, from this and its other reactions, is Cl_2.

We now possess other criteria for distinguishing monatomic and polyatomic molecules. One of these is furnished by the different heat capacities of gas molecules of differing complexity, as set forth briefly in Chapter III, Table 2.

3. If this reasoning seems at all puzzling it is because it is difficult to carry out a logical process in unfamiliar terms, where one's imagination cannot serve as a prop. A problem involving the price of bandersnatches in rupees would bother persons who could solve the same problem on the price of sheep in dollars. The difficulty is one that can be minimized

by training, and such training is an important element in one's education. The aim should be to learn to reason just as confidently and correctly with "unknowns," such as x and y, as with familiar terms such as apples and boys. Let us illustrate the simple nature of the argument in the preceding paragraph by using familiar units.

Suppose you were told that an unknown number of apples had been divided equally among a certain number of baskets, and, further, that the apples in these baskets had later been divided equally, without cutting any apples, among twice as many boys as baskets. What conclusion could you draw about the number of apples in each basket? You would doubtless have little hesitation in stating your conclusion somewhat as follows: If the apples in a certain number of baskets, all filled alike, can be distributed evenly among twice as many boys as baskets, then each basket must contain an even number of apples, at least two. The reasoning in paragraph 2 is no more difficult than this. It is, simply: If the atoms in a certain number of molecules of oxygen (all alike, since it is pure substance) can be distributed evenly among twice as many molecules of water, then each molecule of oxygen must contain an even number of atoms, at least two. It sometimes pays to substitute familiar for unfamiliar terms just to overcome one's inhibitions.

4. Molecules of Elements. We have seen that the molecules of hydrogen, oxygen, and chlorine each contain two atoms. The same is true for nitrogen, fluorine, bromine, and iodine. Another variety of oxygen exists, called ozone, formed from oxygen by the silent electric discharge, with a diminution in volume in the ratio of 3 to 2, indicating that the equation must be written

$$3 O_2 = 2 O_3.$$

The molecule of ozone, therefore, contains three oxygen atoms. The molecule of phosphorus vapor at low temperatures is P_4, at higher temperature P_2, that of sulfur may be S_8, S_2, or S, according to the temperature. When metals are vaporized their molecules nearly always consist of single atoms. The same is true of argon, neon, and helium, gases existing in small amounts in the atomsphere.

5. Changes in Volume or Pressure in Gas Reactions. The connection we have traced between the volumes of gases in chemical reactions and the relative number of molecules may be used conversely to deduce the change of volume or pressure to be expected when reactions take place between substances whose formulas are known. Consider, for example, the reaction represented by the equation

$$2 \, SO_2 + O_2 = 2 \, SO_3.$$

If this reaction is carried out at a temperature at which all of the substances represented are gaseous, then we see that three molecules have formed two. If the temperature and volume have been kept the same during the reaction, this will result in a decrease of the pressure to two thirds of its former value. If the temperature and pressure are the same as before, then the volume will be two thirds of its former value.

It is important, whenever an equation will be used to deduce relative volumes, to use the correct formulas of the substances in the gaseous form. For example, the same weight, 28 g., is indicated both by N_2 and $2N$, but the second formula is incorrect, and would lead us to expect twice the volume which would actually be involved.

6. Volume of One Mole of Any Gas. The double meaning attached to chemical symbols and formulas was explained in Chapter II, one referring to single atoms and molecules, and furnishing a basis for reasoning, and the other referring to the gram-atom and gram-molecule, or mole, and furnishing a basis for experimental work. Having determined that equal numbers of gaseous molecules are contained in equal volumes, at equal temperatures and pressures, and that the mole of all substances consists of the same number of molecules, it becomes important to ask what is the actual volume occupied by the mole of gas. This rests upon the measurement of gas densities, as illustrated by the following table:

Gas	Wt. of 1 liter 0° C., 1 atm.	Vol. of 1 g. 0° C., 1 atm.	g. per mole	Vol. of 1 mole 0° C., 1 atm.
H_2	0.08988 g.	11.126 l.	2.016	22.43 l.
O_2	1.4291 g.	0.6998 l.	32.00	22.39 l.
N_2	1.2507 g.	0.7995 l.	28.02	22.40 l.
NH_3	0.7621 g.	1.3122 l.	17.03	22.35 l.

These values for the volume of the mole of gas under standard conditions, as well as others that might be added, are all very close to 22.4 liters, which may therefore be selected as the molal volume of a gas under standard conditions. (This is the volume of a cube 28.2 cm. or $11\frac{1}{8}$ inches on the side.) We may take this volume as the basis of our working definition of molecular weight, saying that **the molecular weight of a substance is the number of grams of it which occupy 22.4 liters when it is in the gaseous form and under standard conditions.** Very frequently, of course, substances cannot exist in the vapor state under these conditions, so that the relation between the weight and the volume of vapor must be found experimentally at some higher temperature, and perhaps lower pressure, after which it is possible to calculate the weight that 22.4 liters of the vapor would have at 0° C. and 1 atmosphere, if no condensation took place.

7. We may illustrate by examples the various types of problems it is possible to solve with the aid of this relationship.

Calculation of the Weight of a Given Volume or the Volume of a Given Weight of a Gas. *Example:* What is the volume of 10 g. of O_2 at 127° C. and 0.5 atmosphere? The answer to this is obtained by the following obvious steps:

32 g. of O_2 occupy 22.4 l. at 273° K. and 1 atm.

32 g. of O_2 occupy 44.8 l. at 273° K. and 0.5 atm.

32 g. of O_2 occupy $\frac{400}{273} \times 44.8$ l. at 400° K. (127° C.) and 0.5 atm.

1 g. of O_2 occupies $\frac{1}{32} \times \frac{400}{273} \times 44.8$ l. at 400° K. and 0.5 atm.

10 g. of O_2 occupy $\frac{10}{32} \times \frac{400}{273} \times 44.8$ l. or 20.5 l. at 400° K. and 0.5 atm.

Example: What is the weight of 50 l. of CO_2 measured at 25° C. and 3 atm.?

At 273° K. and 1 atm. 22.4 l. of CO_2 weigh 44 g.

At 273° K. and 3 atm. $\frac{1}{3} \times$ 22.4 l. of CO_2 weigh 44 g.

At 298° K. (25° C.) and 3 atm. $\frac{298}{273} \times \frac{1}{3} \times$ 22.4 l., or 8.16 l., of CO_2 weigh 44 g.

At 298° K. and 3 atm. 1 l. of CO_2 weighs $\frac{44}{8.16}$ g.

At 298° K. and 3 atm. 50 l. of CO_2 weigh $50 \times \frac{44}{8.16}$ g., or 270 g.

8. Determination of the Relative Weights of a Gas and Air. It is often important to know whether a gas is heavier or lighter than air. The proportion of nitrogen to oxygen in air is very nearly 4 to 1 by volume, so that in 22.4 liters of air four fifths of the molecules would be nitrogen and one fifth would be oxygen. Taking four fifths of 22.4 liters of nitrogen under standard conditions, weighing four fifths of 28.0 g., and mixing it with one fifth of 22.4 liters of oxygen, weighing one fifth of 32.0 g., we would get 22.4 liters of air weighing 28.8 g., under standard conditions. Suppose we wish to know the relative density of the following gases with respect to air: CO_2, NH_3, HCl, Cl_2. We can find their molecular weights with the aid of the atomic weight table, and conclude that 22.4 liters under standard conditions would have the following weights: CO_2, 44 g.; NH_3, 17 g.; HCl, 36.5 g.; Cl_2, 70 g.; air, 28.8 g. This shows at once the relative weight of each with respect to the air.

9. Determination of Molecular Weight. *Example:* What is the molecular weight of phosphorus vapor and what is its formula, given the atomic weight, P = 31.0, and the experimental determination that a flask having a volume of 583 cc. was filled with the vapor at 310° C. and a pressure of 756 mm., and that it was found on cooling to contain

1.49 g. of phosphorus? The molecular weight is found from the number of grams occupying 22.4 liters at 273° K. and 760 mm., which must therefore be calculated.

Since 1.49 g. of phosphorus vapor occupied 583 cc. at 756 mm. and 583° K.,

     1.49 g. of phosphorus vapor would occupy $\frac{756}{760} \times 583$ cc. at 760 mm. and 583° K.,

     1.49 g. of phosphorus vapor would occupy $\frac{273}{583} \times \frac{756}{760}$ $\times$ 583 cc. at 760 mm. and 273° K.,

     1.49 g. of phosphorus vapor would occupy 0.2715 l. at 760 mm. and 273° K.,

     $\frac{22.4}{0.2715} \times$ 1.49 g., or 123 g., of phosphorus vapor would occupy 22.4 l. at 760 mm. and 273° K.

Since 123 g. would occupy 22.4 l. under standard conditions, if it did not condense, 123 is approximately the molecular weight. Since the atomic weight is 31, there are evidently 4 atoms in the molecule, so that the formula is P_4.

10. As another example we may determine the formula of a compound, found by analysis to contain 40 per cent of carbon, 6.67 per cent of hydrogen, and 53.33 per cent of oxygen, and of which 0.50 g. gave 328 cc. of vapor at 200° C. and 750 mm. We will first find the relative number of atoms of each element in the molecule of the compound. From the per cents given we may say that

    40 g. C combines with 6.67 g. H and 53.33 g. of O

∴ 12 g. "   "   " $\frac{12}{40} \times$ 6.67 g. = 2 g. H and

                             $\frac{12}{40} \times$ 53.33 = 16 g. O

or 1 g.-atom C "   "   2 g.-atoms H and 1 g.-atom O

or 1 atom C   "   "   2 atoms H and 1 atom O.

The formula might therefore be CH_2O. However, the same proportions by weight would be found if the formula were $C_2H_4O_2$ or $C_3H_6O_3$, or any other multiple of CH_2O. In order to distinguish between them we must therefore determine the number of grams per mole, which is numerically equal to the molecular weight.

Since 0.5 g. occupies 328 cc. at 750 mm. and 473° K. (200° C.), 0.5 g. would occupy $\frac{750}{760} \times 328$ cc. at 760 mm. and 473° K., and 0.5 g. would occupy $\frac{273}{473} \times \frac{750}{760} \times 328$ cc., or 187 cc. at 760 mm. and 273° K.

Now the weight of gas contained in 22.4 liters, or 22,400 cc., is 1 mole, and since 187 cc. weigh 0.5 g., 1 cc. would weigh 0.00267 g. and 22,400 cc. would weigh $22{,}400 \times 0.00267$ g., or 60 g. Of the various multiples of CH_2O the one having a molal weight of 60 g. is $C_2H_4O_2$; hence this is the correct formula.

11. Direct Relation between Volumes of Gases and Weights of Other Substances in Reactions. *Example:* When limestone is heated to a sufficiently high temperature, it decomposes, as represented by the following equation:

$$CaCO_3 = CaO + CO_2.$$

Suppose we wish to calculate how many liters of CO_2, measured at 20° C. and 10 atmospheres pressure, should be obtained from 2 kilograms (2000 g.) of $CaCO_3$. It is not necessary to calculate the weight of CO_2, since the equation can be interpreted so as to give directly the relation between the weight of $CaCO_3$ and the volume of CO_2. We may indicate this relationship as follows:

$$CaCO_3 \longrightarrow CO_2$$

$$\left.\begin{array}{l} 1 \text{ mole} \\ 100 \text{ g.} \end{array}\right\} \text{ gives } \left\{\begin{array}{l} 1 \text{ mole} \\ 22.4 \text{ l. at } 273° \text{ K. and 1 atm.} \end{array}\right.$$

∴2000 g.   "   448 l.   "   "   "   "   "

"   " $\frac{293}{273} \times 448$ l. at 293° K. and 1 atm.

"   " $\frac{1}{10} \times \frac{293}{273} \times 448.$ l at 293° K. and 10 atm.

The resulting volume is 48.1 l.

12. Complete Interpretation of Chemical Equations. It is possible now to summarize what has been presented in this chapter and the preceding one concerning the interpretation of chemical equations, both as to weight and volume relations, bearing in mind that **a formula signifies a certain weight of substance, and, when the substance exists in the**

gaseous state, a certain volume under standard conditions.
The molal volumes of liquids and solids can be calculated
from the measured density, d grams per cc., whence 1 g.
occupies $1/d$ cc. and M grams M/d cc. We may recall that
formulas are interpreted in two ways, one referring to atoms
and molecules, the other to gram-atoms and gram-molecules,
or moles. This double interpretation may be illustrated by
using an equation as in the following table, writing under
each formula its significance in both senses.

$$CO_2 \text{ (gas)} + C \text{ (solid)} = 2 CO \text{ (gas)}$$

(1) Weights in terms of			
oxygen atom = 16	44	12	56
Number of molecules	1	1 atom	2
Relative volumes	1	0 +	2

$$CO_2 \text{ (gas)} + C \text{ (solid)} = 2 CO \text{ (gas)}$$

(2) Weight in grams	44	12	56
Number of moles	1	1 g.-atom	2
Volume of 0° C., 1 atm.	22.4 l.	$\dfrac{12}{d}$ cc.	44.8 l.
Number of molecules	6×10^{23}	6×10^{23} (atoms)	12×10^{23}

The last row of figures is added for the sake of interest,
not because it will be used in problems. The other data
represent all that is necessary in order to solve any problem
involving weights, or volumes of gases, provided that one
knows how to apply the gas laws to get the relation between
the volumes of gases at standard conditions and at other
conditions. It must be noted that this generalization connecting weights and volumes is possible only where gases
are involved. With liquids and solids the densities of the
particular substances must be determined by experiment.
The great difference between the volumes of equivalent
quantities of gases, liquids, and solids should be appreciated.

If the carbon in the above equation is in the form of graphite, whose density is 2.25, the volume of 12 g. of it is 5.33 cc. The relative volumes of 12 g. of graphite and 44 g. of CO_2 in both liquid and gaseous forms are represented to scale in Fig. 1.

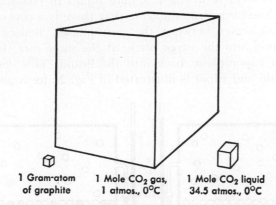

1 Gram-atom   1 Mole CO_2 gas,   1 Mole CO_2 liquid
of graphite   1 atmos., 0°C   34.5 atmos., 0°C

Fig. 1.   Relative volumes.

13. Molecular Weights of Dissolved Substances. It is frequently impossible to determine the molecular weight of a substance from the volume of its vapor, owing to decomposition on heating. Sugar, for example, decomposes instead of vaporizing when heated, turning first to caramel and then charring. Some property other than the density in the vapor state is therefore necessary in order to determine its molecular weight, and to decide which multiple of its empirical formula, $C_{12}H_{22}O_{11}$, is the correct one. Hydrogen peroxide, likewise, is very unstable, except when in a dilute solution, decomposing often with explosive violence when in the pure state. Analysis shows that it contains twice as much oxygen in proportion to the hydrogen as does water; hence, having decided that water is represented by the formula H_2O, we may conclude that hydrogen peroxide must be represented by one of the formulas HO, H_2O_2, H_3O_3, etc. These are alike in the proportion of hydrogen to oxygen, 1 to 16, but differ in the total weight of the molecule, i.e., the molecular weight. To distinguish between these possible formulas, therefore, we must find out whether the mole weighs 17 g. or 34 g. or 51 g., etc. For such substances the molecular weight must be determined under conditions such that the substance does not decompose, which is the case often in dilute solutions.

14. Among the properties of a solution which depend upon the molecular weight of the dissolved substance (called the solute) are the vapor pressure, the boiling point, and the freezing point. To understand the nature of the effect of a solute we may apply again the kinetic theory. If we have a pure liquid in contact with its vapor in a closed vessel, we imagine that there is a constant interchange of molecules between the two phases, molecules going from the liquid into the vapor phase at the same rate that others go from the vapor phase back into the liquid. This distribution between liquid and vapor is illustrated in Fig. 2a for a pure liquid.

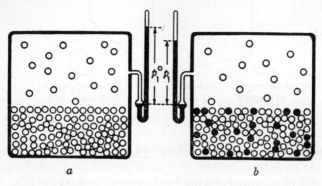

Fig. 2. *a*, vapor pressure of pure liquid, and *b*, of the same liquid in which 0.2 of the molecules have been replaced by molecules of a nonvolatile solute having approximately the same intermolecular force of attraction.

Suppose, now, that a certain proportion of the solvent moelcules, say 0.2, is replaced by molecules of some solute which is not appreciably volatile and which does not alter the attractive forces holding the molecules of solvent in the liquid phase. Since there are now only 0.8 as many molecules of solvent present in the liquid phase as before, the number in the vapor phase and hence their pressure will be reduced to 0.8 its former value, as illustrated in Fig. 2b. Of course, if the molecules of the solute introduced exert a stronger attraction on the solvent molecules, they will be individually less able to escape into the vapor than before, so that their number and therefore their aggregate pressure would be less than 0.8, and vice versa. The effect on vapor pressure in the ideal case, where there is no alteration in the attractive forces, is represented graphically in Fig. 3. If the solution is composed of n_1 moles of solvent and n_2 moles of solute (these roles are actually interchangeable) then the fraction of solvent molecules in the solution is $n_1/(n_1 + n_2)$ and their vapor pressure, p_1, is the same fraction of the vapor pressure of the pure solvent, p_1^0, or

$$p_1 = p_1^0 \frac{n_1}{n_1 + n_2}. \qquad (1)$$

This is known as **Raoult's Law.**

Evidently Raoult's Law can be used to determine the number of moles, n_2, represented by a certain weight of solute in n_1 moles of solvent. Suppose, for illustration, that it was found by experiment that 19.40 g. of iodine dissolved in 38.0 g. of CS_2 lowered the vapor pressure of the CS_2 from 433 mm. at 30° C., the value for pure CS_2, to 404 mm. for the iodine solution. Putting p_1 = 404 and p_1^0 = 433 in equation (1) gives 0.933 = $n_1/(n_1 + n_2)$. The molecular weight of CS_2 is 76.0, therefore the number of moles of it in 38.0 g. is 0.500, which is n_1. Substituting this in the preceding equation

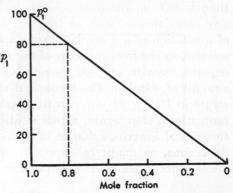

Fig. 3. Lowering of vapor pressure of a solvent when its mole fraction is reduced by adding a solute. Raoult's Law.

gives the value of $n_2 = 0.0718$, the number of moles of iodine represented by 19.40 g. One mole of iodine is, accordingly, $19.40/0.0718 = 270$ g. Since the atomic weight of iodine is 127 its molecule must be I_2, rather than I, or I_3, etc., with a molecular weight 254. The discrepancy between 254 and 270 must be attributed to experimental errors and to deviations of this solution from Raoult's Law.

15. Instead of measuring the number of dissolved moles by the lowering of the vapor pressure of the solvent, the temperature being kept the same, we may, on the other hand, keep the pressure the same, say 1 atmosphere, and determine how much the temperature must be increased in order to make the vapor pressure of the solvent great enough to continue boiling, i.e., we may measure the rise in the boiling point produced by the added solute. The relation between the rise in temperature when solute is added in order to continue the boiling under 1 atmosphere pressure, and the lowering of vapor pressure when solute is added at constant temperature, as shown in Fig. 2, depends on the change in vapor pressure caused by changing the temperature. This is related to the heat of vaporization of the solvent by Equation (6), Chapter III. In the case of water, the theoretical rise in the boiling point is 0.52° C. for 1 mole of solute in 1000 g. of water. Other concentrations produce proportionate rises, i.e., 0.26° C. for 0.50 mole per 1000 g., etc.

16. Just as it is harder to vaporize the solvent from a solution than it is from the pure solvent, so it is harder to remove it by any other means, such as freezing, and just as the boiling point of a solution of a nonvolatile substance is higher than that of the solvent, so the freezing point of the solution will be lower, and will depend, likewise, only on the number of moles of solute in a given amount of solution. The theoretical value is 1.86° C. for 1 mole of solute in 1000 g. of water, with proportionate values at other concentrations. Here again, actual solutions show deviations from the theoretical lowerings due to unequal attractive forces, and these deviations, as might be expected, are greater at higher than at lower concentrations, as illustrated in Table 1.

TABLE 1

Freezing Point Lowerings for Aqueous Solutions

Moles per 1000 g. H_2O	0.01	0.1	1.0
Acetone, $CO(CH_3)_2$	0.0186	0.185	1.79
Hydrogen peroxide, H_2O_2	—	0.184	1.88
Ethyl alcohol, C_2H_5OH	0.0183	0.183	1.83
Propyl alcohol, C_3H_7OH	0.0186	0.183	1.79
Glycerol, $C_3H_5(OH)_3$	0.0186	0.187	1.92
Cane sugar, $C_{12}H_{22}O_{11}$	0.0186	0.188	2.06

17. *Example:* It was found that a solution of 7.29 g. of sugar in 100 g. of water had a freezing point 0.395° lower than that of water. What is the molecular weight of the sugar? For each 1000 g. of water in a solution of the same concentration there would be 72.9 g. of sugar. Now, 1 mole of sugar in this amount of water would produce a lowering of 1.86°, and since 72.9 g. produces a lowering of only 0.395°, which is $\frac{0.395}{1.86}$ or 0.213 of the lowering produced by 1 mole, there must be only 0.213 of a mole present. If, then, 72.9 g. is 0.213 mole, 1 mole is $\frac{72.9}{0.213}$ g. or 342 g. Comparing this with the empirical formula of sugar, $C_{12}H_{22}O_{11}$, as determined by analysis, we see that the simplest formula is the correct one.

Exercises

1. Define (a) compounds, (b) solutions, (c) elements in terms of the atomic and molecular theories.

2. What is the distinction between a mole and a molecule? Give an example of the former.

3. What conclusion can you draw from the fact that 1 liter of phosphine gas, PH_3, can be decomposed to give 250 cc. of phosphorus vapor, measured at the same temperature and pressure?

4. What volume of oxygen is necessary to burn 3 liters of H_2S gas according to the reaction: $2 H_2S + 3 O_2 = 2 H_2O + 2 SO_2$?

5. State a simple piece of evidence to show that the molecule of oxygen contains two atoms.

6. If ordinary oxygen is O_2, how could you prove that ozone is O_3?

7. How many moles of oxygen, O_2, are 40 g. of oxygen?

8. (a) How many moles of NO_2 gas are there in 23 g. of it? (b) What volume would 23 g. occupy under standard conditions?

9. A closed vessel contains ammonia gas at 1 atm. and 27° C. A spark is passed through the gas till it is all decomposed into hydrogen and nitrogen. What will the pressure be if the temperature is (a) 27° C., (b) 127° C.? The equation for the reaction is: $2 NH_3 = N_2 + 3 H_2$.

10. Give the specific gravity of each of the following gases referred to air under the same conditions: N_2, O_2, CO, H_2S, Cl_2, NH_3, H_2O vapor, HCl, NO, SO_2.

11. What is the volume of 34 g. of NH_3 at 546° C. and 4 atm.?

12. What would be the relative efficiencies of the following gases as filling for balloons: H_2, He, CH_4?

*13. How efficient is hot air, at a temperature of say 200° C., in lifting a balloon? (Make reasonable assumptions for any further necessary data.)

14. (a) A certain compound of carbon and hydrogen contains 20% of hydrogen; the atomic weights are H = 1 and C = 12; what is its simplest formula? (b) What is its formula if 1.5 g. of the gas occupy 1.12 l. under standard conditions?

---

* These are questions of greater difficulty, which should not be attacked until the others are mastered.

15. How many liters of CO_2, measured (*a*) under standard conditions, (*b*) at 22° C. and 5 atm. pressure, could be obtained by heating 1000 g. of $CaCO_3$?

16. At a certain pressure and temperature 2 g. of CO_2 occupied a volume of 1250 cc. What is the molecular weight of another gas 2 g. of which occupied a volume of 720 cc. under the same temperature and pressure?

17. What volume of CO, measured at 0° C. and 0.8 atm., could be obtained from 25 g. of carbon by the reaction: $2 C + O_2 = 2 CO$?

18. A certain gas is known to have a formula of the type CH, C_2H_2, C_3H_3, etc. Given that 295 cc. of it weighs 0.317 g. at 22° C. and 1 atm., which formula is correct?

19. Write the equation for the combustion of CO to CO_2, and interpret it in terms of (*a*) moles, (*b*) liters at standard conditions, (*c*) grams.

20. 4.0 g. of scandium react with an excess of HCl to give 3.054 liters of hydrogen at 0° C. and 760 mm. At. wt. of Sc = 44. (*a*) What weight of scandium is equivalent to 1 g. of hydrogen? (*b*) What is the formula of scandium chloride? (*c*) What would be the volume of hydrogen at 25° C. and 784 mm. if collected over water? Vapor pressure of water at 25° C. is 24 mm.

21. What is the formula of a gas containing 46.1% of carbon and 53.9% of nitrogen, 2.60 g. of which has a volume of 560 cc. at 0° C. and 2 atm.?

22. If M grams of a gas occupy 22.4 liters at 1 atm. and 273° K., what volume, v, will W grams of it occupy at p atm. and $T°$?

*23. Hydrogen peroxide contains 1 part by weight of hydrogen to 16 parts of oxygen, and a solution of 0.369 g. of it in 25 g. of water had a freezing point of − 0.805° C. What is its formula?

24. The following gas reactions are carried out in closed vessels kept at constant temperature. If the initial pressure is 1 atm., what will the final pressure be in each case? (*a*) $2 HI + H_2 + I_2$, (*b*) $2 O_3 = 3 O_2$, (*c*) $4 PH_3 = P_4 + 6 H_2$, (*d*) $2 SO_3 = 2 SO_2 + O_2$.

*25. Arrange the following gases in order of increasing rate of diffusion through still air: NH_3, Cl_2, $COCl_2$, H_2, H_2S, SO_2.

*26. The radius of a helium atom is approximately 10^{-8} cm. What fraction of the volume occupied by helium gas at 1 atm. and 0° C. is actually occupied by the atoms themselves?

*27. Calculate the ratio of the density of air containing 0.01 mole per cent of Cl_2 to that of pure air at the same temperature.

28. What volume of liquid benzene, density 0.82 g. per cc., would be formed by condensing 1 liter of benzene vapor, measured at 100° C. and 1 atm.? Benzene, C_6H_6.

29. 68,000 calories of heat are given out when one mole of hydrogen burns. How many calories are liberated by the burning of the hydrogen in a soap bubble of 500 cc. volume? Assume 1 atm. pressure and 25° C.

*30. AsH_3 is toxic at a partial pressure of 0.04 mm. What weight of Mg_3As_2 would be necessary to infect one cubic meter of air to this concentration?

*31. In deriving the number 28.8 for the weight of 22.4 l. of air at standard conditions, in paragraph 8, the presence of argon was neglected and the fraction of oxygen molecules was taken roughly as $\frac{1}{5}$. Calculate a more accurate value from the following figures for the per cent of each kind of molecule: 78% N_2, 21% O_2, 1% A.

*32. The pressure of water vapor at 20° C. is 17 mm. Calculate the weight of 1 l. of (a) dry air at 20° C. and 760 mm. (~~use the result of exercise 26~~), and (b) air saturated with water vapor at the same temperature and pressure.

*33. The value of pv for H_2 at 200 atm. and 20° C. is 1.206 of the value of pv at low pressures and the same temperature. What balloon capacity could be filled by the hydrogen in a steel "bottle" of 1.00 cu. ft. capacity and a pressure of 200 atm. at 20° C.?

*34. How many molecules of gas per cc. are there in an X-ray tube evacuated to a pressure of 10^{-5} mm. at 20° C.?

CHAPTER V

THE RELATION OF CHEMICAL AND PHYSICAL PROPERTIES TO ATOMIC STRUCTURE

1. The nature of chemical union prior to the last few decades was clothed in mystery. Such pictures of it as were drawn were the product of pure speculation. The older generation of living chemists had to accumulate their knowledge of chemical behavior piecemeal, with little to guide them in the way of general principles. The students of today, however, can be saved much of this long process by availing themselves of the deductive approach made possible by the flood of light recently thrown upon the structure of matter. This chapter is intended only as a preliminary survey, details and proofs will be given later, particularly in Chapters XVI and XVII. The student should not be discouraged if he should feel after studying it that he is far from being expert in understanding atomic structure and relating it to chemical and physical properties. That facility is something to build up gradually by repeated practice in connection with an ever-widening range of phenomena, not a task that can be completed in a few lessons.

There are three common ways of presenting a subject. They may be designated, respectively, the logical, the chronological, and the psychological. The first consists in building up an argument, step by step, each complete and conclusive. It is the form which a subject finally assumes in an orderly mind, the one, therefore, which it tends to assume in a textbook. The second way follows the historical order in which the subject was developed. This is likely to be interesting and worth retracing, but it may not be the most significant to the learner because the clearest experimental evidence has not always been the first to come to light. The way which is here called the psychological way takes account of the fact that a scientific principle is usually not a simple proposition to be grasped the moment it is logically demonstrated, but rather a concept, which may have many and far-reaching implications. To use it with true understanding requires skill only to be developed by practice. It is like an athletic skill, such as diving, which cannot be acquired by explanations and demonstrations alone, but by repetition under increasingly difficult conditions.

TABLE 1
Ultimate Particles

	Atomic weight $O = 16.0000$	Electric charge Unit $= 1.60 \times 10^{-19}$ coulombs	Radius, cm.
Electron	0.000,548	− 1	$\gg 10^{-13}$
Proton	1.0073	+ 1	2×10^{-13}
Neutron	1.0087	0	2×10^{-13}
cf. Oxygen atom	16.0000	0	6000×10^{-13}

This chapter is neither logical nor chronological; it is a sort of brief aerial reconnaissance of scientific territory of great importance to students of physical science. It gives a preview of what is to be later proved by evidence and logic. The student will have abundant opportunity throughout the course to learn to find his own way about in this region.

2. **Ultimate Particles.** Atoms were formerly defined as the ultimate particles of matter and regarded as indivisible. We have recently learned, however, that the numerous different species of atoms are themselves composed of three species of still smaller particles, electrons, protons, and neutrons. Their significant properties, mass, electric charge, and size are given in Table 1. The figures for size are to be regarded as somewhat uncertain, for they depend on the method used in calculating them. The properties of the electron are such that a definite radius cannot be measured;

all we are justified in saying is that an electron occupies much more space than a proton or a neutron.

3. Composition of Atoms. The atoms of the different elements are all made up of these three kinds of elementary particles. The weight of an atom depends almost entirely on the number of protons and neutrons it contains, since the electrons are so light that they contribute but little to atomic weight. The charge of an atom, however, is not affected by the number of neutrons present but depends on the balance between electrons and protons. A neutral atom contains the same number of electrons and protons; an atom with unit negative charge has one extra electron, etc.

4. Structures of Atoms. The protons and neutrons in an atom are packed tightly in a very small **nucleus** around which the electrons travel at relatively great distances, a little like the planets of the solar system, which travel around the sun. The size of the solar system is fixed by the planetary orbits, its mass mainly by the mass of the sun.

A neutral atom of oxygen, for example, has 8 electrons and 8 protons. Since its atomic weight is 16, it contains 8 neutrons in addition to its 8 protons in the nucleus. If the diameter of the whole atom is called 1, the diameter of the nucleus is only 0.0001; the diameter of a single electron is perhaps, roughly 0.001. If the nucleus is represented by a small pea, the electrons could be large oranges, the farthest 100 yards away from the pea. It would be a queer kind of pea, however, since it would weight about one ton if the oranges were ordinary oranges. It is evident that an atom, like the solar system, is mostly empty space.

5. Electron Orbitals. The Danish physicist, Bohr, assigned definite circular and elliptical orbits to the electrons, on the basis of certain assumptions, but it is now realized that it is impossible to verify these orbits experimentally. The orbit of a comet can be fixed from a series of observations of its successive positions, but anything we do to an electron to find out where it is diverts it from its path, and we can never find out where it would have been later if left alone.

It is possible, however, in effect, to shoot electrons at a great many atoms of one species and learn how the percentage of successful hits on the electrons of the atom varies with the distance from the nucleus. Figure 1 shows how this probability or "electron density" varies with the distance. The results of such experiments and calculations permit the drawing of the only kinds of atomic pictures that have any actual significance. Figure 2a shows such a picture. It is a picture such as would result if it were possible to take a photograph of the electron of a hydrogen atom by time exposure

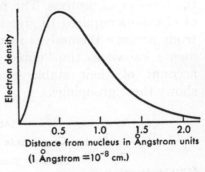

Fig. 1. Probability of finding the electron of a hydrogen atom at varying distance from its nucleus.

without disturbing it. The electron appears to be moving in and out from the nucleus in different directions, giving the effect of a spherical "cloud." Figure 2b shows the "cloud" for an electron which is temporarily moving in

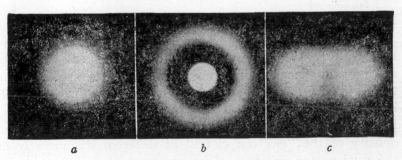

a   b   c

Fig. 2. "Electron clouds."

a state farther from the nucleus. It will later revert to the more stable state, emitting a "quantum" of radiant energy of definite frequency. Figure 2c shows the dumbbell shaped "cloud" made by an electron moving in still another temporary state in a magnetic field.

6. The Grouping of Electrons in Atoms. The number of neutrons in the nucleus of an atom, while contributing to the atomic weight, has little effect upon its chemical behavior. This is determined by the nuclear charge, which depends on the number of protons. The nuclear charge fixes the number of electrons required to give a neutral atom, and these electrons arrange themselves in certain stable groups. The elements known as the "noble gases" are inert chemically on account of their stable electron arrangements. Table 2 shows these groupings.

TABLE 2

Electron Groupings in the Noble Gas Elements

	Helium	Neon	Argon	Krypton	Xenon	Radon
Nuclear charge atomic number (No. of protons)	+2	+10	+18	+36	+54	+86
No. of electrons						
1st group K	2	2	2	2	2	2
2nd " L		8	8	8	8	8
3rd " M			8	18	18	18
4th " N				8	18	32
5th " O					8	18
6th " P						8

We see that 2 electrons form a stable group nearest the nucleus in all these atoms. All but helium have stable octets as their outermost groups. We need not bother at this time to discuss the significance of the buried groups of 18 and 32, but we shall focus our attention on the pair and the octet. Figure 3 shows the probability of finding an electron, or the density of the "electron cloud" at different distances from the nucleus for an atom of krypton, which has 2, 8, 18, 8 electrons in the K, L, M, N groups, respectively.

7. Gain or Loss of Outer Electrons. Elements with intermediate atomic numbers have either too many or too few electrons to give these stable groupings. Table 3 shows the distribution of electrons in the elements with nuclear charges from 1 to 20. These nuclear charges, serving as they do to

orient the series of elements, are called **atomic numbers.**
The elements not possessing the stable outer electron groups
shown in Table 2 tend to acquire these groups by gaining or
losing electrons, as the case may be. The element fluorine,
whose electron groups are 2,7, could assume the neon structure by acquiring an extra electron, but since its nuclear
charge is only $+ 9$, the electrons 2,8, would give the resultant
atom a unit negative charge, which we write F⁻ and call

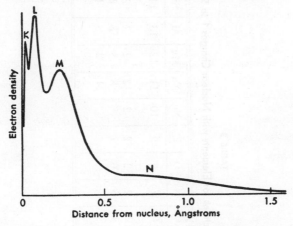

Fig. 3. "Electron density" for a krypton atom.

fluoride ion. Sodium, Na, $+ 11$, has 2,8,1 electrons, and can
assume the neon structure by losing its outer electron, making
it Na⁺, sodium ion. Similarly, magnesium, Mg, can become
Mg⁺⁺; aluminum, Al, can become Al⁺⁺⁺; oxygen, O, can
become O⁻⁻, etc. The elements near argon, A, can assume
the argon structure, 2,8,8, by gaining or losing electrons,
as the case may be, giving S⁻⁻, Cl⁻, A, K⁺, Ca,⁺⁺ etc., all
having 2,8,8 electrons. Lithium, Li, becomes Li⁺ in assuming
the helium structure. Hydrogen, like Li, Na, K, can lose its
only electron, since it is not part of a pair or an octet.

This is so important that it is summarized for the first
20 elements, in Table 3, for emphasis.

8. Chemical Reaction by Electron Transfer. Atoms which
can lose outer electrons can react chemically with atoms which

TABLE 3

Distribution of Electrons for Elements with Nuclear Charges 1 to 20

Element	H	He	Li	Be	B	C	N	O	F	Ne	Na	Mg	Al	Si	P	S	Cl	A	K	Ca
Nuclear charge, + No. of electrons, −	1	2	3	4	5	6	7	8	9	10	11	12	13	14	15	16	17	18	19	20
Group 1	1	2	2	2	2	2	2	2	2	2	2	2	2	2	2	2	2	2	2	2
Group 2			1	2	3	4	5	6	7	8	8	8	8	8	8	8	8	8	8	8
Group 3											1	2	3	4	5	6	7	8	8	8
Group 4																			1	2

can gain electrons, giving charged atoms which can arrange themselves in solid crystal lattices. If we represent a fluorine atom by $^-\overline{\underline{(+7)}}^-$, the circle inclosing what is called the "kernel," consisting of the nucleus and the inner pair of electrons, the part not disturbed in chemical reactions, whose

TABLE 4

Gain and Loss of Electrons to give Stable Structures

Neutral atoms	O	F	Ne	Na	Mg	Al
	2	2	2	2	2	2
	6	7	8	8	8	8
				1	2	3
Charged atoms, neon structure	O^{--}	F^-	Ne	Na^+	Mg^{++}	Al^{+++}
	2	2	2	2	2	2
	8	8	8	8	8	8
Neutral atoms	S	Cl	A	K	Ca	Sc
	2	2	2	2	2	2
	8	8	8	8	8	8
	6	7	8	8	8	8
				1	2	3
Charged atoms, argon structure	S^{--}	Cl^-	A	K^+	Ca^{++}	Sc^{+++}
	2	2	2	2	2	2
	8	8	8	8	8	8
	8	8	8	8	8	8

charges add up to $+7$, and, represent a sodium (natrium) atom by $^-\underline{(+1)}$, whose kernel consists of the nucleus, the inner electron pair, and the electron octet, whose charges add up to $+1$, then the chemical reaction between these two atoms may be represented as follows:

$$^-\overline{\underline{(+7)}}^- \text{ and } ^-\underline{(+1)} \text{ give } ^-\overline{\underline{(+7)}}^= \text{ and } (+1)$$

These resulting charged atoms, F^- and Na^+, attract each other, and, if there are many of them, build up a cubic crystal lattice in which the oppositely charged atoms alternate as illustrated in the one in Fig. 6 labeled "ionic." Sodium chloride crystals, common salt, NaCl, are constructed on this plan.

If magnesium and fluorine atoms are used, one atom of the former, with its two outer electrons, can satisfy two fluorine atoms. The reaction can be pictured as follows:

$$^-\!\!\overline{\underline{(+7)}}^{\,-} \text{ and } ^-(+2)^{\,-} \text{ and } ^-\!\!\overline{\underline{(+7)}}^{\,=} \text{ to give } ^=\!\!\overline{\underline{(+7)}}^{\,=}(+2)^{\,-}\overline{\underline{(+7)}}^{\,-}$$

The resulting MgF_2 necessarily forms a somewhat more complicated crystal lattice than the simple cubic mentioned above.

It can be seen, in general, that the numbers of outer electrons determine the ratios in which atoms combine, their combining values, or "valences" (cf. Chapter IX), and allow us to write compounds of the elements in Table 4, such as: KCl, $CaCl_2$, $ScCl_3$, K_2S, CaS, Sc_2S_3. **The outer electrons of an atom, the ones which are involved in chemical changes, are called its valence electrons.**

The terms we have been using may be clearer for future use if summarized in the following diagram.

Atom	Na	Cl	Ca	
Nucleus	+ 11	+ 17	+ 20	⎞
Electrons				⎟
1st group	2	2	2	⎬ Kernel
2nd group	8	8	8	⎟
3rd group	1	7	8	⎠
4th group			2	Valence electrons

9. It is often convenient to represent the kernel of an atom by its symbol in boldface type, remembering the + charge each kernel would have and the outer electrons that would have to be present in a neutral atom. The following comparison illustrates the relation between these kernel symbols and the ordinary symbols, using dots to denote valence electrons.

Ordinary symbol	H	H$^+$	Cl	Cl$^-$	Cl$_2$	HCl	H$_2$O
Kernel symbol	**H**·	**H**	·**C̈l**:	:**C̈l**:	:**C̈l**:**C̈l**:	**H**:**C̈l**:	**H**:**Ö**:
							H

10. Electron-Shared or Covalent Bonds. In the cases considered in the preceding paragraph, the charged atoms resulting from electron gains and losses are held together mainly (there is also another component) by electrostatic attraction. There is, however, another type of force, not electrostatic, capable of forming very strong bonds. Its simplest example is the hydrogen molecule, H_2. The separate atoms consist of 1 proton and 1 electron each, and, being alike, there is no reason why one should permanently acquire the electron of the other. We see with helium, however, that 2 electrons can form a very stable group. In fact it requires a work of 24.5 electron volts (the energy that an electron would acquire in traveling 1 cm. in an electric field of 24.5 volts per cm.; one electron volt is equivalent to 23,066 calories per gram-atom) to remove one electron from a helium atom, as compared with 13.5 electron-volts for a hydrogen atom and only 5.1 electron volts for a sodium atom.

This can be explained, in part, by the fact that an electron moving in a circular or elliptical orbit is accompanied by a magnetic field, just as a current in a loop of wire has its magnetic field. These orbits or loops are free to orient themselves so as to neutralize these fields. There is good reason to believe, also, that the electrons spin on their axes, and thereby create a further magnetic field. A north-south adjustment of their spin magnetic fields is an additional factor in giving stability to a pair of electrons. Single atoms which have one valence electron respond to an external magnetic field while those with two do not unless the field is strong enough to unpair their electron orbits and spins.

Our concept of a hydrogen molecule must therefore be two protons with two electrons moving about both of them in some sort of stabilized orbits, giving a "cloud" shaped like Fig. 4. A similar stability is achieved by the pairing of the odd electrons of 2 chlorine atoms. Unable otherwise to gain undisputed possession of 8 electrons, they satisfy their need for 8 electrons by going into partnership, as represented by :C̈l:C̈l:. We have such pairing and sharing also in the molecules: F_2, Br_2, I_2.

11. Electron-pair bonded molecules can be very stable, as illustrated by the heat necessary to dissociate them into atoms, shown in Table 5. The figure for NaCl vapor illustrates the fact that electrostatic bonds and electron-pair bonds can be of comparable magnitude.

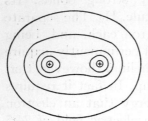

Fig. 4. Electron "cloud" density for a hydrogen molecule.

12. Metals and Nonmetals. The pairing of the outer electrons of two like atoms that we see in the molecule, H_2, does not occur, at least with any strength, in the case of the larger, metallic atoms, whose valence electrons, even in the solid state, are more or less free to move about within the metal, in consequence of which they are **electric conductors.** The ability of metals to reflect light from their surfaces, called metallic luster, is due to these loosely

TABLE 5

Heat of Dissociation of One Mole into Atoms, Kilogram Calories

H_2	103.7	Br_2	45.2
F_2	62.6	I_2	35.4
Cl_2	56.9	NaCl(gas)	100.

held electrons. These electrons can easily be detached from the solid metal, the potential required in the case of sodium being only 2.1 electron volts. Elements whose outer octets are complete, either alone, as with the noble gas atoms, neon, argon, etc., or by sharing, as with Cl_2, O_2, N_2, etc., hold their electrons so firmly that they are nonconducting and nonmetallic in the solid state. The work of removing an electron from a molecule of gaseous Cl_2 is 13.2 electron volts.

13. Nonpolar, Polar, and Ionic Compounds. As stated above, two like atoms usually combine by sharing outer electrons, if possible, so as to complete pairs and octets, as illustrated by chlorine in Fig. 5. The molecule is symmetrical and electrically neutral, and is called **nonpolar**. If the atoms differ somewhat in their affinity for electrons due to differing sizes or structures, the bonding or shared electrons will be closer to, or spend more of the time traveling about one atom than the other, making this atom on the whole more negative, as illustrated by iodine chloride, Fig. 5. Such a molecule is called **polar**. If the difference in electron affinity is sufficiently great, the outer electrons of the one may be

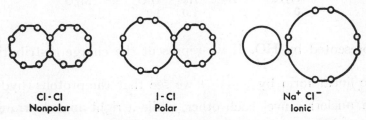

Cl - Cl
Nonpolar

I - Cl
Polar

Na⁺ Cl⁻
Ionic

Fig. 5. Types of molecules.

completely lost to the other so that there is no true chemical bond but only the electrostatic attraction of the now positive and negative atoms for each other, as illustrated by potassium chloride. Such a molecule is called **ionic,** since the two parts are easily detached from each other on going into solution where they are free to wander off in different directions.

14. The degree of polarity, or displacement of + and − charges in a molecule is expressed by its **dipole moment.** The dipole moment of a molecule determines the force which an electronic field can exert to orient the molecule, as shown in Fig. 6. It obviously depends upon the magnitude of the charge separation in the molecule, i.e., it is greater the larger the charge difference between different parts of the molecule and the distance of separation. The transition from nonpolar through increasingly polar to ionic compounds is illustrated in Table 6.

The dipole moment often gives important evidence of molecular structure. For example, the large moment of the water molecule shows that it is not linear and symmetrical as represented by HOH, but approximately right angled, as

TABLE 6

Polarity

(The figures are for dipole moment $\times 10^{18}$ electrostatic units)

Electron displacement

Zero	Increasing			Complete
H_2, Cl_2	HI	HCl	HF	NaCl
0 0	0.4	1.0	2	
PI_3	PBr_3	PCl_3	$SbCl_3$	BiF_3
0	0.6	1.0	3.6	
H_2Te	H_2Se	H_2S	H_2O	MgO
0		1.0	1.9	

represented by HO. If we represent the charge distribution
　　　　　　　　H
of a linear form by $+ = \overset{..}{O} = +$ we see that the protons (hydrogen nuclei) cancel each other, while a right-angled arrangement $+ = \overset{..}{O} =$ throws the positive charges to one side, the
　　　　　　 $\dotplus$
negative to the other so that the molecule would tend to orient in an electric field as shown in Fig. 6.

A study of dipole moments indicates that the negative character of some of the commoner elements increases in the following order:

K, Na, Ba, Ca, Mg, Al, Sn, Sb, B, As, H, P, I, S, C, Br, Cl, N, O, F.

15. Types of Crystal Lattices. The various types of atoms and molecules arrange themselves in solid crystal lattices of rather distinct kinds with characteristic properties. Metallic atoms hold their electrons so loosely that even when massed together in the solid form the electrons can migrate more or less freely through the solid under the impulse of an electric field giving metallic conduction, the most distinctive property of metals. This is crudely illustrated in Fig. 7. Moreover, since the positive "kernels" of the atoms—the atoms stripped of their outer electrons—are not bound to each other by specific bonds, they can be dis-

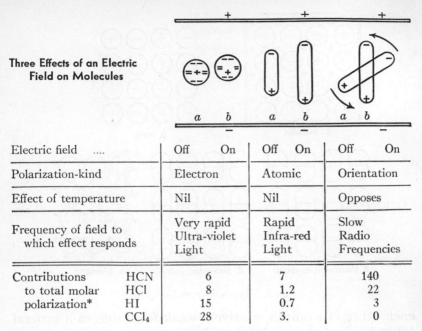

Three Effects of an Electric Field on Molecules						
	a	*b*	*a*	*b*	*a*	*b*
Electric field	Off	On	Off	On	Off	On
Polarization-kind	Electron		Atomic		Orientation	
Effect of temperature	Nil		Nil		Opposes	
Frequency of field to which effect responds	Very rapid Ultra-violet Light		Rapid Infra-red Light		Slow Radio Frequencies	
Contributions to total molar polarization* HCN	6		7		140	
HCl	8		1.2		22	
HI	15		0.7		3	
CCl₄	28		3.		0	

*Calculated from dielectric constant, ϵ, and the volume per mole, v, by the formula, $v(\epsilon - 1)/(\epsilon + 2)$.

Fig. 6

placed relatively to each other without destroying the general attraction between kernels and electrons; hence the metals are ordinarily malleable.

Ionic substances, on the other hand, form crystals with alternately + and − atoms or, better, ions, which are too large to change places unless the structure is melted and greatly expanded; hence they are nonconductors in the solid form but conductors in the liquid state. To split the crystal requires the overcoming of the electrostatic forces between the ions. They are not malleable or plastic since the sliding of one layer over another would bring together ions of like sign which would repel each other resulting in breaking the crystal before a new position of attraction is attained.

Nonpolar molecules and the single stable atoms of helium, neon, argon, etc., exert no electrostatic attractions upon

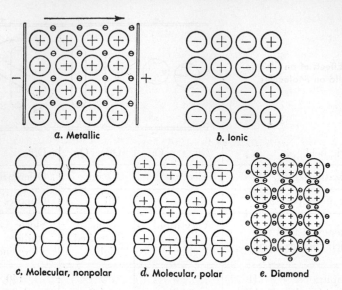

a. Metallic   b. Ionic

c. Molecular, nonpolar   d. Molecular, polar   e. Diamond

Fig. 7. Types of crystal lattices.

each other but only a relatively weak force due to a general interaction of the rapidly moving electrons of one molecule with those of another, analogous, very roughly, to the interaction of vibrating tuning forks. Nonpolar substances, therefore, are relatively soft, and are easily melted and vaporized. A number of the lighter molecules exist as gases at ordinary temperatures and pressures. Figure 7 includes a crude picture of a lattice of nonpolar molecules, e.g. Cl_2.

If the molecules are more or less polar like ICl, in Fig 5, we may expect them to strive for crystal arrangements in which oppositely charged parts of molecules are as near as possible together, giving enhanced attractions, melting points and crystal strengths, other things being equal, as in Fig. 7, for polar molecules. In the liquid state, unlike the ionic substances, they cannot conduct the electric current by migrating independently to the poles, but they will tend to orient, except as opposed by thermal agitation, so that the charged ends of the molecules will lie in the direction of oppositely charged plates thrust into the liquid, as illustrated in Fig. 6.

This figure illustrates three effects of applying electric

fields to molecules. The first is the displacement of electrons with respect to nuclei; the second, the stretching or bending of molecules, called atomic polarization; the third, the orientation of dipoles already existing within the molecule. The distinguishing characteristics of each effect are stated.

One other important lattice type exists, that represented by diamond. Carbon atoms have 4 outer electrons, as shown in Table 1. When 2 such atoms form a chemical bond by sharing a pair of electrons the possibilities of sharing are not exhausted, as they are with chlorine atoms, but each can form electron pairs with 3 other atoms. The result is represented in 2 dimensions in Fig. 7, "diamond lattice." Actually each atom has 4 others around it arranged like the corners of a tetrahedron as illustrated in Chapter XVIII, Fig. 1. We see that there are no molecules of carbon in such a crystal, but that all the atoms are firmly bound together with electron-pair bonds, continuing throughout the crystal. To scratch or split such a crystal would require the rupture of a large number of these bonds, which are particularly strong with carbon due to its small atomic size. In fact, carbon is the hardest known substance, and neither dissolves nor vaporizes at any ordinary temperature.

16. Relative Stabilities of Ionic Compounds. In the cases of compounds in which the atoms may be regarded as definitely positive or negative by reason of the passage of electrons from the metallic to the nonmetallic atoms, we may relate the stability of the compound in large part to the ease with which the electrons can be detached from the former and acquired by the latter. If the formation of one compound from its elements liberates more energy than the formation of another, it is evident that to recover the free elements from the former would require more energy, whether electrical or chemical, than in the case of the latter; the former is therefore more stable. This energy of formation may be divided into a number of parts corresponding to carrying out the synthesis in a number of distinct steps. For example, if one mole (58.5 g.) of solid sodium chloride is to be synthesized from solid sodium and gaseous chlorine, instead of allowing the elements to react with each other directly to form the salt, a process which liberates 98 kg. cals. of heat per mole of NaCl, it is possible to melt one gram-atom of sodium, Na (solid), with absorption of its heat of fusion, next to vaporize it to give gaseous atoms, Na (gas), absorbing its heat of vaporization, then to strip it of its outer electron, giving Na^+ (gas), then let it unite with Cl^- (gas), prepared by splitting Cl_2 (gas) into atoms, Cl (gas), and adding an electron per atom, to give gaseous NaCl molecules, which are then liquefied, and finally solidified.

This synthesis in steps is indicated in the following diagram along with the amount of heat, in kg. cals., involved in each step. A + sign means that heat has been absorbed, increasing the heat content of the material involved, and a − sign that heat has been evolved or lost.

TABLE 7

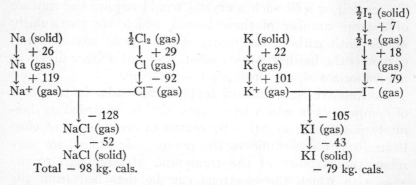

Na (solid) $\frac{1}{2}Cl_2$ (gas)   K (solid) $\frac{1}{2}I_2$ (solid)
  ↓ + 26   ↓ + 29   ↓ + 22   ↓ + 7
Na (gas)   Cl (gas)   K (gas) $\frac{1}{2}I_2$ (gas)
  ↓ + 119   ↓ − 92   ↓ + 101   ↓ + 18
Na^+ (gas)————————Cl^- (gas) K^+ (gas)————————I (gas)
            ↓ − 128   ↓ − 79
       NaCl (gas) I^- (gas)
        ↓ − 52   ↓ − 105
       NaCl (solid)   KI (gas)
Total − 98 kg. cals.   ↓ − 43
                                          KI (solid)
                                          − 79 kg. cals.

By comparing the different steps for the two substances, sodium chloride, NaCl, and potassium iodide, KI, it can be seen how differences between the several respective steps affect the total. For example, the greater total heat of formation of NaCl is due in part to the much greater heat evolved when its gaseous ions unite; they are smaller and can approach closer to each other. The totals are made to differ in one direction by the greater heat absorbed in removing the electron from the gaseous metallic atom, in the case of the sodium, and in the other direction, by the greater heat evolved upon adding the electron to the nonmetallic atom, in the case of chlorine. The smaller energy involved in vaporizing the metal in the case of potassium contributes to the stability of its compounds.

These comparisons may be clearer if the magnitudes are represented graphically to scale, as in Fig. 8. Each step which naturally evolves energy is represented as occurring downward, while each step which absorbs energy is represented as occurring upward. The net evolution of energy on forming a compound is thus the excess of all the downward over the upward processes. The greater the evolution of energy when the compound is formed, the more stable it is, because this would have to be expended in separating the compound again into its elements. The diagram shows that the main "downhill" steps are bigger for forming KF than for forming KI, and, conversely, that to decompose KF would require more energy than to decompose KI, principally because, first, more energy is required to "lift" apart K^+ and F^- than

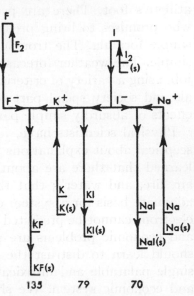

Fig. 8. Graphic representation of magnitude of steps involved in heats of formation.

K^+ and I^-—the former are closer together—and, second, because it takes more energy to "lift" the electron from F^- than from the larger I^-. If we compare KI and NaI, where the difference lies in the metals, we see that "lifting" the electron from a K-atom requires less energy than to "lift" one from the smaller Na-atom, hence more energy is left over to be evolved when KI is formed than when NaI is formed, and, conversely, more would have to be expended to get K and I_2 from KI than to get Na and I_2 from NaI.

17. It may be rather disappointing at this early stage to learn that so many factors have to be considered in order to make accurate predictions. Most of us would prefer to have the matter much simpler. Some profess to predict the weather by looking at the new moon, to see whether its horns point up or down. Some are impressed by claims that a single patent will cure many ailments, from dandruff down to athlete's foot. There are people who vote for a candidate who promises to bring prosperity by means of some single, simple formula. The trouble is that matters are seldom so simple. The weather forecaster, spending all his time on the job, using a variety of criteria, still makes mistakes. Individuals and society spend part of the time recovering from the effects of absurdly simple panaceas.

Physical scientists have, for the most part, learned to be sceptical about explanations that are too simple. They have learned that there are about 92 elements, not four, "earth, air, fire, and water"; that the law of gravitation is not an adequate basis for a system of physics; that the behavior of electrons cannot be predicted from that of baseballs. Political and economic problems are still more complicated, and we should learn to distrust the social scientist who offers in a single palatable and intoxicating elixir to cure a sick social and economic system. We should learn that a spree and a cure may begin with similar feelings of elation but they end very differently.

18. Electrochemical Series. It may be worth while to simplify a problem provided we remember what we have done and do not rely too heavily on the result. We decide in the morning whether or not to take along an umbrella on the basis of an admittedly unreliable prediction regarding the weather. After all, most of us can do better than tossing a coin to protect ourselves from getting wet. Indeed, the making of an accurate analysis of a problem may take so long, even when we know how, as not to be worth the effort. We find, fortunately, that we can correlate chemical stabilities with only a small proportion of error if we focus our attention on only a few of the factors presented in paragraph 16. In that case it is important only not to be surprised if we make a few mistakes.

It is evident from the values in Table 7 that, while the stability of a compound depends upon a number of factors, the electron changes are comparatively large; hence the energies involved in gaining and losing electrons largely determine stability. This will be discussed at more length later (Chapters XVI and XVII) in relation to atomic structures, and we will content ourselves here with simply giving a list, in Table 8, of some of the elements arranged roughly

TABLE 8

Heat in Kg. Cals. Evolved in Formation per Gram-atom of Negative Element

	Oxides	Chlorides	Iodides
Potassium	86	105	79
Sodium	99	98	70
Calcium	152	104	64
Aluminum	133	56	24
Zinc	85	49	25
Iron (ferrous)	64	41	24
Tin (stannous)	70	40	18
Lead	52	43	20
Hydrogen	66	41	− 6
Copper (cuprous)	40	33	16
Silver	7	30	15
Gold (aurous)	—	10	2

according to the stabilities of their compounds. The order is not quite uniform because the charged atoms do not arrange themselves in the same patterns in crystals of different compounds, but the only great discrepancies are in the positions of Na_2O and K_2O.

19. The order of the elements in Table 8 is worth remembering. This will not be difficult for one who will see its correlation, first with its historical significance. The noblest metal in the list, gold, has the greatest tendency to retain its electrons in the metallic state rather than to become positive in compounds, and, accordingly, has doubtless been known from earlier times than any other metal. Neither gold

nor silver, however, were sufficiently abundant to have any great cultural significance. Copper, on the other hand, is more abundant and is easily obtained from its ores and was the first metal to play a significant role in making tools and utensils. The alloy of copper with tin gave bronze, which is harder than either, and gave rise to the "bronze age." Iron is harder to obtain, hence the "iron age" came later. Only in recent times have metals such as sodium and aluminum been obtained. The order of the elements in Table 8 can be further correlated with their ordinary properties and uses. For example, gold is not subject to corrosion, silver tarnishes slightly, copper and lead more readily, but they can still be used where iron would rust badly. Aluminum seems to be stable but this is because the thin oxide coating first formed is very adherent and impervious; if the surface is wet with mercury the film no longer adheres and the metal oxidizes with great rapidity.

20. Salts, Acids, and Bases. Substances which crystallize in ionic lattices, except those whose negative ion is OH^-, are usually called **salts,** by analogy with NaCl, common salt. Most of them are more or less soluble in water, whose polar molecules (cf. paragraph 12) are able to attract the ions of the salt crystal sufficiently to overcome the forces holding them in the lattice. They are then able to wander about independently in the solution (cf. Chapter VIII).

The ions of salts are not confined to single charged atoms, but may consist of charged groups. Figure 5, Chapter XVIII, represents the structure of such salts as $CaCO_3$ and $NaClO_3$, where the ions are Ca^{++} and CO_3^{--} or Na^+ and ClO_3^-, respectively. The following polyatomic ions are frequently encountered:

SO_3^{--}	sulfite	$C_2H_3O_2^-$	acetate
SO_4^{--}	sulfate	ClO_3^-	chlorate
CO_3^{--}	carbonate	ClO^-	hypochlorite
NO_3^-	nitrate	NH_4^+	ammonium
		$Ag(NH_3)_2^+$	silver ammonia complex.

Such ions, like monatomic ions, owe their charges to an excess or deficiency of electrons.

21. Acids. There are a number of hydrogen compounds which, although not giving ionic lattices, react with water to give hydrogen ion, which may be written H^+ (aq.), H_3O^+ (i.e., $H_2O + H^+$), but is usually abbreviated to H^+, the water of hydration being understood. Such a solution is readily recognized as acid by such familiar tests as sour taste, reaction with base metals, such as zinc, to produce hydrogen, $2 H^+ + Zn = H_2 + Zn^{++}$; reaction with a carbonate to produce CO_2 gas, $2 H^+ + CaCO_3$ (solid) $= Ca^{++} + H_2O + CO_2$; and colors imparted to certain highly colored substances called indicators (cf. Chapter XIII). There are a number of more or less familiar acids which we may recall and characterize briefly. Hydrochloric acid, HCl, is a gas when in the pure state at ordinary pressure and temperature, but it is very soluble in water, forming the solution known industrially as "muriatic acid." Sulfuric acid, H_2SO_4, in the absence of water, is a dense, syrupy liquid, and has the trade name, "oil of vitriol." It is manufactured in larger quantities than any other substance for purely chemical purposes. Nitric acid, HNO_3, is a fuming, corrosive liquid extensively used to dissolve the nobler metals and in the manufacture of explosives. Acetic acid, $HC_2H_3O_2$ (only one of the hydrogen atoms of which has acid properties), is the acid of vinegar. Phosphoric acid, H_3PO_4, is used in the phosphate drinks at soda fountains. Boric acid, H_3BO_3, or "boracic acid," is a solid giving a solution of very faintly acid properties. It finds use as a mild antiseptic. Oxalic acid, $H_2C_2O_4$, a solid in the pure state, finds frequent use as a chemical reagent. The various fruit juices contain characteristic acids, such as citric acid, found in lemons, tartaric acid in grapes, malic acid in apples, etc.

When acids dissolve in water, there is formed, along with H^+, an equivalent amount of negative ion, e.g.,

$$HCl \text{ (gas)} \quad = H^+ + Cl^-,$$
$$HNO_3 \text{ (liquid)} = H^+ + NO_3^-,$$
$$H_2SO_4 \text{ (liquid)} = 2 H^+ + SO_4^{--}.$$

22. Bases. Certain solid lattices contain the hydroxide ion OH^- which is liberated, if the substance is soluble, on going into water solution. Such substances are called bases. The positive ion is nearly always that of a metal. Most of them are insoluble in water, or nearly so, the chief exceptions being sodium hydroxide, $NaOH$, sometimes called "caustic soda," potassium hydroxide, KOH, sometimes called "caustic potash," the solution of which is often called "lye," and barium hydroxide, $Ba(OH)_2$. Calcium hydroxide, $Ca(OH)_2$, "slaked lime," is sparingly soluble; its solution is known as "lime water." To these should be added ammonium hydroxide, NH_4OH, formed when ammonia gas, NH_3, is dissolved in water. The soluble bases, especially the first two, are often called **alkalis,** and their solutions alkaline.

The most significant property common to bases is their ability to neutralize acids. If the base and acid are both soluble and largely split into ions, the reaction is simply, $H^+ + OH^- = H_2O$. If the base is insoluble, for example, $Pb(OH)_2$, and the acid soluble, the reaction is expressed by $Pb(OH)_2 + 2\ H^+ = 2\ H_2O + Pb^{++}$. Of course, in order to have a solution of H^+ some negative ion must be present, e.g., NO_3^-, but where this does not take part in the reaction there is no more necessity for representing it in the equation than there is to include the vessel, the operator, or other necessary concomitants; nevertheless, it is often important not to forget its presence in connection with any later treatment of the solution. Some teachers, for this reason, prefer to represent the above reaction by the equation, $Pb(OH)_2 + (2\ H^+,\ 2\ NO_3^-) = 2\ H_2O + (Pb^{++},\ 2\ NO_3^-)$.

The soluble bases, like acids, can be recognized by the colors they give to indicators. We shall see that it is possible by selecting proper indicators to construct a scale to measure all degrees of acidity and alkalinity (cf. Chapter XIII).

23. Basic and Acidic Oxides; Anhydrides of Bases and Acids. Certain oxides of metals can react with water to produce bases, e.g.

$$CaO + H_2O = Ca(OH)_2 = Ca^{++} + 2\ OH^-,$$

or, they may remain after a base is dehydrated by heating; or, again, they may neutralize an acid directly, without first reacting with water, e.g., $CaO + 2 H^+ = H_2O + Ca^{++}$. Their close relation to bases is justification for calling them **basic oxides** or **basic anhydrides,** or even, briefly, bases.

Certain other oxides, chiefly those of nonmetals, react with water to yield H^+, e.g., $H_2O + SO_3 = H_2SO_4 = 2 H^+ + SO_4^{--}$, hence may be called **acidic oxides** or **acid anhydrides.**

24. Other Systems of Acids and Bases. The definitions of acids and bases given in this chapter are the ones most generally used, particularly for inorganic chemistry, where reactions receiving most attention are those occurring in aqueous solutions. Acids and bases are substances that can give, respectively, H^+ and OH^-, the ions of the solvent, H_2O. Other points of view have, however, proven useful for dealing with other classes of compounds and reactions. In dealing with reactions in liquid ammonia, a solvent showing many similarities with water, it is desirable to use the "ammonia system," in which an acid is any substance which gives the positive ion of the solvent, NH_4^+, and a base any substance which gives its negative ion, NH_2^-. Neutralization is $NH_4^+ + NH_2^- = 2 NH_3$. The organic chemist has for study a large number of acids which give H^+ but few bases which give OH^-, and he uses a variety of solvents, hence he usually prefers a system which is not restricted in these respects: one which defines an acid as any species, whether charged or uncharged, which can give off a proton, H^+, and a base as any substance which can unite with H^+. Thus H_2CO_3, HSO_4^-, and NH_4^+ are all acids, by virtue of the reactions:

$$H_2CO_3 = H^+ + HCO_3^-,$$
$$HSO_4^- = H^+ + SO_4^{--},$$
$$NH_4^+ = H^+ + NH_3,$$

and HCO_3^-, SO_4^{--}, and NH_3 are all bases, though varying widely in strength. A fourth system is used which is still more general, in that it escapes also from the limitation of H^+ as the criterion of an acid. For over a century chemists have been accustomed to speak of "basic oxides" and "acid oxides," influenced by the close resemblance between the neutralization of a base and an acid, such as

$$Ca(OH)_2 + H_2SO_4 = CaSO_4 + 2\,H_2O$$

and the union of their anhydrides,

$$CaO + SO_3 = CaSO_4$$

The nature of such a union is seen from their electron formulas (cf. paragraph 9):

$$Ca \;\Big|\; \ddot{\underset{\cdot\cdot}{O}}: \;+\; \overset{:\ddot{O}:}{\underset{:\ddot{O}:}{S:\ddot{O}:}} \;=\; Ca \;\Big|\; \overset{:\ddot{O}:}{\underset{:\ddot{O}:}{\ddot{O}:S:\ddot{O}:}}$$

Charges $\quad +2 \quad -2 \qquad\quad 0 \qquad\quad +2 \qquad\quad -2$

The S-atom of SO_3 lacks 2 electrons to complete its octet, and these are furnished by sharing a pair with the O of CaO. The "acid," SO_3, is an "electron acceptor," and the "base," CaO, an "electron donor." (These different systems are explained at length in Chapter XXII.) A student who, in the meantime, becomes skilled in using the "water system" should have little difficulty in extending his viewpoint to include the other three.

10^{-30} $1-11$ **Exercises**

1. State as briefly as possible the essential distinctions between the terms:

(*a*) alkali and base, (*b*) halide and halogen, (*c*) concentration and amount, (*d*) mole and molecule, (*e*) noble metal and base metal, (*f*) electron and proton, (*g*) proton and neutron.

2. What is meant by each of the terms: electron, proton, kernel, nucleus, noble metal, alkali, alkaline reaction, neutralization, anhydride?

3. Four different atoms, A, B, C, D, have nuclear charges of 6, 9, 13, 19 respectively.

(*a*) Give the electron groupings in these atoms.

(b) Which of these elements are metals, and which nonmetals?

(c) Which of these elements will be gaseous, with diatomic molecules, under ordinary laboratory conditions?

(d) Which, if any, of the other elements will unite with B to form an ionic compound?

(e) Which, if any, of the other elements will unite with B to form a compound with electron-pair bonds?

4. Element X is made up of atoms in which the nucleus contains 12 protons and 12 neutrons. What is (a) its atomic weight, (b) its atomic number, (c) the number of valence electrons, (d) its character as a metal or a nonmetal?

5. A certain atom has 11 protons in its nucleus. (a) How many valence electrons does it have? (b) Is the solid element metallic? (c) What additional fact could be stated if the atomic weight were also given?

6. Given that Li has 1 valence electron, Be has 2, C has 4, O has 6, and F has 7, write the formula and state what kind of bonds you would expect in each of the following: (a) Li element, (b) O element, (c) F element, (d) compound of Be and F, (e) compound of Li and O, (f) compound of Li and F, (g) compound of O and F.

7. Which of the following reactions would you expect to take place with least evolution of heat, and which with the greatest?

$$Fe + Cl_2 = FeCl_2,$$

$$Ca + Cl_2 = CaCl_2,$$

$$Cu + Cl_2 = CuCl_2,$$

$$Ca + I_2 = CaI_2.$$

8. Knowing that zinc displaces copper from its chloride, would you expect the decomposition of $ZnCl_2$ or of $CuCl_2$ to require the greater electrical energy?

9. Complete the following equations:

$$Ba(OH)_2 + HCl =$$

$$Ba(OH)_2 + HNO_3 =$$

$$Ba(OH)_2 + H_3PO_4 =$$

$$C_3H_8 + O_2 = CO_2 + H_2O$$

10. Determine, by subtracting H_2O in proper proportion, what are the anhydrides of the following substances: HNO_3, H_2CO_3, $Fe(OH)_3$, $Fe(OH)_2$, H_3PO_4, HPO_3, H_3PO_3, $CuOH$, H_2SO_3.

11. Give, by formulas, two examples of each of the following: (a) alkali, (b) acid, (c) basic anhydride.

***12.** The radius of the atom of Cl is 1.1×10^{-8} cm., that of I is 1.3×10^{-8} cm. How would this difference affect the relative heats of formation of solid $BaCl_2$ and BaI_2 from the reaction of metallic Ba with gaseous Cl_2 and I_2? Explain.

13. Do you expect HF or HI to have the larger dipole moment? Explain.

* Questions of greater difficulty.

CHAPTER VI

CONCENTRATION, ACIDIMETRY AND ALKALIMETRY

1. Gravimetric Analysis. The determination of the composition of any material is termed its **analysis. Qualitative analysis** is the determination of the kinds of matter composing the material; **quantitative analysis,** their amounts. The qualitative analysis of a mineral would give the information that it contains certain constituents; its quantitative analysis would yield the amount of each. Quantitative analysis may be carried out by separating each constituent from the others in a form that can be weighed; this is called **gravimetric analysis.** For example, the amount of sulfuric acid in a solution may be determined by adding a solution of barium chloride, which produces a nearly insoluble **precipitate** (meaning a substance thrown down) of barium sulfate; this is filtered out on a suitable filter, dried and weighed. The amount of sulfuric acid present in the sample of solution analyzed can then be calculated from the relation that 98.08 g. of H_2SO_4 yields 233.45 g. of $BaSO_4$.

2. Volumetric Analysis. There is another procedure, called volumetric analysis, where the amount of constituent is determined from the amount of a **reagent** (a reacting substance) necessary to complete some reaction with it, the amount of the reagent being found by having it in a solution of known concentration and measuring the volume of this solution necessary to complete the reaction, a process called **titration.** This method is usually preferred to the gravimetric method on account of its greater rapidity. Since it is important not only for analysis but for many other purposes to have clear ideas respecting concentration, we will use volumetric analysis at this point to develop them.

The amount of an acid or alkali present in a solution is usually determined by volumetric analysis, since the exact amount of the one necessary to neutralize the other is easily determined by the aid of an **indicator,** a substance showing different colors in acid and alkaline solutions, which shows the **end point** of the titration. Suppose that we wish to determine the amount of sulfuric acid in, say, 50.0 cc. of a certain solution. We can titrate it in the presence of an indicator with a solution of NaOH of known concentration, say 10.0 g. per liter, using a **buret** (cf. Fig. 1), a tube provided at its lower end with a stopcock and graduated in cubic centimeters so that the volume of solution used can be read. Suppose that 20.0 cc. of the alkaline solution is necessary to neutralize the acid, as shown by the change of color of the indicator. Since 1000 cc. of the alkaline solution contain 10.0 g. of dissolved NaOH, 20.0 cc. of it contain 0.02×10.0 g. or 0.200 g. To calculate how much sulfuric acid this can neutralize we write the equation, $2 NaOH + H_2SO_4 = 2 H_2O + Na_2SO_4$, from which, by the aid of the atomic weights, we see that $2(23.0 + 16.0 + 1.0)$ or 80.0 g. of NaOH can neutralize $2.0 + 32.0 + 4 \times 16.0$ or 98.0 g. of H_2SO_4. Then 1.00 g. of NaOH can neutralize $\frac{1}{80} \times 98.0$ g. or 1.225 g. of H_2SO_4 and 0.200 of NaOH, the amount used in the titration, can neutralize 0.245 g. of H_2SO_4, which is the amount in the 50.0 cc.

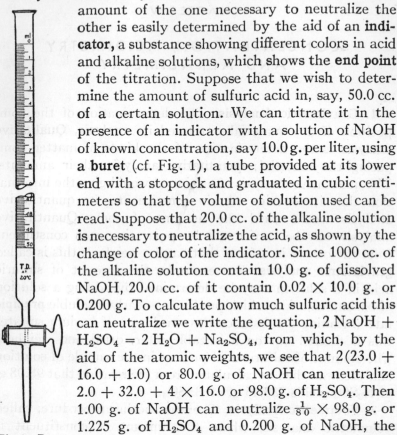

Fig. 1. Buret.

sample of the acid solution. It is not necessary for this purpose to consider degree of ionization since all acids or bases, whether highly ionized or not, must be titrated by aid of a suitable indicator to an end point where acid and base are equivalent, even though the solution is not neutral (cf. Chapter XIII, paragraph 30).

3. The amounts of acid and alkali involved in the neutralization are much more simply expressed if the mole is used as the unit instead of the gram. Instead of saying that 80 g. of NaOH can neutralize 98 g. of H_2SO_4, we write simply that 2 moles of NaOH can neutralize 1 mole of H_2SO_4. We should then express the concentration in terms of moles per liter, and 10.0 g. of NaOH per liter becomes 0.25 mole per liter since 40 g. of NaOH is 1 mole. **We designate concentration in terms of moles per liter by the letter M following the number and preceding the formula,** thus 0.25 M-NaOH means a solution containing 0.25 moles of NaOH for every liter. It should be noted carefully that **it expresses a concentration of NaOH, not the quantity of it used;**

For example,

1 liter of 0.25 M-NaOH contains	0.25	mole of NaOH
2 liters " " " contain	0.5	" " "
100 cc. " " " "	0.025	" " "
20 cc. " " " "	0.005	" " "

and so forth, for any volume of solution taken.

Since solutions expand with increasing temperature, a given volume of solution will not contain exactly the same amount of dissolved substance if measured out at different temperatures. The magnitude of the possible error can be inferred from the expansion of pure water with temperature. The volume of 1 kg. of water is 1000.87 cc. at 15° C. and 1001.77 cc. at 20° C., a difference of approximately 1 cc. in 1000 cc. This change in temperature would therefore produce a detectible error in a titration only if the error in end point and buret readings also did not exceed 1 part per 1000, e.g., 0.05 cc. in measuring 50 cc. of solution.

It is possible, by exercising great care, to reduce the other errors to such small amounts that the fluctuations in room temperature could interfere with a desired high degree of accuracy. Since it is usually not convenient to keep the temperature of a room sufficiently constant, the difficulty is avoided by weighing the amount of solution used instead of measuring its volume. A weight buret, suitable for this purpose, is shown in Fig. 2. It is made short in order to suspend it from an analytical balance. The concentrations of solutions to be used for this purpose are generally stated in terms of the number of moles per 1000 g. of water. Where it is desired to distinguish the two methods, **molar** concentration refers to the number of moles per 1000 cc. of solution and **molal** to the number of moles per 1000 g. of water.

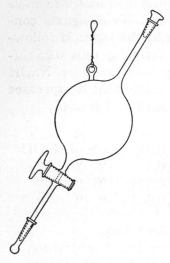

Having supposedly used 20.0 cc. of this 0.25 M-NaOH in titrating the 50 cc. sample of sulfuric acid solution, we can now say that 0.005 mole of NaOH was used. Since, from the equation, we see that 2 moles of NaOH neutralize 1 mole of H_2SO_4, evidently 0.005 mole of NaOH neutralize 0.0025 mole of H_2SO_4, which is the amount present in the sample. If we want this amount in grams we simply take 0.0025×98 g. If we wish to know the molar concentration of the acid, i.e., the number of

Fig. 2. Weight buret.

moles per liter, we see that since 50.0 cc. of the acid solution contain 0.0025 mole of H_2SO_4, 1000 cc. or 1 liter would contain $\frac{1000}{50} \times 0.0025$, or 0.05 mole; hence it is 0.05 M-H_2SO_4. This calculation is obviously simpler than the one involving grams, which necessitated the use of atomic weights.

4. The Equivalent: Normal Concentration. It is very convenient, in titration, to have various solutions of the same neutralizing power. Although it is true that solutions of such acids as HCl and HNO_3 of the same molar concentration may be used interchangeably in titrating bases, solutions of molar HCl and molar H_2SO_4, for example, could not be used indiscriminately, since 1 mole of H_2SO_4 has twice the power that 1 mole of HCl has to neutralize alkali. Similarly, while 10 cc. of 0.1 M-HCl would neutralize 10 cc.

of 0.1 M-NaOH, it would neutralize only 5 cc. of 0.1 M-Ba(OH)$_2$. Since, in titrating acids and bases, we are interested in the hydrogen of the acid and the hydroxyl of the base, the simplest basis for making and using such solutions is the amount of acid hydrogen and basic hydroxyl in a liter of each solution. Solutions of NaOH and Ba(OH)$_2$ would have the same neutralizing power if equal volumes contained, not 1 mole of each, but 1 mole and $\frac{1}{2}$ mole, respectively. The amount of acid and base to be dissolved in equal volumes of solution are the amounts which, in the particular reactions involved, will yield 1 g. of acid hydrogen and 17 g. of basic hydroxyl, respectively. This amount is called an **equivalent,**[1] and concentration expressed in equivalents is called **normality** and denoted by the letter N in the same way that molal concentration is indicated by M. Thus 2 N-H$_2$SO$_4$ denotes 2 equivalents of this acid per liter; 0.5 N-KOH denotes 0.5 equivalent of KOH per liter. Obviously, whenever the acid and base contain one acid hydrogen atom and one hydroxyl group in the molecule, the mole and equivalent are the same, and so molar and normal concentrations for such acids and bases are the same.

5. The previous example can now be reconsidered in the simpler units. We found that 20.0 cc. of 0.25 M-NaOH neutralized 50.0 cc. of H$_2$SO$_4$ solution of unknown concentration. In terms of true acid and alkaline equivalence, or neutralizing power, it is evident that the H$_2$SO$_4$ solution is less concentrated than the NaOH in the ratio 2 to 5, since the corresponding volumes are in the ratio of 5 to 2. The concentration of the NaOH is 0.25 N, as well as 0.25 M, since 1 mole is 1 equivalent in this case. The concentration of the H$_2$SO$_4$ is therefore $\frac{2}{5} \times 0.25$ or 0.1 equivalent per liter, which is written 0.1 N-H$_2$SO$_4$. This calculation is simpler than the one using molar concentration, as the

---

[1] The following is a more general definition: The **equivalent weight** for any substance for any reaction is that weight in grams which will yield 6×10^{23} unit reactions, or 1 equivalent of reaction. The unit reaction involves the making or breaking of a bond, or the participation of one elementary particle such as the proton or electron.

equation need not be used, and the concentrations can be directly compared instead of calculating the moles present in each volume used. It may be made to yield the same results as the other, for 1 equivalent of H_2SO_4 is 0.5 mole and 49 g.; hence a solution which is 0.1 N-H_2SO_4 is 0.05 M-H_2SO_4 or contains 4.9 g. per liter.

6. The use of equivalents and normal concentration is likely to seem more difficult at first, but this is only because these terms are new. As soon as the initial difficulty is overcome by a little wrestling with it, these units will be found to make matters simpler. The following illustration should

TABLE 1

Base and acid	Ratio of base to acid expressed in		
	Grams	Moles	Equivalents
NaOH + HCl	40 : 36.5	1 : 1	1 : 1
KOH + HNO$_3$	56 : 63	1 : 1	1 : 1
2 KOH + H$_2$SO$_4$	112 : 98	2 : 1	2 : 2
Ba(OH)$_2$ + 2 HNO$_3$	171 : 126	1 : 2	2 : 2
3 NaOH + H$_3$(C$_6$H$_5$O$_7$)(citric acid)*	120 : 192	3 : 1	3 : 3
3 Mg(OH)$_2$ + 2 H$_3$(C$_6$H$_5$O$_7$)	123 : 384	3 : 2	6 : 6

* Only the hydrogen atoms outside the parentheses react as acid.

make clear why this is true. The use of grams corresponds to the ordinary grocery store in which a price list is required to convert pounds to cents. Using moles is like a "groceteria" in which all commodities are in packages worth $1, $2, $3, etc. The clerk would not need to know as much arithmetic. A still less educated clerk could get along, however, if every package were worth just $1.00. He would be very stupid, indeed, if he should allow himself to worry over the different sizes, weights, and shapes of the packages.

Table 1 should suffice to show that the arithmetic involved becomes progressively simpler as we go from grams to moles to equivalents.

7. **Summary.** By way of summary it may be stated that any kind of problem involved in titrating acids and bases may be solved by understanding the three following factors

and utilizing them in the connection demanded by the problem:

First, **the number of equivalents and the number of grams per mole of substance,** as indicated by the formula; e.g., $Ca(OH)_2$ denotes 1 mole, 2 equivalents, 74 g.

Second, **the meaning of the symbols expressing concentration;** e.g., 0.01 M-$Ca(OH)_2$ denotes a solution of 0.01 mole (hence, by the first step, 0.02 equivalent or 0.74 g.) of $Ca(OH)_2$ in a liter.

Third, **the relation between the amount of acid and base used, which is given by the equation, if amounts are expressed in moles or grams, or, if equivalents are used, 1 equivalent of any acid neutralizes 1 equivalent of any base, by the definition of the term equivalent.**

8. *Examples:* What is (1) the molar concentration and (2) the normal concentration when 7.4 g. of $Ca(OH)_2$ are in 2 liters of solution? 1 mole of $Ca(OH)_2$ is 2 equivalents, and weighs 74 g.; hence 7.4 g. is 0.1 mole and 0.2 equivalent. Since this is dissolved in 2 liters, 1 liter contains 0.05 mole or 0.1 equivalent, so that the solution is 0.05 molar or 0.1 normal, expressed briefly as 0.05 M-$Ca(OH)_2$ and 0.1 N-$Ca(OH)_2$, respectively.

9. How many cc. of 0.2 N-HCl will be required to neutralize 40.0 cc. of 0.5 N-NaOH? By 0.5 N-NaOH we mean 0.5 equivalent of NaOH in 1 liter of solution; hence 40.0 cc. of it, which is 0.040 liter, will contain 0.040 × 0.5, or 0.02 equivalent of NaOH. Since 1 equivalent of any acid neutralizes 1 equivalent of any base, the amount of acid neutralized by 0.02 equivalent of NaOH is 0.02 equivalent. Since 0.2 N-HCl means 0.2 equivalent of it per liter of solution, to get 0.02 equivalent we would have to take 0.1 liter, or 100 cc.

10. It was found that the acetic acid in 10 cc. of vinegar was neutralized by 14.0 cc. of 0.5 M-KOH solution. How many grams of acetic acid were in 100 cc. of the vinegar? The formula of acetic acid is $HC_2H_3O_2$, and only one of the hydrogen atoms in the molecule has acid properties. By 0.5 M-KOH we mean a solution containing 0.5 mole of KOH per liter. Since 14 cc. is 0.014 liter, this volume of solution will contain 0.014 of 0.5 mole, or 0.007 mole of KOH. By writing the equation,

$$KOH + HC_2H_3O_2 = H_2O + KC_2H_3O_2,$$

we see that 1 mole of the acid neutralizes 1 mole of the base, so that 0.007 mole of the base will be neutralized by 0.007 mole of the acid, which is the amount present in 10 cc. of vinegar. Since 1 mole of acetic acid weighs 60 g., 0.007 mole weighs 0.42 g. Since this amount is contained in 10 cc. of vinegar, 100 cc. would contain 4.2 g.

11. If 0.654 g. of zinc is completely dissolved in 100 cc. of 0.5 M-H_2SO_4, what will be the concentration of the acid after the reaction, in terms of: (*a*) moles per liter, (*b*) equivalents per liter? The atomic weight of zinc is 65.4, so that 0.654 g. is 0.01 gram-atom of zinc. From the equation for the reaction,

$$Zn + H_2SO_4 = ZnSO_4 + H_2,$$

we see that 1 gram-atom of zinc will use up 1 mole of acid; hence, 0.01 gram-atom of zinc would use up 0.01 mole of the acid. Now 1 liter of 0.5 M-H_2SO_4 contains 0.5 mole and 100 cc. would contain 0.05 mole. The zinc used up 0.01 mole of this, leaving 0.04 mole of H_2SO_4 in 100 cc., which corresponds to 0.4 mole per liter. Since 1 mole of $H_2SO_4 = 2$ equivalents, 0.4 mole = 0.8 equivalent and the solution may be called 0.8 normal.

12. Titration Involving Other Types of Reaction. It will be seen from the last example above that solutions of known concentration may be used to measure amounts of material in other reactions besides those where acids and bases neutralize each other. The speed with which volumes of solutions can be measured in titrations, makes the former preferable wherever speed is desired. When neutralization of acids and bases does not take place, some other means of indicating the end point of the reaction is necessary. Where a highly colored substance disappears in the reaction, this may be used to indicate when the exact amount required has been added. Any excess makes itself evident by reason of the color.

One such substance frequently used is potassium permanganate, $KMnO_4$, a substance with a deep purplish red color, which is a very strong oxidizing agent. As an example of the type of reaction now being considered, let us determine how much iron is in an ore, 1.016 g. of which, when dissolved in acid so as to give a solution containing $FeSO_4$, required 45.0 cc. of 0.05 M-$KMnO_4$ to change the $FeSO_4$ to $Fe(SO_4)_3$, according to the equation,

$$10\ FeSO_4 + 2\ KMnO_4 + 8\ H_2SO_4 =$$
$$5\ Fe_2(SO_4)_3 + 2\ MnSO_4 + K_2SO_4 + 8\ H_2O.$$

The actual amount of $KMnO_4$ used is evidently 0.045 of 0.05 mole or 0.00225 mole. According to the equation 2 moles of $KMnO_4$ react with 10 moles of $FeSO_4$, so that 0.00225 mole of $KMnO_4$ would react with 5×0.00225 mole or 0.01125 mole of $FeSO_4$. Now 0.01125 mole of $FeSO_4$ contains 0.01125 gram-atom of iron, and since 1 gram-atom of iron is 55.8 g., 0.01125 gram-atom would weigh 0.01125×55.8 g., or 0.626 g. Since, finally, this amount of iron was found from 1.016 g. of the ore, the iron is 61.7 per cent of the ore.

13. Standardizing Solutions. In making solutions of known concentration for titration we must start with some substance that can be weighed, such as benzoic acid, $HC_7H_5O_2$ (only one of the hydrogen atoms has acid properties), or sodium carbonate, Na_2CO_3. If it were desired to make 0.05 M-H_2SO_4, which contains 0.05 mole or 4.9 g. of H_2SO_4 per liter, we would make up a quantity of the solution a little more concentrated than 0.05 M by dissolving about 3 cc. of concentrated acid (density 1.8) in a liter of water. We would next determine accurately the concentration of acid in this solution by titrating a known weight of Na_2CO_3. Suppose that it takes 43.0 cc. of our solution to react with 0.248 g. of Na_2CO_3, according to the equation

$$Na_2CO_3 + H_2SO_4 = H_2O + CO_2 + Na_2SO_4.$$

Since 1 mole of sodium carbonate reacts with 1 mole of the acid, and since 0.248 g. of Na_2CO_3 is 0.00234 mole, the amount of H_2SO_4 is also 0.00234 mole, and as this is dissolved in 43.0 cc. the amount in one liter is $\frac{1000}{43} \times 0.00234$ mole, or 0.0545 mole. This solution may be used in titrations just as it is, or by diluting with the right amount of water the concentration may be adjusted to exactly 0.05 molal. Since 0.05 mole per liter is the same as 0.0545 mole in

1090 cc., if water is added to a liter of the 0.0545 molal solution until the volume becomes 1090 cc., then the concentration of the resulting solution is 0.05 molal, as desired. From this an alkaline solution of desired concentration may then be made up by a similar process.

Chemists are, however, prone to take unnecessary pains to adjust their standard solutions to concentrations expressed by simple numbers. By the aid of a slide rule it is just as easy to calculate the results of titrations where the acid is 0.0545 M as it is when it is exactly 0.05 M.

Exercises

See Appendix II for Answers

1. Write equations expressing the neutralization of sodium hydroxide with hydrochloric acid; sodium hydroxide with sulfuric acid; calcium hydroxide with nitric acid; barium hydroxide with sulfuric acid.

2. Write under each substance involved in the above equation the number of moles, grams, and equivalents represented.

3. How many grams are there in 1 equivalent of each of the following substances: KOH, H_2SO_4, $Al(OH)_3$? From your answers state how many grams of aluminum hydroxide and of sulfuric acid would combine to form aluminum sulfate.

4. How many moles of sulfuric acid will be neutralized by 4 equivalents of sodium hydroxide?

5. If 0.98 g. of sulfuric acid is in 1 liter of solution, what is (*a*) the molar concentration? (*b*) the normal concentration?

6. When 3.7 g. of calcium hydroxide are in 5 liters of solution, what is (*a*) the molar concentration? (*b*) the normal concentration?

7. (*a*) How many equivalents of barium hydroxide are in 200 cc. of 0.1 normal solution? (*b*) How many moles? (*c*) How many equivalents of hydrochloric acid could this solution neutralize? (*d*) How many grams?

8. If 10 cc. of a certain solution of sulfuric acid neutralized 20 cc. of a normal solution of potassium hydroxide, what was the concentration of the former in (*a*) equivalents per liter; (*b*) moles per liter; (*c*) grams per liter?

9. If 25 cc. of 0.2 normal acid neutralized some base, how many equivalents of base were there? How many grams of base were there if the base was (*a*) sodium hydroxide; (*b*) calcium hydroxide?

10. If 10 cc. of $N/5$ ammonium hydroxide neutralizes 20 cc. of sulfuric acid, what was the concentration of the latter?

11. How many cc. of 0.2 normal acid are necessary to neutralize 25 cc. of 0.5 normal alkali?

12. How many cc. of 0.2 M-HCl will exactly neutralize 0.02 mole of (a) KOH; (b) Ba(OH)$_2$; each dissolved in 500 cc. of water?

13. What volume of hydrogen, measured at 18° C. and 1.02 atm., could be obtained by the action of zinc in excess upon 200 cc. of 0.5 M-H$_2$SO$_4$?

14. What is the equivalent weight of an acid 1.25 g. of which is neutralized by 25 cc. of 0.4 N-Ba(OH)$_2$?

15. (a) How many equivalents of oxalic acid, H$_2$C$_2$O$_4$, are necessary to neutralize 1 equivalent of KOH? (b) How many moles of the former for 1 mole of the latter? (c) How many grams of the former for 1 gram of the latter?

16. 11.2 liters of Cl$_2$ at 0° C. and 760 mm. react with an excess of H$_2$. The product is dissolved in water. What is the molar concentration of HCl in this solution if its final volume is 500 cc.?

17. 30 cc. of 0.1 M-HCl are mixed with 100 cc. of 0.05 M-Ba(OH)$_2$ and the resulting solution is evaporated to dryness. (a) What substances are present in the residue? (b) How many moles of each? (c) How many equivalents of each?

CHAPTER VII

THERMOCHEMISTRY

1. There are many chemical reactions in which our interest lies ordinarily not in the substances produced but in the heat evolved or absorbed. The burning of fuel is a chemical reaction, but our purpose in burning them is not to produce the carbon dioxide and water that usually result. These substances we take pains to dispose of by means of chimneys and ventilation. Our purpose is rather to obtain the heat or light that accompanies the reaction. In buying fuels, therefore, the important consideration is not the relative cost of the various available fuels but the relative cost of the heat obtained from each. The chemist should therefore know how the heat of such a reaction may be measured and expressed.

Again, in many reactions of importance, a knowledge of whether heat is absorbed or evolved helps to determine the most desirable conditions for carrying it out, as will be explained in Chapter XIV. Also in technical processes, if heat is absorbed during a reaction, this may have to be considered in estimating the cost, since the heat thus absorbed may have to be supplied by means of fuel or electrical energy.

2. Heat Units. A quantity of heat is conveniently measured by absorbing it in a definite weight of water and measuring the rise in temperature of the water. The units chosen depend on the units of weight and temperature which are used. These heat units and the relation between them are set forth in Table 1. The joule is 10^7 ergs, and is also a volt-coulomb, that is, the electrical work done when a coulomb of electricity flows through a resistance under a drop of potential of 1 volt, or, in equivalent terms, when a current of 1 ampere flows for 1 second under a 1-volt drop in potential.

TABLE 1

Heat Units

Amount of heat necessary to raise the temperature of	Name	Abbreviation	equivalent
1 g. of water 1° C. at 15° C.	calorie	cal.	4.185 joules
1 kg. " " 1° C. " "	large calorie	kcal.	1000 cal.
1 pound of water 1° F. at 60° F.	British Thermal Unit	B.T.U.	1054.6 joules / 0.252 kcal.

3. Experimental Determination of Heats of Reaction. The amount of heat involved in a chemical reaction is determined in an apparatus known as a calorimeter. It consists of a vessel holding perhaps a liter of water, provided with a stirrer and a more or less delicate thermometer. This vessel must be well surrounded by some effective heat insulator, so that the temperature of the water within shall be affected only to the least possible extent by the room temperature. This insulation may be furnished by felt, a water jacket, or, by a vacuum jacket, as in a Dewar flask. The reacting substances may be introduced into the calorimeter in various ways. When the heat of solution of a solid is to be measured, the substance may be sealed in a thin glass bulb immersed in water in the calorimeter. After uniform temperature has been reached the bulb is broken and the solid allowed to dissolve. If the reaction is one like the precipitation of an insoluble substance from dilute solutions, or the neutralization of an acid by a base, one liquid may be inclosed in a thin

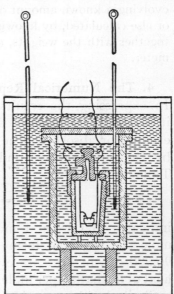

Fig. 1. Bomb calorimeter.

glass vessel, or in one with a valve, and immersed in the other liquid. The liquids may then be mixed at the proper time. If the reaction is one taking place at a high temperature, it may be carried on within a "bomb" immersed in the water of the calorimeter, (Fig. 1). A small weighed portion of the material under investigation is placed within this bomb, which is then closed and filled through a tube in the top with oxygen under high pressure. It is then placed in the calorimeter and when uniform temperature is attained the combustion is brought about by means of an electrical connection through the lid of the bomb.

The amount of heat liberated by the reaction is measured by the rise in temperature of the calorimeter contents and the heat capacity of the latter. If water alone were involved, the number of calories liberated would be found simply by multiplying the rise in temperature by the weight of the water. Various other substances are present, however, such as the stirrer, the containing vessel, the thermometer, etc., so that their power of absorbing heat compared with that of water must be measured or calculated and added to the weight of the water as the "water equivalent" of the calorimeter. This may be measured by allowing a reaction evolving a known amount of heat to take place in the calorimeter, or else calculated, by knowing the heat capacities or specific heats, together with the weights, of the various substances in the calorimeter.

4. The Numerical Representation of Heats of Reaction. In expressing the results of thermochemical measurements it is usual to include in the equation the number of calories evolved or absorbed. The amounts of substances represented by the equation are understood to be expressed in moles. Thus the equation,

$$C + O_2 = CO_2 + 96,500 \text{ cal.},$$

indicates that when 1 mole (12 g.) of carbon burns with 1 mole of oxygen to form 1 mole (44 g.) of carbon dioxide, 96,500 cal. of heat are evolved. This amount of heat is the **heat of formation** per mole of carbon dioxide from its elements.

Similarly, the equation

$$N_2 + O_2 = 2 NO - 43,200 \text{ cal.}$$

means that when 1 mole (28 g.) of nitrogen reacts with 1 mole (32 g.) of oxygen to form 2 moles (60 g.) of nitric oxide, 43,200 cal. of heat are *absorbed*. This reaction might equally well be written

$$N_2 + O_2 + 43,200 \text{ cal.} = 2 NO.$$

The ordinary rules of algebra apply to the sign of the heat if the number is thus transposed. Either way of writing the equation signifies that nitrogen, oxygen, and heat are all used up in the formation of nitric oxde.

The symbol, ΔH, is used to express changes in "heat content" of the system. In the preceding reactions the values of ΔH are — 96,500 cal. and + 43,200 cal., respectively.

The term **exothermic** is often applied to reactions which evolve heat and **endothermic** to those which absorb heat. It may be mentioned that the former predominate in reactions occurring at ordinary temperatures and the latter in those occurring at very high temperatures, in the electric furnace.

5. Effect of the State of the Reacting Substances. The heat of a reaction depends upon the temperature at which it is carried out and upon the state of the substances involved. For example, in the union of hydrogen and oxygen to form water, it makes a difference whether the water produced is at a temperature at which it is liquid or vapor. Since the condensation of steam to liquid takes place with the evolution of heat, it is evident that where the final product is liquid the heat of formation will be greater than when it is a gas. To make this clear we will need to specify in the equation the state of the substance, which we would do in this case as follows:

$$2 \, H_2 + O_2 = 2 \, H_2O \text{ (gas)} + 115,640 \text{ cal., or}$$
$$= 2 \, H_2O \text{ (liq.)} + 136,540 \text{ cal.}$$

Or, again, we might find it desirable to express the states of all substances in the equation where ambiguity might otherwise arise, as in the equation,

$$Hg \text{ (liq.)} + Cl_2 \text{ (gas)} = HgCl_2 \text{ (solid)} + 53,300 \text{ cal.}$$

It makes a difference also whether or not a substance is in solution, and what its concentration is in the solution. We might, therefore, have an equation such as the following:

$$NaOH \text{ (0.1 molal)} + HCl \text{ (0.1 molal)}$$
$$= H_2O + NaCl \text{ (0.05 molal)} + 13,200 \text{ cal.}$$

Where the concentration is small and does not need to be specified exactly, it may suffice to use the abbreviation, aq., after the formula of the dissolved substance, which signifies the presence of a large amount of water. (From the Latin *aqua*, water.)

6. In a gaseous reaction in which the number of molecules of gaseous substances changes, the heat will be somewhat different if the reaction is carried out in a closed vessel so that the volume remains constant, from what it will be if the reaction is carried out so as to keep the pressure constant. Since a gas does work in expanding against an external pressure, heat must be absorbed during the expansion in order to maintain the original molecular velocity and hence the original pressure. This behavior finds illustration in the fact that a ball thrown against a yielding surface rebounds with less speed than when thrown against a rigid surface. The heat of a chemical reaction at constant pressure will therefore be greater or less than that of the same reaction at constant volume according as the number of gaseous molecules decreases or increases during the reaction.

7. Indirect Determination of Heats of Reaction. In many cases the heat of a reaction cannot be determined directly on account of the difficulty of carrying out the reaction in a calorimeter. In such cases it is usually possible to determine it indirectly. Moreover, even though the reactions may be easily carried out in the calorimeter, it is unnecessary to measure the heats of all, since some may be calculated from others. To do this we use a well-founded law (Hess' Law) stating that all heats of reaction depend only on the state of the initial or final substances and not upon the steps into which the reaction may be divided. This law is a consequence of the more fundamental law of the conservation of energy, which states that though energy be transformed from one form to another, none of it is ever lost. The different forms of energy include heat, potential energy, or energy of position, kinetic energy, or energy of motion, electrical energy, chemical energy, etc. As an example, $ZnSO_4$ might be formed from its elements in either of the following ways:

FIRST WAY

$$Zn + \tfrac{1}{2} O_2 = ZnO + 85 \text{ kcal.}$$
$$S + O_2 = SO_2 + 70 \text{ kcal.}$$
$$SO_2 + \tfrac{1}{2} O_2 = SO_3 + 22 \text{ kcal.}$$
$$ZnO + SO_3 = ZnSO_4 + 53 \text{ kcal.}$$

Total: $Zn + S + 2 O_2 = ZnSO_4 + 230 \text{ kcal.}$

SECOND WAY

$$Zn + S = ZnS + 40 \text{ kcal.}$$
$$ZnS + 2 O_2 = ZnSO_4 + 190 \text{ kcal.}$$

Total: $Zn + S + 2 O_2 = ZnSO_4 + 230 \text{ kcal.}$

The total result in either case is the formation of $ZnSO_4$ from Zn, S, and $2 O_2$ with the evolution of heat. Our law tells us that the total heat liberated is the same in either case, as shown by the above figures.

As a consequence of this, thermochemical equations may be added or subtracted like any algebraic equations. Suppose that the following heats of reaction have been measured:

$$C + O_2 = CO_2 + 96.5 \text{ kcal.,} \tag{1}$$

and

$$2 CO + O_2 = 2 CO_2 + 135.0 \text{ kcal.,} \tag{2}$$

and we wish to learn the heat of the reaction:

$$2 C + O_2 = 2 CO.$$

All that is necessary is to eliminate CO_2 from equations (1) and (2) by multiplying (1) by 2 and subtracting (2) from it, obtaining

$$2 C - 2 CO + O_2 = 58 \text{ kcal.,}$$

or, transposing,

$$2 C + O_2 = 2 CO + 58 \text{ kcal.}$$

If, on the other hand, we eliminate O_2 by subtracting (1) from (2), we obtain the equation for a different reaction,

$$2 CO = C + CO_2 + 38.5 \text{ kcal.,}$$

which, since it usually reacts in the reverse direction, we may prefer to write

$$C + CO_2 = 2\ CO - 38.5\ kcal.$$

Again, it is not possible to synthesize H_2O_2 aq. from its elements in the calorimeter, but the heat that would be evolved if the reaction were possible may be calculated from the following:

$$H_2O_2\ aq. = H_2O + \tfrac{1}{2}\ O_2 + aq. + 23.0\ kcal.,$$
$$H_2 + \tfrac{1}{2}\ O_2 = H_2O + 68.4\ kcal.$$

Subtracting the first from the second to eliminate H_2O we obtain:

$$H_2 + \tfrac{1}{2}\ O_2 - H_2O_2\ aq. = -\tfrac{1}{2}\ O_2 - aq. + 45.4\ kcal.,$$

or, transposing to make the signs positive,

$$H_2 + O_2 + aq. = H_2O_2\ aq. + 45.4\ kcal.$$

From this we learn that H_2O_2 is an exothermic compound, formed *from its elements* with the evolution of heat.

8. Fuel Value of Foods. The heat evolved by the combustion of dry food materials in a calorimeter bomb serves for an approximate valuation of their ability to furnish the heat and muscular energy needed by the body. Accordingly, the amount of food materials needed per day can be estimated roughly by the aid of a knowledge of the fuel values of the foods. An adult needs from 2000 to 3500 kcal. per day, according to his weight and to the amount of his muscular activity. This makes it possible, for example, to calculate roughly the quantity of food needed, and the relative costs of different foods, which aids in reducing costs of food in the home and in institutions, and furnishes a valuable means in determining the least weight of food necessary for a camping or exploring expedition. It may be of interest to have the few figures given in the following table:

	Approximate number kcal. per pound
Foods	
Starchy foods, cereals, flour, rice, beans, etc.	1650
Sugar	1860
Fats and oils	3650
Cheese	2000
Chocolate	2850
Milk, evaporated, unsweetened	800
Milk, condensed, sweetened	1500
Dried fruit	1300
Fish	1000
Meat	1600

Of course, other considerations must also enter to secure a wholesome, well-balanced diet, but these cannot be discussed here.

Exercises

See Appendix II for answers

1. What is the distinction between heat and temperature?
2. Calculate the heat of the reaction:

$$CaO + CO_2 = CaCO_3$$

from the following:

$$CO_2 + Ca(OH)_2 = CaCO_3 + H_2O + 30.5 \text{ kcal.}$$
$$CaO + H_2O = Ca(OH)_2 + 11.5 \text{ kcal.}$$

3. Calculate the heat of the reaction:

$$Zn + Cl_2 + aq. = ZnCl_2 \text{ aq.}$$

from the following determinations:

$$Zn + 2 HCl \text{ aq.} = ZnCl_2 \text{ aq.} + H_2 + 36 \text{ kcal.,}$$
$$H_2 + Cl_2 = 2 HCl \text{ (gas)} + 44 \text{ kcal.,}$$
$$HCl \text{ (gas)} + aq. = HCl \text{ aq.} + 17 \text{ kcal.}$$

4. (*a*) Calculate the heat of the reaction:

$$N_2 + 3 H_2 = 2 NH_3$$

from the following:

$$4 NH_3 + 3 O_2 = 2 N_2 + 6 H_2O \text{ (liq.)} + 364 \text{ kcal.}$$
$$6 H_2 + \tfrac{1}{2} O_2 = H_2O \text{ (liq.)} + 68.3 \text{ kcal.}$$

(*b*) The above figures are for constant pressure; would the heat of formation of NH_3 be greater or less at constant volume?

5. Given that $C + O_2 = CO_2 + 96.5$ kcal., and that anthracite coal, considered as 95 per cent carbon, costs $10 per ton (= 1000 kg.), determine the cost of 1000 kcal. from the burning of this coal.

6. Considering "water gas" to consist of CO and H_2 only, as indicated by the equation of its formation,

$$C + H_2O = CO + H_2,$$

and given the heats of combustion of CO and H_2, i.e.

$$CO + \tfrac{1}{2}O_2 = CO_2 + 68.0 \text{ kcal.,}$$
$$H_2 + \tfrac{1}{2}O_2 = H_2O + 68.3 \text{ kcal.,}$$

calculate the cost of 1000 kcal. from this gas if it costs 90¢ per 1000 cu. ft. (= 28,300 liters) when measured at 20° C. and 1 atm. pressure.

7. If kerosene were pure $C_{10}H_{22}$, whose heat of combustion is 1626 kcal., and costs 15¢ per gallon (3.781 liters) and has a density of 0.79 g. per cc., calculate the cost of 1000 kcal. obtained by burning kerosene.

8. From the table on page 125 make out a "grub-list" for two men on a ten-day walking tour, endeavoring to get the minimum weight consistent with variety and palatability.

CHAPTER VIII

ELECTROLYTIC DISSOCIATION

1. Such a large proportion of the reactions with which we concern ourselves take place in water solution that the behavior of substances dissolved in water is a subject of great importance. We will consider a number of the properties and reactions of substances in aqueous solution, and see that conclusions that may be drawn as to the nature of these solutions are in agreement with the picture in Chapter V.

2. **Solvents for Different Types of Solids.** We can better understand the nature of aqueous solutions if we first consider the process of solution in general. In relation to the different types of solids outlined in Chapter V, paragraph 15, a solid composed of distinct molecules is best dissolved by a liquid whose intermolecular forces are of approximately the same strength and nature as those existing in the solid. For example, solid sulfur, containing molecules of S_8, is readily dissolved by liquid CS_2. Naphthalene, $C_{10}H_8$, is readily dissolved by hexane, C_6H_{14}. Water is a very poor solvent for these substances because the field of force around a water molecule is different from the fields of force surrounding the molecules just mentioned. The electrons are much more the property of the oxygen than of the hydrogen, hence the water molecule is relatively positive in one part and negative in another. Such a molecule is called an electric dipole (cf. Chapter V) and is surrounded by an electrostatic field, very different in nature from the field of force surrounding a sulfur molecule. Water is, however, a good solvent for a substance like sugar, whose molecules contain a number of OH groups, each an electric dipole similar to the water dipole. Solids of the diamond type are usually nearly insoluble in all solvents.

Solids of the salt type are not dissolved by liquids whose molecules are surrounded by symmetrical fields of force such as benzene or gasoline but they are dissolved by liquids whose molecules contain electrostatic dipoles, including water, liquid ammonia, and a few others. The process of solution in such a case is easily pictured (Fig. 1). When the water molecule reaches the surface of a salt crystal it tends to

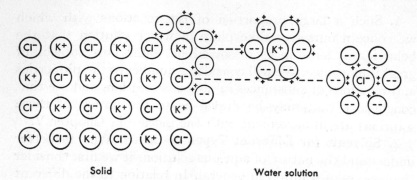

Solid   Water solution

Fig. 1. The process of solution of a salt in water.

orient with its negative part towards the positive potassium atom and its positive part towards the negative chlorine atom. This weakens the force between the charged atoms of the crystal so that, if it is not too strong, the charged atoms may be detached from the crystal and wander off into solution each surrounded by an envelope of oriented water molecules. These charged atoms in solution are but weakly attracted to each other and can move about in the solution more or less independently. They are accordingly called **ions,** from the Greek word meaning to wander.

We will now examine certain properties of salt solutions to see how they harmonize with this conception regarding their nature.

3. Abnormally Great Lowering of the Freezing Point. It has been pointed out in Chapter III that the molecular weight of substances may be determined by two essentially identical methods. Both methods depend upon the fact that (a standard number of molecules $(6 \times 10^{23}$ or 1 mole) produce certain effects which are independent of the mass, structure, or identity of the molecules.)

Thus, 1 mole of *any* gas $(6 \times 10^{23}$ molecules) occupies 22.4 l. at 0° C. and 1 atm. Again, 1 mole of any soluble substance produces the same effect, in general, as 1 mole of any other substance with respect to lowering the freezing point, or raising the boiling point of water solutions.

It is even possible as an alternative to define a mole from the empirical viewpoint as the number of grams which in the gaseous state at 0° C. and 1 atm. will occupy 22.4 l., or else as the number of grams which, dissolved in 1000 g. of water, will lower the freezing point of the solution 1.86° C. below that of pure water. If we determine the effect of various substances in lowering the freezing point of water, we find that a large number of them show concordant behavior. Other substances, including (acids, bases, and salts, show an abnormally great lowering of the freezing point.) This is illustrated in the following table:

TABLE 1

Substance	Freezing points of 0.1 molal solutions, °C.
Sugar	− 0.188°
Glycerine	− 0.186°
Alcohol	− 0.184°
NaCl	− 0.348°
HCl	− 0.356°
KNO_3	− 0.330°
$BaCl_2$	− 0.478°
Na_2SO_4	− 0.459°

It will be seen that the first three substances in the table behave as would be expected, but that the others give an abnormally great lowering of the freezing point. There are two ways of accounting for this abnormality. Either the law of the uniform molal lowering does not hold universally, or else acids, bases, and salts dissociate into two or more independent parts when dissolved in water. If this law still holds, then 1 mole of NaCl, HCl, or KNO_3, when dissolved in a large quantity of water, seems to yield nearly 2 moles of dissolved substances, whereas 1 mole of $BaCl_2$, or of Na_2SO_4, seems to yield nearly 3 moles of dissolved substances.

These results harmonize perfectly with the picture of such solutions given above according to which 1 mole of KCl in solution exists as 1 gram-ion of K^+ and 1 gram-ion of Cl^-, nearly independent of each other, and each exerting its effect upon the freezing point. This effect is proportional chiefly to the total concentration of ions or molecules in solution and is scarcely influenced by their nature, size, or charge. Thus 0.1 mole of Br_2, CH_3OH, Na^+, Cl^-, and SO_4^{--} would each affect the freezing point to the same extent.

4. The theory that acids, alkalis, and salts may be dissociated into charged ions was advanced by Arrhenius in 1881, long before it had been shown that the solid salts also contain charged atoms, and it seemed absurd to many to think of sodium chloride dissolving as atoms of sodium and chlorine, sodium being a metal that reacts violently with water and chlorine a poisonous gas. *Such a difficulty is avoided by realizing that an uncharged atom and a charged ion are quite different substances*. Thus Cu is copper, a reddish metal; Cu^{++} or cupric ion, existing in water as a greenish blue substance, is very different from Cu in all its properties. Again, H_2 is a light, combustible gas, while H^+ is a substance existing in solution, along with some negative partner, and having a sour taste, etc.

5. **Independent Migration of Ions in Electrolysis.** It has been found that all dissolved substances that give the abnormal effect on the freezing point of water also give solutions which conduct the electric current, depositing materials at the electrodes, or else dissolving the electrodes. Because of this behavior they are called **electrolytes**. Those conducting very well, the strong acids and alkalis, and most salts, are called **strong electrolytes**.

6. This conductivity is quite in accord with the presence in the solution of charged ions, which must necessarily migrate

towards an electrode of opposite charge when voltage is applied. The negative electrode, called the cathode, the one which is receiving electrons from the dynamo or battery, attracts the positive ions, which are accordingly called **cations,** while the positive electrode, the anode, attracts the negative ions, called **anions.** It is possible to detect this migration experimentally. If, for example, we have a **U**-tube containing, say, dilute copper sulfate in the bottom, with dilute potassium nitrate carefully superimposed as shown in Fig. 2a, and allow an electric current to pass through the solution for a time, we will find that the blue color characteristic of copper salts travels towards the negative pole, while the sulfate ion travels towards the positive pole, as might be shown by testing layers of solution with a solution of barium chloride. The state of affairs after the passage of a current is depicted in the figure at b. Whenever electrolysis

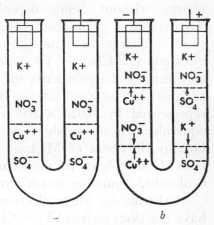

Fig. 2.   Independent migration of the ions in electrolysis.

takes place it is possible to show such independent migration of the two parts of the salt, acid, or base, by appropriate experiments similar to the above.

7. Discharge of the Ions at the Electrodes. Since in electrolysis it is observed that current continues to flow so long as sufficient voltage is applied and there are ions in the solution, it is obvious that electrons must be able to pass from the solution to the wire, or external circuit, and vice versa. The pole at which the electrons enter the solution is called the cathode or reducing electrode; conversely, the pole at which they leave the solution is called the anode or oxidizing electrode. (Note that anode and oxidation begin with vowels, cathode and reduction begin with consonants.)

If we represent an electron by the symbol, e^-, the discharge of ions at a cathode may be represented by equations such as the following:

$$H^+ + e^- = H, \text{ followed by } 2\,H = H_2;$$
$$Ag^+ + e^- = Ag;$$
$$Cu^{++} + 2\,e^- = Cu.$$

In some cases an ion may be reduced to an ion of lower charge without being deposited, as $Fe^{+++} + e^- = Fe^{++}$. To deposit 1 gram-atom of an element whose ion has 1 positive charge, such as Ag^+ or H^+, requires 6.0234×10^{23} electrons (cf. Chapter V), 1 equivalent of electricity; twice as much, or 2 equivalents for ions with 2 positive charges, such as Cu^{++} or Zn^{++}, and so on. The quantity of electricity represented by 6.023×10^{23} electrons, the electrochemical equivalent, is obviously very important and is called one faraday, in honor of Michael Faraday, who discovered the laws of electrolysis. Its magnitude in practical units is 96,540 coulombs,[1] a number worth remembering.

At the anode, where electrons leave the solution, we may have reactions such as $Cl^- = Cl + e^-$, followed by $2\,Cl = Cl_2$. Frequently the electrons may come from some source other than the anions in solution. Thus, if the anode were made of copper, the electrons removed from the anode would come not from Cl^- in solution but from atoms of copper going into solution as Cu^{++}. Again, when SO_4^{--} is present, although it carries part of the current to the anode it is the water, not the SO_4^{--}, which eventually gives up electrons to the anode; $H_2O = 2\,H^+ + \frac{1}{2} O_2 + 2\,e^-$. (It is sometimes said that the reaction is $SO_4^{--} = SO_3 + \frac{1}{2} O_2 + 2\,e^-$, followed by $SO_3 + H_2O = 2\,H^+ + SO_4^{--}$. The sum of these two is the reaction previously written, which is the final result in either case. There is probably no evidence that electrons are any more

---

[1] A coulomb is the amount of electricity carried by a current of 1 ampere in 1 second; e.g., 10 amperes flowing for 1 minute would amount to 600 coulombs, and if 1000 coulombs are delivered in 50 seconds, the current strength is 20 amperes. Practically it is defined as the amount of electricity that will deposit 0.001,118 g. of silver.

easily removed from SO_4^{--} than from H_2O, and the net result is all we are sure of.) In any case Faraday's Law holds, and 1 faraday of electricity releases $\frac{1}{2} Cl_2$, $\frac{1}{2} O_2$, etc., or dissolves $\frac{1}{2} Cu^{++}$, etc.

8. The following further examples may serve to make the matter clearer. Since 108 g. of silver is 1 gram-atom, deposited by 96,500 coulombs, to deposit 1 g. would require $\frac{1}{108}$ of 96,500 coulombs, and to deposit 5 g. would require $\frac{5}{108}$ of 96,500 coulombs, or 4470 coulombs. If this were done by a current of 2 amperes (2 coulombs per second), the time required would be 2235 seconds, or 37 minutes, 35 seconds. However, to deposit 63.6 g. of copper, from ordinary copper salts, 65.4 g. of zinc, etc., requires twice as much electricity, or 2 faradays. Similarly, certain other ions require 3 faradays per gram-ion.

9. It is worth noting that the fact that whole numbers of faradays are required to discharge 1 gram-atom of different elements implies that 1 or more elementary electric charges are involved in changing ions to atoms, or, in other words, that electricity, like matter, is atomic in structure, not a continuous "fluid," as it was once often called. The experimental facts constitute, essentially, laws of "definite and simple multiple proportions" for electricity as for other forms of matter.

10. Formulas of Ions. The formulas of ions are simply related, in many cases, to the number of outer or valence electrons upon the free atom, which, in turn, is correlated with the group of the Periodic System to which an element belongs (cf. Chapter XVII). Thus, the hydrogen atom has one electron and gives H^+, the calcium atom has two electrons and gives Ca^{++}, etc. The student should learn the formulas of the common ions, such as Na^+, K^+, Ag^+, Cu^{++}, Zn^{++}, Ba^{++}, Al^{+++}, Fe^{++} and Fe^{+++}, OH^-, Cl^-, Br^-, NO_3^-, SO_4^{--} and CO_3^{--}. When the formula of one ion is known, that of its accompanying ion can be derived; for example, knowing that $Th(SO_4)_2$ must give SO_4^{--}, it is obvious that thorium ion is Th^{++++}. Similarly, the formulas of solids or

undissociated molecules follow from the ionic charges, such as $2 Al^{+++} + 3 SO_4^{--} = Al_2(SO_4)_3$; $4 K^+ + Fe(CN)_6^{----} = K_4Fe(CN)_6$; $Ca^{++} + 2 H_2PO_4^- = Ca(H_2PO_4)_2$; $Ca^{++} + HPO_4^{--} = CaHPO_4$; $3 Ca^{++} + 2 PO_4^{---} = Ca_3(PO_4)_2$.

11. The properties of dilute aqueous solutions of strong electrolytes are the sum of independent sets of properties, hence independent substances are present. The properties of solids cannot be simply referred to the properties of their constituent ions, since these ions, in crystals, are so close together as to modify each other's properties. Solid $CuCl_2$, $CuBr_2$, and $Cu(NO_3)_2 \cdot 6 H_2O$, for example, are colored green, brown, and blue, respectively. The copper ions are the source of color but their color is modified differently by each different species of adjacent colorless ions, or, in the $Cu(NO_3)_2 \cdot 6 H_2O$, by the water surrounding the Cu^{++}. All three salts, however, give the same blue color when dissolved in dilute water solution, indicating the presence of the same Cu^{++} aq. in each case. The ions are influenced now mainly by the water molecules surrounding them; the different ions are too far apart to have more than slight effect upon each other. The properties of a dilute solution of a strong electrolyte are, therefore, the sum of the properties of the water and of the constituent hydrated ions. This applies to all properties, including density, electric conductivity, color, refractive index, and chemical behavior. It makes no difference, for example, whether we make a solution by dissolving 0.1 mole each of $NaCl$ and KNO_3 or by dissolving 0.1 mole each of $NaNO_3$ and KCl, the result in either case is a solution containing 0.1 mole each of Na^+, K^+, Cl^-, and NO_3^-. The conductivities of these four salts at 25° C. in 0.1 molal solution are given in Table 2. We see that there is scarcely any difference between the sums corresponding to the presence of equal amounts of the same four ions. Obviously the conductivity of any one of these solutions could be calculated with good accuracy from measurements on the other three.

Most striking of all, perhaps, are the chemical reactions. It is not possible to predict the properties of gaseous HCl from the properties of hydrogen and those of chlorine, but it is possible to predict the properties of a dilute aqueous solution of HCl from the properties common to all other acids, on the one hand, and those common to all soluble chlorides on the other hand. The hydrogen ion in this solution reacts in the same way and has the same properties as the hydrogen ion obtained from any other acid, as explained in Chapter V. It affects indicators in the same way, it reacts

TABLE 2

Conductivities of 0.1 Molal Solutions at 25° C.

NaCl	0.01066	NaNO$_3$	0.00987
KNO$_3$	0.01201	KCl	0.01286
Sum	0.02267	Sum	0.02273

with carbonates, dissolves zinc, tastes sour, just as it always does unless the other ion present exerts some complicating effect on these tests. The chloride ion gives precipitates with the same reagents, such as AgNO$_3$ or Hg$_2$(NO$_3$)$_2$ solutions, as are obtained from all other chloride electrolytes. Knowing the properties of chloride ion, as obtained from some chloride, and knowing the properties of a cation, say barium ion, we can predict the properties of dilute solutions of barium chloride, without the aid of direct experiment. This makes it possible to simplify enormously the labor of learning the chemical reactions of electrolytes upon each other. It is necessary only to know the reactions given by the important ions in order to predict the reactions of the enormous number of electrolytes which might be obtained by combinations of these ions. Instead of remembering the action of a large number of sulfates individually upon all soluble barium salts, it suffices to remember that barium ion, Ba^{++}, reacts with sulfate ion, SO$_4^{--}$, to give a very insoluble white precipitate of barium sulfate, BaSO$_4$. Such generalizations cannot be made with any degree of assurance with substances that are un-ionized. Alcohol and phenol (carbolic acid) both contain the hydroxyl group (OH), their formulas being C$_2$H$_5$OH and C$_6$H$_5$OH, respectively, but these are not appreciably ionized, and when dissolved in water react very differently, having no set of properties in common. Again, it is not correct to conclude that silver nitrate is a "test for chlorine," as is sometimes stated. Chloroform, $CHCl_3$, will give no such test unless it is heated with silver nitrate for a long time. A solution of potassium chlorate gives no precipitate with silver ion, Ag^+, because, although it contains chlorine, it yields no chloride ion, Cl^-, but, instead, chlorate ion, ClO_3^-.

The value of the ionic theory is very great in reducing equations to their simplest terms and focusing the attention on the essential reactions taking place.

12. Heats of reaction in dilute solutions of strong electrolytes depend on the reacting ions only. Heats of reaction between ions in dilute solution are independent of the nature of any other ions present. This is not true for substances not in solution. Solid $NaOH$ and solid KOH do not give the same heat of neutralization with concentrated hydrochloric or nitric acid, but when both acid and base are dilute, the amount of heat liberated is always the same, 13,700 calories per equivalent. Since the heat liberated is the same, the reaction liberating it is likely to be the same, and the ionic theory indicates that this should be the case. Instead of writing

$$NaOH + HCl = H_2O + NaCl$$

and

$$KOH + HNO_3 = H_2O + KNO_3,$$

for the reactions in dilute solution, which would lead us to expect different heats of reaction, we should, according to previous evidence, write

$$Na^+ + OH^- + H^+ + Cl^- = H_2O + Na^+ + Cl^- + 13,700$$
$$\text{cal.}$$

$$K^+ + OH^- + H^+ + NO_3^- = H_2O + K^+ + NO_3^- + 13,700$$
$$\text{cal.}$$

The ionic form of the equations indicates that nothing happens to anything except H^+ and OH^-, which unite to form H_2O;

the other ions, being unaffected, may be canceled from the equation, leaving simply

$$H^+ + OH^- = H_2O + 13,700 \text{ cal.}$$

as the fundamental and only reaction in both cases.

The same would apply to precipitations. Any soluble barium salt would give the same heat effect per mole with any soluble sulfate, since, no matter what other ions are present in the solution, the essential reaction is

$$Ba^{++} + SO_4^{--} = BaSO_4 + 5600 \text{ cal.}$$

If, however, $Ba(OH)_2$ and H_2SO_4 solutions be used, the heat of reaction would, of course, be no longer the same as above, for then we would have occurring simultaneously two independent reactions, each with its own heat effect, and the ionic equation

$$Ba^{++} + 2\,OH^- + 2\,H^+ + SO_4^{--} = BaSO_4 + 2\,H_2O + 2 \times$$
$$13,700 \text{ cal.} + 5600 \text{ cal.}$$

shows that nothing should be canceled out.

13. Degree of Ionization of Strong Electrolytes. In very dilute solutions, the ions of strong electrolytes are so far apart as to be without influence on each other, but as concentration increases, electrostatic attractions and repulsions come into play, each positive ion tending to surround itself with negative ions, and vice versa. This attraction restricts their independence and prevents them from exerting their full individual effects. For example, they suffer a drag as they move in opposite directions while conducting an electric current, as shown in Table 3, which gives the current that would be carried by a mole of KCl at 18° C. between parallel electrodes 1 cm. apart when diluted by different volumes of water. The limiting conductivity in very dilute solution is evidently about 128, but this is greatly reduced as higher concentrations are reached. The effect of ions on the freezing point is likewise additive only at extremely low concentrations. If a salt gives two ions, the ratio of the freezing point lowering to the concentration should be $2 \times 1.86° = 3.72$ (cf. paragraph 3). This is closely approached by 0.001 M-KCl, as seen in Table 3 on page 138, but becomes less at higher concentrations.

There are other factors that may contribute to these deviations beside the one mentioned above. One of these may be the repulsions suffered by the ions when they happen to come very close to each other; another may be their varying degrees of hydration. In many cases, also, a given pair of ions may temporarily unite to form a molecule. This union is strong in the case of the weak acids and

TABLE 3
Effects of Ionic Interaction for KCl

Concentration moles per 1000 g. of water	0.0002	0.001	0.01	0.1	1
Conductivity divided by concentration	127.9	127.1	122.2	113.7	98.1
Freezing point lowering divided by concentration	——	3.65°	3.61°	3.45°	3.25°

bases and a few salts, and is appreciable in the case of many salts. Even such a strong acid as nitric shows evidence of the presence of HNO_3 molecules in concentrated solutions. The weak salts mentioned below, in paragraph 15, represent cases of incomplete dissociation. In some cases intermediate ions are formed, as $Pb^{++} + Cl^- = PbCl^+$, and $PbCl_2 + Cl^- = PbCl_3^-$.

The various formulas connecting the concentrations of the ions with the properties of their solutions all require modification to take into account the several kinds of interaction. Students who pursue this subject further into the realm of quantitative relationships will encounter factors called activity coefficients, which correct the ionic concentrations so as to allow for the variations here discussed. However, the qualitative reasoning called for in this book will yield sufficiently accurate results if we treat strong acids and bases and nearly all salts as completely ionized, the ions having effects proportional to their concentration.

It should be understood that the omission from an equation of ions which are unaffected by the reaction does not imply that they can be absent from the solution. Although the equation $H^+ + OH^- = H_2O$ represents the only chemical change that occurs in the neutralization of solutions of strong acids with strong bases, the solutions mixed must contain other ions; it is impossible to make one solution containing only H^+ and another containing only OH^-; some ion of opposite charge must be present in each, but it makes practically no difference whether the ion associated with H^+ is Cl^-, NO_3^-, or ClO_4^-, nor whether the ion associated with OH^- is Na^+, K^+, Rb^+, or Cs^+. The fact that some other ion must be in the solution is no reason for putting it into the equation if nothing happens to it. Indeed, one cannot have these solutions without vessels to hold them, test tubes, or beakers, or flasks, or some other, but that fact is no reason for adding test tubes to both sides of an equation. A chemical equation should show only the chemical changes, and not be overburdened by the formluas of molecular species which are not reacting.

14. Weak acids and bases are less ionized than strong acids and bases in solutions of the same concentration. There are some acids and bases which show the properties of hydrogen and hydroxide ions, respectively, to a much less extent than do strong acids and bases in solutions of the same concentration. Solutions of HCl, HNO_3, and H_2SO_4, at the same concentration, say 0.01 normal, would have about the same sour taste, but 0.01 normal acetic acid, $HC_2H_3O_2$, would not taste nearly so sour. The first three acids would show almost identical colors with an indicator like methyl violet, sensitive to that degree of acidity, but it would require approximately normal acetic acid to show the same color. The same weakness on the part of acetic acid is shown in power to conduct current. While, therefore, the properties of acetic acid indicate that it yields hydrogen ion in water, they also indicate that only a little of the hydrogen of the acid is ionized. Again, while the effect of acetic acid on the freezing point of water is greater than that of an un-ionized substance like sugar, it is not double the latter, as is approximately the case with an acid like hydrochloric acid. Its heat of neutralization is no longer 13,700 cal., as with a strong acid, but has a different value, 13,400 cal., which includes the heat of dissociation of the acid during its neutralization.

There are a number of such weak acids, including carbonic acid, H_2CO_3, boric acid, H_3BO_3, hydrogen sulfide (hydrosulfuric acid), H_2S, silicic acid, H_2SiO_3 (also many polysilicic acids), nitrous acid, HNO_2, arsenous acid, H_3AsO_3, arsenic acid, H_3AsO_4, sulfurous acid, H_2SO_3, and hydrocyanic acid, HCN, hypochlorous acid, $HClO$, etc. Table 4 gives the con-

TABLE 4

Approximate Concentration of H^+ in Solutions of Various Acids

Moles of Acid Dissolved per Liter		1	0.1	0.01
Hydrochloric	HCl	1	0.1	0.01
Nitric	HNO_3	1	0.1	0.01
Bisulfate ion ($NaHSO_4$ soln.)	HSO_4^-	0.2	0.04	0.008
Acetic	$HC_2H_3O_2$	0.004	0.0013	0.0004
Carbonic	H_2CO_3 (CO_2 in water)	—	0.0002	0.00006
Hydrosulfuric	H_2S	—	0.0001	0.00003

centration of H^+ in solutions of four weak acids compared with two strong acids, and indicates clearly the different extent of the ionization. The **degree of ionization** is the fraction, or per cent of the total electrolyte present, which has broken down into ions. For example, the figures for acetic acid show that if 0.1 mole of acetic acid is dissolved in 1 liter, 0.0013 mole of H^+ is liberated; since every H^+ produced requires one molecule of $HC_2H_3O_2$ to split up, 0.0013 moles of the acid have dissociated, which is 0.0013 $\approx$ 0.1 or 1.3 per cent of the acid taken. It is to be noted that as a weak acid is diluted the degree of ionization increases although the concentration of H^+ diminishes.

The most important weak base ordinarily encountered is ammonium hydroxide, NH_4OH. It is this weakness which makes it useful in cleansing, for although it does not yield enough free hydroxide ion to be injurious in washing, yet, if the little it does yield is used up, more can dissociate, the undissociated portion acting as a sort of reserve for hydroxide ion.

15. Weak Salts. Most salts are highly ionized when in solution, even though they be salts of weak acids or bases, like sodium acetate or ammonium chloride. (There are, however, a few exceptions, including lead acetate, $Pb(C_2H_3O_2)_2$, the iodide of cadmium, CdI_2, mercuric chloride, $HgCl_2$, mercuric cyanide, $Hg(CN)_2$, and ferric thiocyanate, $Fe(SCN)_3$. These salts are poor electrolytes, and their reactions in solution show the presence of relatively few ions. For example, (all ordinary soluble chlorides give a precipitate of lead chloride, $PbCl_2$, on the addition of lead ion to their solutions) With mercuric chloride, however, no precipitate is obtained, indicating that there is less chloride ion in a concentrated solution of mercuric chloride than in a saturated solution of the rather insoluble lead chloride.) If, however, silver ion is taken, a precipitate is formed, for silver chloride, $AgCl$, is much less soluble than lead chloride, and $HgCl_2$ yields enough chloride ion to precipitate it.

16. Ionization of Weak Polybasic Acids in Steps. It is found that the two or more hydrogen atoms in the molecule of a polybasic acid, like H_2CO_3, H_2S, or H_3PO_4, tend to dissociate with unequal readiness into ions. While the first hydrogen atom of H_2CO_3 is but slightly ionized, it is possible to neutralize it with OH^-, forming water and HCO_3^-, before the neutralization of the second hydrogen atom, in the HCO_3^-, begins. This explains the ease with which it is possible to form acid salts in such cases. The first atom of hydrogen in H_3PO_4 ionizes readily, corresponding to a moderately strong acid; the second ionizes from $H_2PO_4^-$ with much less ease, so that the ion $H_2PO_4^-$ is a rather weak acid, while the third is hard to neutralize, HPO_4^{--} being a very weak acid. Conversely, when hydrogen ion, H^+, is added to an ion like PO_4^{---} it is taken up very completely at first until the latter is converted into HPO_4^{--}, then less completely until $H_2PO_4^-$ is formed, and then only a little to form H_3PO_4. Similarly, when H^+ is added to CO_3^{--}, the first step is the formation of HCO_3^-, the second is the formation of H_2CO_3, or CO_2. Even H_2SO_4 forms some HSO_4^- in more concentrated solutions.

17. Ionization in Other Solvents Than Water. Water is the chief solvent in which we are interested, but there are others which can dissolve electrolytes with ionization. The most important of these are liquid ammonia and the alcohols. Ionization in all other solvents that have been investigated is less than in water, and seems to be roughly proportional to the dielectric constant of the liquid. The following values for the dielectric constants for several liquids are of interest in this connection:

Water	80	Ammonia	16
Methyl (wood) alcohol	31	Chloroform	5
Ethyl alcohol	26	Ether	4
Acetone	22		

18. Ionization of Fused Salts. Fused salts appear to be highly ionized, conducting the electric current very readily. This corresponds to the fact that melting a salt like NaCl merely releases the charged atoms, Na^+ and Cl^-, already present, held in fixed positions in the solid state, but free to move in the molten state towards charged electrodes. On account of this high conductivity many substances are obtained industrially by the electrolysis of fused salts rather than of aqueous solutions. This is the case especially with metals such as sodium, calcium, and aluminum, where, instead of the desired metal, the hydrogen from the water would be deposited at the cathode. Sodium and calcium are obtained, along with chlorine gas, by the electrolysis of their fused chlorides. Aluminum is obtained by the electrolysis of Al_2O_3 dissolved in fused cryolite, Na_3AlF_6.

19. Ionization of Water. Water itself is very slightly ionized. The purest water that can be prepared has a very slight conductivity due to H^+ and OH^-. Knowing the conductivities of these ions in more concentrated solution, as we do from measurements with acids and bases, it is possible to calculate the concentration of these ions in water to be approximately 10^{-7} molal[1] at ordinary temperatures. This corresponds to 0.1 milligram of H^+ and 1.7 milligrams of OH^- per ton of water. Other methods of measurement confirm these figures.

---

[1] This number is equivalent to writing $\frac{1}{10^7}$ or $\frac{1}{10,000,000}$.

20. The method of calculation from conductivity is illustrated by the following scheme.

Solution measured	Ions present	Conductivity at 18° C.
0.001 M-HCl	0.001 M-H$^+$ + 0.001 M-Cl$^-$	377×10^{-6}
0.001 M-KOH	0.001 M-K$^+$ + 0.001 M-OH$^-$	234×10^{-6}
	Sum	611×10^{-6}
0.001 M-KCl	0.001 M-K$^+$ + 0.001 M-Cl$^-$	127×10^{-6}
	0.001 M-H$^+$ + 0.001 M-OH$^-$	484×10^{-6}
	if they could exist together	
Pure water	x molal H$^+$ + OH$^-$	0.042×10^{-6}

Conductivity is proportional to concentration, therefore

$$\frac{484}{.042} = \frac{10^{-3}}{x}, \text{ or } x = 0.9 \times 10^{-7}.$$

Exercises

See Appendix II for answers

1. How would you define acid, base, salt, in terms of the ionic theory?

2. Summarize in writing the evidence in favor of the theory of electrolytic dissociation.

3. State in writing all the evidence you have learned, showing that a solution of acetic acid is much less ionized than one of hydrochloric acid of the same concentration.

4. Divide the following substances into two lists, one for those slightly ionized in water, the other for those highly ionized: ammonium hydroxide, ammonium chloride, hydrochloric acid, sodium acetate, carbonic acid, sodium chloride, mercuric chloride.

5. Write the formulas of all the salts that can be formed from the following ions: Ca^{++}, Mg^{++}, Fe^{+++}, Al^{+++}, SO$_4^{--}$, Cl$^-$.

6. What are the properties of H$_2$ and H$^+$? How might each one be converted into the other?

7. What are the properties of the following substances: Cu, Cu^{++}, Ag, Ag$^+$, Cl$_2$, Cl$^-$?

8. Describe some of the properties of the dilute aqueous solutions of the following: HCl, KNO$_3$, H$_2$SO$_4$, Na$_2$SO$_4$, KCl, CuCl$_2$, CuSO$_4$.

9. How does the evidence obtained from the heat of neutralization support the ionic theory?

10. Write the principal reaction occurring when (a) NaCl dissolves in water; (b) a solution of sodium sulfate is evaporated; (c) concentrated HCl solution is warmed.

11. In writing the following equations represent all substances by formulas indicating that they are mainly ionized or un-ionized, as the case may be: a solution of acetic acid is neutralized by one of sodium hydroxide; silver nitrate and potassium chloride solutions are mixed, giving a precipitate of silver chloride; dilute hydrochloric acid acts on a solution of sodium carbonate, giving CO_2 gas, water, and sodium chloride solution; zinc is put into a solution of copper sulfate, giving a precipitate of metallic copper; concentrated sulfuric acid acts on solid sodium chloride, giving hydrogen chloride gas and solid sodium sulfate; mercuric chloride solution is treated with hydrogen sulfide gas, giving a precipitate of mercuric sulfide, etc.

12. What is the concentration of OH^- in (a) equivalents per liter, and (b) grams per liter, when 0.37 g. of $Ca(OH)_2$ is dissolved in 400 cc.?

13. A solution of HAc is found to give the same color with methyl violet as a certain solution of HCl. Which would neutralize the larger proportion of base? Explain.

14. Define or explain the following terms: ion, electrolyte, degree of ionization, faraday, electron.

15. What is the degree of ionization of a weak monacid base if the concentration of the OH^- in a 0.5 normal solution is 0.002 normal?

16. (a) What is the concentration of H^+ in a 2 molal solution of acetic acid if it is 0.006 ionized? (b) What is the concentration of Ac^- (i.e., $C_2H_3O_2^-$)? (c) Of the un-ionized HAc?

17. How many (a) faradays, (b) coulombs are required to deposit 1 g. of each of the following ions at the appropriate electrode; and (c) how long will it take using a current of 1 ampere: (1) H^+, (2) Ni^{++}, (3) Cl^-, (4) Al^{+++}?

18. Arrange the following in order of their freezing points, starting with the highest: (a) 1 N-HCl; (b) 0.1 N-HCl; (c) 1 N-HAc; (d) 0.1 M-sugar; (e) 0.1 M-H_2SO_4; (f) water.

19. 0.1-g. atom of Zn is added to 0.05 moles of HCl in 500 cc. H_2O. (a) What substances are present in the final solution? (b) What is the quantity of each in moles? (c) What is the concentration of each in moles per liter?

20. State what electron changes occur when (1) an electric current is passed through a copper wire; (2) metallic zinc dissolves in acid; (3) chlorine gas acts upon metallic sodium.

21. Outline experiments to show whether glutaric acid is stronger or weaker than succinic acid.

CHAPTER IX

COMBINING PROPORTIONS

1. Ionic Charges. The proportions in which ions combine to form neutral substances are readily derived from their charges. Conversely, when the formula of an ionizing substance is known, together with that of one of its ions, the formula of the other ion is readily obtained. Examples have been given in Chapter VIII, paragraph 10.

The ionic charges, as explained in Chapter V, depend on the number of electrons an atom gains or loses. The elements, H, Li, Na, K, have but one outer electron to lose, hence, on combining with other elements, take a charge of $+1$. The elements, Be, Mg, Ca, Sr, Ba, have two outer electrons and give the ions Be^{++}, Mg^{++}, etc. The atoms, F, Cl, Br, I, with seven outer electrons, add one to complete an octet, becoming F^-, Cl^-, Br^-, I^-.

2. Oxidation Number. A substance may be insoluble in water and fail to give in that way a direct indication of the number of electrons each atom has lost or gained; nevertheless, we may feel confidence in the conclusions from more indirect evidence. For example, FeO and Fe_2O_3 are insoluble in water but they dissolve in H^+ as follows: $FeO + 2\,H^+ = Fe^{++} + H_2O$; $Fe_2O_3 + 6\,H^+ = 2\,Fe^{+++} + 3\,H_2O$. They can also be formed from Fe^{++} and Fe^{+++} as follows: $Fe^{++} + 2\,OH^- = Fe(OH)_2 = FeO + H_2O$; $2\,Fe^{+++} + 6\,OH^- = 2\,Fe(OH)_3 = Fe_2O_3 + 3\,H_2O$. Now H^+ is a substance which becomes H_2 when it acquires electrons at a cathode and OH^- becomes O_2 and H_2O when it loses electrons at an anode; hence we conclude that the iron in FeO and Fe_2O_3, respectively, has the same number of electrons as in Fe^{++} and Fe^{+++}. We shall call the charge which an element appears to have its **oxidation**

number or state. The reason for using the word oxidation may be illustrated by comparing the following reactions:

$Zn + 2H^+ = Zn^{++} + H_2$	Solution of zinc in acid
$Zn = Zn^{++} + 2\,e^-$	Solution at an electrode
$Zn + \frac{1}{2} O_2 = ZnO$	Oxidation by burning
$Zn + Cl_2 = ZnCl_2$	Chlorination
$Zn + Cu^{++} = Zn^{++} + Cu$	Displacement of Cu by Zn.

Each of these processes involves essentially the removal of the two electrons from each zinc atom. Although the third reaction only is literally oxidation, the term is extended in a figurative sense to include them all. Accordingly, the oxidation number of zinc has been increased in each case from 0 to $+2$.

3. The reverse process, a gain in electrons, or decrease in oxidation number, is designated by an obviously general term, **reduction.** In the above reactions involving Zn, the H^+, O_2, Cl_2, and Cu^{++} have been reduced, the oxidation numbers having changed as follows: hydrogen, $+1$ to 0; oxygen, 0 to -2; chlorine, 0 to -1; copper, $+2$ to 0.

4. The oxidation number can be assigned with little ambiguity to elements that always lose the same number of electrons, such as H, Na, K, Mg, Ca, Al; however, there are exceptions to ordinary behavior. Thus Li and H_2 react to form LiH, which fuses to give a conducting melt from which H_2 separates at the anode, or pole from which electrons are being removed. The hydrogen apparently has the unusual charge, or oxidation number -1, and the reaction is evidently $H^- = \frac{1}{2} H_2 + e^-$. Again, the oxygen in most of its compounds has an oxidation number of -2, having gained 2 electrons per atom to complete the octet, as we might expect. It is otherwise, however, in a class of compounds called peroxides, including H_2O_2, BaO_2, Na_2O_2. Evidence for this is seen in the following contrasting reactions:

$$BaO + 2\,H^+ = Ba^{++} + H_2O,$$
$$BaO_2 + 2\,H^+ = Ba^{++} + H_2O_2,$$
$$SnO + 2\,H^+ = Sn^{++} + H_2O,$$
$$SnO_2 + 4\,H^+ = Sn^{++++} + 2\,H_2O.$$

It is evident that the oxidation numbers of Ba and O cannot be the same in both BaO and BaO_2; however, both give the ordinary Ba^{++} on reaction with acid, hence it is the oxidation number of the oxygen which changes. In the case of SnO and SnO_2, on the other hand, it is the tin that changes. Evidently in both BaO_2 and H_2O_2 the oxidation number of the two atoms of oxygen together is -2. If there were any evidence that the electrons were unequally distributed between the two oxygen atoms, one might assign different oxidation numbers accordingly to the two atoms, for -2 and 0, for example, would add up to -2 just as do -1 and -1, but not only is such evidence lacking but since the two atoms àre quite alike it is improbable that any such inequality could be more than instantaneous. The question has no practical significance; it suffices to assign the oxidation number -1 to oxygen in peroxides.

5. Compounds whose atoms are held together by electron-pair bonds range gradually from those in which the electron pair is equally shared to those in which the pair is largely displaced towards one of the atoms. Such gradations are shown in Table 2, Chapter V. To assign the bonding electrons entirely to the more negative atom is evidently rather arbitrary except where the substance is ionic as with MgO, but it is customary in such cases to assign the electrons to the more negative element. Usually, though not always, there is sufficient experimental evidence to reveal the direction of electron displacement, permitting useful classifications of the compounds of an element according to the several oxidation numbers it assumes, and the balancing of equations for reactions in which the element changes its state of oxidation by simple formal procedures (cf. Chapter XV).

6. Thus, SF_6, SO_3, SO_4^{--}, and H_2SO_4 are classed together as compounds containing sulfur with an oxidation number of $+6$; with SCl_4, SO_2, and SO_3^{--} it is $+4$; while in H_2S, SH^-, and ZnS it is -2. These oxidation numbers are assigned by aid of the knowledge that oxygen has a very strong tendency to add 2 electrons in all its compounds except the peroxides; chlorine is usually -1, hydrogen is usually $+1$, and zinc $+2$. Furthermore, the changes involving no change in oxidation number are simpler than those which do.

Compounds of arsenic are readily classified according to oxidation number in the accompanying table.

TABLE 1

Oxidation Numbers of Arsenic

-3	0	$+3$	$+5$
H_3As	As	$AsCl_3$	AsF_5
Mg_3As_2		As_2O_3	As_2O_5
		AsO_2^-	AsO_3^-

7. An interesting case is presented by the sulfur in sodium thiosulfate, $Na_2S_2O_3$, the "hyposulfite of soda" of photography. The thiosulfate ion probably has the structure,

$$\left[\begin{array}{c} :\ddot{O}: \\ :\ddot{O}:\!S\!:\!\ddot{S}: \\ :\ddot{O}: \end{array} \right]^{-}$$

like that of SO_4^{--}. This ion can decompose to give off the extra sulfur as free sulfur, whose atoms are $:\ddot{S}$, or as sulfide ion, $:\ddot{S}:$, depending upon the reagents used. We might accordingly say that the inner and outer sulfur atoms are respectively either $+4$ and 0, or $+6$ and -2, depending upon which behavior we are considering, or, neglecting these behaviors, we might assign $+2$ as the average for the two atoms. Decision between these alternatives is quite unnecessary for balancing an equation for the oxidation of this ion, since a total of 8 electrons would be necessary to oxidize $S_2O_3^{--}$ to $2SO_4^{--}$.

8. There is another kind of combining value called **coordination number, that expresses the number of atoms, irrespective of charge, that group themselves around the atom in question.** In sulfate ion and thiosulfate ion the coordination number of the central atom is 4. In SF_6 it is 6. Silver, with a charge of $+1$, has a coordination number of 2 in the compounds, $Ag(NH_3)_2^+$ and $Ag(CN)_2^-$. Platinum, in $PtCl_6^{--}$, has a coordination number of 6, although it may be regarded as containing Pt at the $+4$ oxidation level.

TABLE 2

Examples of Coordination and Oxidation Numbers of the Central Atom

	Coordination number	Oxidation number
SO_4^{--}	4	6
SF_6	6	6
K_2SiF_6	6	4
$Fe(CN)_6^{---}$	6	3
$Fe(CN)_6^{----}$	6	2
$Ag(NH_3)_2^+$	2	1
$Ag(CN)_2^-$	2	1
K_3PO_4	4	5
K_2SO_4	4	6
$KClO_4$	4	7
$Cr(NH_3)_6^{+++}$	6	3
CrO_4^{--}	4	6

Table 2, which gives examples of coordination numbers and oxidation numbers for a number of substances, should be of assistance in distinguishing them.

The coordination number seems to be partly determined by geometrical considerations, depending on the relative sizes of the central and surrounding atoms and upon the symmetry of the resulting structure, especially as packed into a crystal lattice. A larger coordination number is favored by larger size of the central atom and smaller size of the surrounding atoms, as shown by the existence of SF_6 but not SCl_6, OsF_8 but not FeF_8, K_5IO_{10} but only $KClO_4$.

9. Covalence. There is still another term in use, covalence, which signifies the number of electron-shared bonds connecting the element in question with surrounding elements (cf. Chapter V, paragraph 10). This is particularly significant in organic chemistry, where relatively nonpolar, covalent bonds predominate. The element carbon gives no simple ions. Oxidation numbers, if desired, have to be based upon the direction of displacement of the electrons in bonds, often small and uncertain. However, it is the covalence of carbon, the number of electron-pair bonds it can form, which is of far greater significance. This number never exceeds 4. (This matter is set forth in detail in Chapter XVIII.)

10. Writing Equations. In connection with chemical equations it is important to realize that the mere writing of the equation imposes no obligation upon the substance involved to behave as indicated by the equation. The burden is rather upon the one who writes the equation to endeavor to make it correspond to an actual or possible behavior. A complete justification of an equation would require the experimental determination both of the substances produced, their formulas, and their relative amounts. A knowledge of oxidation numbers aids in writing the formulas of substances likely to be formed and also in fixing the numbers of atoms and molecules necessary to make an equation "balance," a necessary feature of an equation.

11. Union of ions. Equations involving the mere splitting of molecules into ions or vice versa are easily balanced with due regard to electric neutrality. For example, if a solution of $Al_2(SO_4)_3$, which contains Al^{+++} and SO_4^{--}, is mixed with one of $BaCl_2$, which contains Ba^{++} and $2\ Cl^-$, the SO_4^{--} unites with the Ba^{++} to form a precipitate of $BaSO_4$; hence we write simply,

$$Ba^{++} + SO_4^{--} = BaSO_4.$$

The Al^{+++} and Cl^- which are present have not reacted, so that they need not be put into the equation any more than the water, the containing vessel, or other necessary feature of the reaction.

12. Let us consider, next, the reaction between aluminum and Fe_3O_4 to form aluminum oxide and iron. To be absolutely certain of the formula of the aluminum oxide produced we would have to determine it by analysis. We do not, however, find aluminum compounds in which the oxidation number of aluminum is other than 3, as we see it in $AlCl_3$. This would lead us to anticipate that the oxide formed would be Al_2O_3, which is correct. Accordingly, we have Al and Fe_3O_4 giving Al_2O_3 and Fe. We must next adjust the number of molecules so that there will be the same number of atoms of each element on each side of the equation. It is obvious that we must take $3 Fe_3O_4$ to get an integral number, 4, of Al_2O_3 molecules. Adjusting the number of atoms of Al and Fe, we have as the equation

$$3 Fe_3O_4 + 8 Al = 9 Fe + 4 Al_2O_3$$

It is always desirable to check the equation written by comparing the number of atoms of each element on each side of the equation. They should, of course, be equal.

13. Oxidation and Reduction of Simple Ions. Equations for simple reactions of this type are readily balanced by balancing the total changes in oxidation numbers; the increase for the substance oxidized must balance the decrease for the substance reduced. Examples of this process may be seen in the following equations:

$$Cu^{++} + Zn = Zn^{++} + Cu.$$

$$2 Ag^+ + Zn = Zn^{++} + 2 Ag.$$

$$Cl_2 + 2 Br^- = Br_2 + 2 Cl^-.$$

$$Fe^{+++} + I^- = Fe^{++} + \tfrac{1}{2} I_2.$$

$$2 Fe^{+++} + Sn^{++} = Sn^{++++} + 2 Fe^{++}.$$

(The balancing of more complicated equations involving oxidation and reduction is explained in detail in Chapter XV.)

Exercises

1. What is the probable oxidation number of each element in each of the following compounds: $CuSO_4$, $Cu(NO_3)_2$, $Pb(NO_3)_2$, $PbCO_3$, $CrCl_3$, MgO, NH_4Cl, CuS, $FeCO_3$, $KClO_3$, K_2CrO_4, $Fe(OH)_2$?

2. Write the formulas of a number of other compounds that might be formed from the constituent parts of the above compounds (omitting the atoms within the ions).

3. Explain the terms: oxidation number, coordination number, oxidation, reduction, covalence.

4. Complete and balance the following incomplete equations:

$$Fe_2O_3 + C = CO +$$
$$Mg(OH)_2 + 2 H^+ =$$

$$MgO + 2 H^+ =$$
$$CrCl_3 + KOH =$$
$$Al + HgCl_2 = Hg + Al^{+++} + Cl^-$$
$$NH_4^+ + Ca(OH)_2 = NH_4OH +.$$

5. Classify according to the state of arsenic the following arsenic compounds: $AsCl_3$, As_2O_3, As_2O_5, As_2S_5, $NaAsS_2$ (consider the oxidation number of S to be $- 2$), H_3As, H_3AsO_4, Ag_3As.

6. In each of the following reactions determine what elements are oxidized and what reduced:

$$2 HgCl_2 + Sn^{++} = Hg_2Cl_2 + Sn^{+++} + 2Cl^-,$$
$$2 Ag^+ + Zn = 2 Ag + Zn^{++},$$
$$Zn + OH^- + H_2O = HZnO_2^- + H_2.$$

7. Explain why both positive and negative oxidation numbers are used.

8. Is As oxidized or reduced when it is changed from (1) $AsCl_3$ to As_2O_5, (2) H_3As to As_2O_3, (3) As_2O_5 to AsO_4^{---}?

9. Classify the following substances according to the state of oxidation of the sulfur in them: H_2S, SO_2, HSO_3^-, SH^-, S, SO_4^{--}, SO_3, $Na_2S_2O_3$, SCl_4, ZnS.

10. Classify the following substances according to the state of oxidation of the iron in them: $Fe_2(SO_4)_3$, FeS, Fe, $FeSO_4$, $FeCl_3$, $Fe(CN)_6^{----}$, Fe_2O_3, $Fe(OH)_2$, $KFe(SO_4)_2 \cdot 12 H_2O$, $BaFeO_4$.

CHAPTER X

CHEMICAL NOMENCLATURE

1. The common names of most familiar substances, given before the development of chemistry as a science, usually give no clue to their composition. However, as the number of known substances has increased it has become necessary to use names which are based upon some system. The multiplication of terms such as "oil of vitriol" (which is not an oil), "copperas" (which contains no copper), "Glauber's salt," "cream of tartar," "muriatic acid," etc., would place an almost impossible task upon the memory if it were extended to the hundred thousand or more known substances. To avoid such a situation as is found in mineralogy, where the terms give little clue to the composition of the substance, chemists have evolved a nomenclature which is based upon the elements composing the compound. This nomenclature has the advantage of being almost international, so far as the European languages are concerned.

2. Names of the Elements. The only generalization possible in the nomenclature of the elements is in regard to the names of the metals. The effort has been to give the Latin neuter suffix, -*um*, to the names of metals, as illustrated by potassium, magnesium, platinum. Where the element was commonly known before the introduction of this systematic nomenclature we may have still surviving the common name without this suffix, as with iron, silver, copper, gold. In such cases the Latin name, from which the symbol is derived, may, however, often be used to designate compounds. For example, instead of copper sulfate we may say cupric sulfate, from the Latin *cuprum*. The reason for this use of the Latin name will become apparent later.

The group NH_4, which gives compounds analogous to those of the metal potassium, is called ammonium.

3. The More Positive Element Named First. It is customary to give the name of the metallic or positive element first in naming the compound (corresponding to the order used in writing the formula), as is seen in the names of aluminum oxide, sodium chloride, copper sulfide, magnesium sulfate, potassium nitrate, hydrogen fluoride, carbon dioxide, etc.

4. Binary Compounds Designated by Suffix -ide. When the compound consists of but two elements it is customary to add the suffix -ide to the name of the second or less metallic element in naming the compound. Thus all compounds of oxygen with a single more positive element are called oxides, those of chlorine are called chlorides, those of phosphorus, phosphides, those of carbon, carbides, etc.

In a few cases this suffix is used where the compound contains more than two elements because of the existence of certain groups acting much like a single element. For example, the cyanide group, CN, acts very much like the halogens; hence KCN is called potassium cyanide, by analogy with KCl, potassium chloride.

5. Designation of Compounds Where the Positive Element May Show Different Oxidation Numbers. As was pointed out in Chapter IX, there are many elements showing more than one oxidation state in their compounds, so that the simple naming of the constituents as above leaves an ambiguity as to which of the possible compounds is meant. There are, for example, two chlorides, oxides, etc., of mercury, iron, tin, lead, copper, etc., so that it is not sufficient, in these cases, to speak of mercury chloride, iron chloride, tin oxide, copper sulfide, etc. In most cases the positive elements exhibit but two oxidation states, and it is possible to distinguish their two series of compounds by adding the suffixes -ous and -ic to the name of the positive element, signifying the lower and higher oxidation states respectively. Accordingly, we designate Hg_2Cl_2 as mercurous chloride and

$HgCl_2$ as mercuric chloride; As_2O_3 as arsenous oxide, and As_2O_5 as arsenic oxide. In many cases the common English name of the element does not lend itself to this usage, as with the elements iron, copper, tin, lead. In such instances the Latin name of the element is used, so that we have $FeCl_2$, ferrous chloride, and $FeCl_3$, ferric chloride, Cu_2O, cuprous oxide, and CuO, cupric oxide, SnS, stannous sulfide, and SnS_2, stannic sulfide.

6. Another way of distinguishing between different compounds of the same element is by the use of the Latin and Greek numeral prefixes to the names of the elements. These prefixes, up to eight, are as follows:

	1	*2*	*3*	*4*	*5*	*6*	*7*	*8*
Latin	*Uni-*	*Bi-*	*Ter-*	*Quadri-*	*Quinque-*	*Sexa-*	*Septi-*	*Octa-*
Greek	*Mono-*	*Di-*	*Tri-*	*Tetra-*	*Penta-*	*Hexa-*	*Hepta-*	*Octo-*

To these we may add the Latin *hemi*, meaning one half, and *sesqui-*, meaning one and a half. By the use of these prefixes we can often designate the compound with less ambiguity than by means of the suffixes *-ous* and *-ic*, especially when more than two compounds exist. As examples of the use of these prefixes we may mention CO, carbon monoxide, and CO_2, carbon dioxide; CS_2, called both carbon bisulfide and carbon disulfide; PCl_3, phosphorus trichloride, and PCl_5, phosphorus pentachloride; Cr_2O_3, chromium sesquioxide, and CrO_3, chromium trioxide; Sb_2S_3, (di)antimony trisulfide (antimonous sulfide) and Sb_2S_5, (di)antimony pentasulfide (antimonic sulfide).

7. The prefix *per-* is used in binary compounds chiefly to denote oxides in which the oxygen is related to the oxygen in hydrogen peroxide, H_2O_2, with an average number of -1. The most important besides hydrogen peroxide are barium peroxide, BaO_2, and sodium peroxide, Na_2O_2. It is doubtless wise to use the term only with oxides of this type, though this is by no means a uniform practice.

A compound like Fe_3O_4, which is doubtless composed of FeO, ferrous oxide, and Fe_2O_3, ferric oxide, may be designated as ferrous-ferric oxide, though it is usually referred to as "magnetic iron oxide." Similarly, Pb_3O_4 is usually known by its commercial name "red lead."

8. Binary Acids. Acids consisting of hydrogen and one other element are designated by the prefix *hydro-* and the suffix *-ic*, like HCl, hydrochloric acid; HN_3, hydronitric acid; H_2S, hydrosulfuric acid.

9. Oxyacids and Salts. Certain elements capable of assuming more than one oxidation state form two or more acids containing oxygen. In such cases the significance of *-ous* and *-ic* in distinguishing higher and lower oxidation state is similar to that used with binary compounds. We have H_2SO_3, sulfurous acid, and H_2SO_4, sulfuric acid; $HCrO_2$, chromous acid, and H_2CrO_4, chromic acid; H_3AsO_3, arsenous acid, and H_3AsO_4, arsenic acid; and HNO_2, nitrous acid, and HNO_3, nitric acid. When more than two oxygen acids of the same elements exist, the prefixes *hypo-* and *per-* are used, as illustrated in the following table, which shows at the same time the salt designations corresponding to the different types of acid, using the acids of chlorine for illustration:

Acid		*Corresponding Salt*	
HCl	Hydrochloric	KCl	Potassium chloride
HClO	Hypochlorous	KClO	Potassium hypochlorite
$HClO_2$	Chlorous	$KClO_2$	Potassium chlorite
$HClO_3$	Chloric	$KClO_3$	Potassium chlorate
$HClO_4$	Perchloric	$KClO_4$	Potassium perchlorate

10. Sulfoacids and Salts. There are many cases where sulfur replaces oxygen in salts, though the corresponding acids are not capable of existing free. These are designated in the same way as the oxysalts, using the prefix *sulf(o)-*, or better, *thio-*. We have $KSbO_2$, potassium antimonite, and $KSbS_2$, potassium thioantimonite; $KSbO_3$, potassium antimonate and $KSbS_3$, potassium thioantimonate; KCNO, potassium cyanate, and KCNS, potassium thiocyanate.

In the case of $Na_2S_2O_3$, which seems to be a sulfate with one oxygen atom replaced by a sulfur atom, the name thiosulfate is given.

11. Complex Halogen Acids and Salts. Similar to the oxy- and sulfoacids we have others containing the halogens, like H_2PtCl_6, chloroplatinic acid, giving salts called chloroplatinates; H_2SiF_6, fluosilicic acid (cf. H_2SiO_3, silicic acid); $HAuCl_2$, chloroaurous acid and $HAuCl_4$, chloroauric acid.

12. Acid and Basic Salts. Many acids have more than one replaceable hydrogen atom in the molecule, and many bases have more than one replaceable hydroxyl group in the molecule. Sulfuric acid, from example, is called a **dibasic acid** on account of its ability to neutralize two hydroxyl groups. Similarly, H_3PO_4, phosphoric acid, is a tribasic acid. On the other hand, $Mg(OH)_2$, magnesium hydroxide, is a **diacid base** for similar reasons. In such cases it is usually possible to have partial neutralization of either acid or base so as to give either an acid salt or a basic salt. The following equations represent the formation of such salts:

$$NaOH + H_2SO_4 = NaHSO_4 + H_2O,$$

$$KOH + H_3PO_4 = KH_2PO_4 + H_2O,$$

$$2\,KOH + H_3PO_4 = K_2HPO_4 + 2\,H_2O,$$

$$Mg(OH)_2 + HCl = Mg(OH)Cl + H_2O.$$

The salts produced in these reactions would be called, respectively, sodium acid (or hydrogen) sulfate, potassium dihydrogen phosphate, dipotassium hydrogen phosphate and magnesium hydroxy chloride or basic magnesium chloride. The names monoprotic, diprotic, etc., are used by some chemists in place of the preceding, signifying 1 proton (hydrogen ion), 2 protons, etc.

Sometimes a basic or hydroxy salt may lose water, becoming an oxysalt. With bismuth hydroxide, for example, $Bi(OH)_3$, the progressive neutralization with HCl would give first $Bi(OH)_2Cl$, then $Bi(OH)Cl_2$, finally $BiCl_3$. The first of these loses water, becoming BiOCl, a well-known substance called bismuth oxychloride. In naming these two kinds of basic salts chemists are not always careful to distinguish between an oxysalt and a hydroxy salt, but there is some justification in this, on account of the uncertainty existing in many cases as to whether the water present in the precipitate is actually combined or not.

Sometimes this oxy group plays the part of a radical, existing throughout various metathetical reactions. The radical is then usually designated by the suffix *-yl*, as in $BiOCl$, bismuthyl chloride, CrO_2Cl, chromyl chloride, UO_2Cl_2 uranyl chloride.

Acid salts may likewise lose water, but the possible types of compounds can best be understood in connection with the various types of partially dehydrated acids.

13. Partially Dehydrated Acids and Their Salts. If an acid salt like $KHSO_4$, potassium acid sulfate, is heated, it loses water according to the equation

$$2 KHSO_4 = H_2O + K_2S_2O_7.$$

The same result is obtained by adding SO_3 to K_2SO_4. With reference to its mode of formation this salt is called potassium pyrosulfate (from the Greek *pyr*, meaning fire). It may also be called potassium bisulfate on account of the extra SO_3 present. This is more evident if the formulas of both the sulfate and the bisulfate are expressed as compounds of acid and basic anhydrides, as was done in Chapter V for many salts, giving $K_2O \cdot SO_3$, and $K_2O \cdot 2 SO_3$, respectively. There are other examples of this type. When acid is added to a chromate, as K_2CrO_4, instead of getting an acid salt, $KHCrO_4$, there results a bichromate, as represented by the equation

$$K_2CrO_4 + HCl = (KCl + KHCrO_4)$$
$$= KCl + \tfrac{1}{2} H_2O + \tfrac{1}{2} K_2Cr_2O_7.$$

There is no great distinction between a bisalt and an acid salt (in solution it is generally impossible to distinguish them), so that the former name is applied somewhat indiscriminately. Thus $NaHCO_3$, sodium acid carbonate, is often called sodium bicarbonate, though the real bicarbonate, which would be $Na_2C_2O_5$, does not exist. Similarly $KHSO_4$ may be called potassium bisulfate. Sometimes it is possible to have still more of the acid anhydride present, as with $K_2Cr_3O_{10}$ and $K_2Cr_4O_{13}$, called potassium trichromate and tetrachromate, respectively, or in general, polychromate (from the Greek *poly*, meaning many). This again becomes most obvious when the formulas are written in terms of the acid and basic anhydrides, giving $K_2O \cdot 3\ CrO_3$ and $K_2O \cdot 4\ CrO_3$. It might be desirable to be more precise, reserving the name potassium acid sulfate for $KHSO_4$ and potassium bisulfate for $K_2S_2O_7$, but it is unlikely that the familiar name for $NaHCO_3$, sodium bicarbonate, would give way in the interest of a finer distinction.

With a tribasic acid like phosphoric acid, H_3PO_4, there exist several partial anhydrides, like HPO_3 and $H_4P_2O_7$. The relations between these acids is best brought out by the equations,

$$3\ H_2O + P_2O_5 = 2\ H_3PO_4,$$

$$H_2O + P_2O_5 = 2\ HPO_3 = 2\ H_3PO_4 - 2\ H_2O,$$

$$2\ H_2O + P_2O_5 = H_4P_2O_7 = 2\ H_3PO_4 - H_2O.$$

In the first, H_3PO_4, we have the maximum amount of water, and it is called orthophosphoric acid (from the Greek *ortho*, meaning straight, direct). The second, metaphosphoric acid (from the Greek *meta*, meaning after), may be derived by the simple abstraction of water from the orthoacid. The third is called pyrophosphoric acid. The application of these terms to several other acids, as in the following table, will make them clearer:

Acids	Boric	Silicic	Phosphorus	Stannic
Ortho	H_3BO_3	H_4SiO_4	H_3PO_3	H_4SnO_4
Meta	HBO_2	H_2SiO_3	(HPO_2)	H_2SnO_3
Pyro	$H_2B_4O_7$ (also called tetra-)	(Many polysilicic acids. $H_2O \cdot nSiO_2$)	$H_4P_2O_5$	

It is evident that there is no distinction between a pyroacid and its salts and a polyacid, and where there are several it is not customary to use the prefix pyro- with its ambiguous significance, for although there is but one pyrophosphoric acid there are a number of polysilicic acids, which require such distinguishing terms as dimetasilicic acid for $H_2Si_2O_5$; trimetasilicic acid for $H_2Si_3O_7$; diorthosilicic acid for $H_4Si_2O_6$, etc. The salts are, of course, designated as for the simpler acids; thus $Na_2H_2P_2O_7$ is disodium-dihydrogen pyrophosphate, $Na_2B_4O_7$ (borax) is sodium tetra- (or pyro-) borate, K_2SnO_3 is potassium metastannate.

Exercises

1. How should each of the following substances be named: CaH_2, H_2S, PbS, $Ni(OH)_2$, $Ni(OH)_3$, Hg_2SO_4, $HgSO_4$, PbO, Pb_3O_4, $CuCO_3$, H_2CO_3, $Hg(NO_3)_2$, $Hg(OH)NO_3$, NH_4Cl, NH_4OH, NH_4HSO_4, $KHNH_4PO_4$, $SbCl_3$, $SbCl_5$, SbOCl, NaCl, NaClO, $AlCl_3$, $Al(OH)_3$, NaH_2AlO_3, $NaAlO_2$, SO_2, H_2SO_3 (cf. H_2SO_4, sulfuric acid), $NaHSO_3$, $Na_2S_2O_7$, SO_3, Sb_2O_3?

2. Give the names of the following substances: (1) ClO_3^-; (2) NaClO; (3) HBr; (4) $HClO_2$; (5) KIO_4.

3. What facts about the following substances can be concluded from their names: thallium; silver arsenide; thallous chloride; carbon bisulfide; phosphorus pentabromide; nitrogen iodide; cerium; ceric chloride; lead dioxide?

4. Give the formulas of the following substances: (*a*) oxygen gas; (*b*) carbonate radical; (*c*) ammonium hydroxide; (*d*) cuprous sulfide; (*e*) aluminum sesquioxide; (*f*) nitrogen trichloride.

5. If H_3AsO_4 is called arsenic acid, what should each of the following be called: $HAsO_3$, H_3AsO_3, $H_4As_2O_7$, $PbHAsO_4$, $KAsS_3$?

6. If K_2MnO_4 is called potassium manganate, what should $KMnO_4$ be called?

7. If H_4SnO_4 is called orthostannic acid, what would you call each of the following: H_2SnO_2, $NaHSnO_3$, $NaHSnO_2$, Na_2SnS_3?

CHAPTER XI

THE SPEED OF CHEMICAL REACTIONS

1. The Problem. The previous chapters have been taken up with various aspects of the nature and composition of substances, and with the representation of substances and their reactions by means of formulas and equations. We are now ready to inquire into the means of controlling chemical reactions so as to realize desirable possibilities or prevent undesirable ones. There are two factors involved in this control, the direction and the speed. For example, at high temperatures the following reaction takes place readily:

$$2 NH_3 = N_2 + 3 H_2.$$

The theory to be developed in Chapter XV shows that it should be possible to reverse this reaction at low temperatures and make ammonia from its elements. We find by experiment, however, that the reaction proceeds so slowly at low temperatures as to be utterly useless as a means of making ammonia, and that we must seek some means for its acceleration in order to make it of any practical use. The means of altering the direction of a reaction will be discussed in the following chapters, this one being devoted to the question of speed in reactions where the direction is already assured. Sometimes we may wish to increase the speed of a reaction, as in the cooking of food, and sometimes we may wish to retard an undesirable reaction, such as the rusting of iron or the decay of wood. How may this be done?

2. Application of the Kinetic Theory. We have seen, in connection with the behavior of gases and solutions, Chapters III and IV, how fruitful is the kinetic theory of matter. We may apply it with equal success to the problem of con-

162

trolling the speed of chemical reactions. In order that reactions may take place between different substances their molecules must come together, or collide. We should therefore expect any means of increasing the number (and perhaps the force) of these collisions to be effective in increasing the speed. What means are available for changing the number and speed of these collisions?

3. Effect of Temperature. Since the kinetic theory connects the temperature of any body with the velocity of the molecules composing it, one way indicated for increasing the number and also the force of the molecular collisions is to increase the temperature. We find, as a matter of fact, that the effect of increasing the temperature is always to increase the reaction velocity. For reactions occurring within a single phase, e.g., between dissolved or gaseous substances, it is found that the effect of increasing the temperature 10° C. is frequently to increase the speed from two to four times. Where the reaction occurs at the boundary line between two phases, as in dissolving a solid, the effect of temperature is usually somewhat less.

4. Chemists constantly make use of the accelerating effect of higher temperature in chemical reactions, and we see it constantly in everyday life. The reactions responsible for the growth of plants, for the decay of dead animal and plant substances, for the souring of milk, are all greatly influenced by the temperature, so that the importance of warmth for growth and of cold storage for preservation is well known to all. The housewife sets her bread to rise in a warm place to hasten the fermentation which produces the carbon dioxide. Those who have lived or camped at high altitudes know of the difficulty of cooking certain foods at the lower temperature at which water boils under such conditions. The difficulty is sometimes solved by means of "pressure cookers," which hold the steam under pressure, allowing a higher temperature to be reached. Such an apparatus may also be used at ordinary altitudes, resulting in a great saving of fuel when cooking such things as beans or the tougher cuts of meat, for it requires scarcely any more fuel to maintain a temperature of 120° C. than it does to maintain one of 100° C., although a reaction that requires 5 hours at the latter temperature might be completed in less than 1 hour at the former. In such processes as extracting glue, gelatin, and fats, "superheated steam" is used with similar effect. The speed of cooking such a thing as a potato is also increased by cutting it into small pieces, so that all parts of it are quickly brought to the temperature of the boiling water in which it is immersed.

5. The process of hardening steel is an interesting case of retarding a reaction by lowering the temperature. Above 766° C. a steel containing 0.9 per cent carbon consists of a hard, tough variety of iron holding the carbon in solid solution, but below that temperature it tends to change into a heterogeneous mixture, shown in Fig. 6, Chapter I, of soft iron (like wrought iron) and a hard, brittle iron carbide, Fe_3C, known as cementite. However, this transition requires an appreciable time, and if the steel, heated above 725° C., is suddenly cooled by quenching in water, so that low temperatures are quickly reached, the tough solid solution may be obtained at ordinary temperatures, where the velocity of the change is practically negligible. This is shown in Fig. 3, page 10. A solution which required 10 seconds for transition at 766° C. to the variety stable at ordinary temperatures would require 300,000 billion years at 20° C. if the reaction velocity were halved for every 10° C. fall in temperature. Hardened steel is thus an unstable substance at ordinary temperatures but we can keep it almost indefinitely by reason of the extreme slowness of its change into the stable variety. If we cool the steel slowly, i.e., anneal it, or if we allow the hardened steel to get too warm for a while, as by too rapid grinding or cutting with a tool, it changes into the stable soft mixture, losing its "temper."

6. Many chemical substances are similarly unstable at ordinary temperatures, existing only because the speed at which they decompose is small. In this class are included

ozone, O_3, hydrogen peroxide, H_2O_2, nitric oxide, NO, and all explosives. Nitric oxide is stable in the true sense only at the temperature of a very hot electric arc and it can be obtained at ordinary temperatures by a process of rapid cooling similar in principle to the hardening of steel.

7. Spontaneous combusion is the result of the preliminary slow oxidation which many combustible substances undergo in contact with air. Ordinarily the heat of these reactions is liberated so slowly that it has time to be conducted away, so that no perceptible rise in temperature of the oxidizing material takes place. When, however, the material is a poor conductor of heat, like oil-soaked cotton waste, and is in large quantities, so that the heat produced is partly retained, then the rise in temperature causes an increase in the rate of oxidation, with a further gradual rise in temperature, until the temperature of ordinary rapid combustion is attained, and the material bursts into flames.

8. Effect of Concentration. Another means of increasing the number of favorable collisions between molecules is to increase the concentration of the reacting substances. The more concentrated a substance is, the more chances there are of its molecules colliding with those of other substances; hence an increase in the concentration of each kind of reacting molecule should increase the speed of reaction. If, for example, two molecules have to collide in order to bring about a certain reaction, then doubling the concentration of either should double the speed of reaction, and doubling the concentration of both should quadruple the speed. Of course, as the reacting substances are used up the speed diminishes.

9. Numerical Relation between Concentration and Speed. If c_1, c_2, c_3, etc., denote the concentrations of the reacting molecules, then the velocity of the reaction, v, as measured by the rate of disappearance of one of the substances or the formation of another, is proportional to, or equal to a constant times the product of the concentrations of the reacting molecules, i.e., $v = kc_1c_2c_3$. . . . If a molecule can decompose without reacting with another the reaction is called

unimolecular and the rate at which the substance disappears is obviously proportional to its concentration at the moment; i.e., $v = kc$, or, if we start with A moles in V liters and after a time, t, the amount decomposed is x, the amount remaining is $A - x$ and its concentration is $(A - x)/V$ and the velocity $\dfrac{\Delta x}{\Delta t} = k\dfrac{A - x}{V}$.

Examples of unimolecular reactions are:

$$N_2O_5 = 2\,NO_2 + \tfrac{1}{2}O_2$$

$$H_3CN_2CH_3 = N_2 + C_2H_6.$$

If two molecules must collide, the reaction is **bimolecular**, and $v = kc_1c_2$. Examples are:

$$2\,NO_2 = 2\,NO + O_2 \qquad\qquad v = k(NO_2)^2$$

$$2\,HI = H_2 + I_2 \qquad\qquad v = k(HI)^2$$

$$H_2 + I_2 = 2\,HI \qquad\qquad v = k(H_2)(I_2)$$

where the parentheses indicate concentrations of the inclosed substance.

Reactions in which the velocity depends on collisions between three or more molecules are very rare because of the fact that simultaneous collisions between three or more molecules are vastly less frequent than collisions between two molecules. One could convince himself of this by throwing three dice repeatedly and comparing the number of triple sixes with the number of double sixes obtained.

Cases in which the total reaction involves a number of molecules are thus usually split up into two or more steps, the slowest of which determines the rate. For example, the reaction

$$2\,H^+ + 2\,Br^- + H_2O_2 = Br_2 + 2\,H_2O$$

might appear to be pentamolecular but it is actually trimolecular; experiments show that its velocity is given by $k(H^+)(Br^-)(H_2O_2)$. There appear to be two steps,

$$(1)\quad H^+ + Br^- + H_2O_2 = HBrO + H_2O.$$

$$(2)\quad HBrO + H^+ + Br^- = Br_2 + H_2O.$$

The first is slower, hence determines the rate, since HBrO can decompose by (2) only so fast as it is being formed by (1). If (2) were slower, a different rate law would be found.

The determination of the "mechanism" or steps of a reaction is often a difficult matter, but is essential for the understanding and hence the control of reactions. The relative speed of the different steps and their reversibility, and the temporary production of intermediate products all play roles in fixing rate laws.

10. Effect of Stirring and of Contact Surface in Reactions Occurring at the Boundaries between Phases. If a reaction occurs at the boundary between phases, as in the solution of a solid in a liquid, it is evident that stirring would have great effect in bringing fresh reacting molecules to the surface of contact, also in removing the products of reaction from the scene of action. The natural tendency of the molecules to diffuse can thus be greatly aided.

Likewise, contact between the materials in the two phases can be aided by having the contact surface large. For this reason powdered sugar will dissolve more rapidly than granulated or lump sugar.

We may summarize and illustrate the foregoing by stating the conditions for the rapid solution of a metal in acid as follows: high temperature, concentrated acid (unless the salt produced would be thereby rendered insoluble, preventing its diffusion away from the surface of the metal), the use of a strong acid like hydrochloric acid, giving a high concentration of hydrogen ion, instead of a weak acid like acetic acid, giving a small concentration of hydrogen ion (assuming that the metal is a base metal which will be dissolved by hydrogen ion), stirring the solution, and using the metal in rather finely divided condition rather than in large pieces.

An undesirable reaction may, of course, be hindered by the converse of the above means.

11. Effect of Catalysts. Many reactions can be accelerated or retarded by the presence of substances which are not themselves permanently used up by the reaction, and which need be present only in small amount to affect the speed for a large amount of reacting mixture. Such substances are called **catalysts.** One class of catalysts acts by furnishing a surface at which the reacting molecules are condensed and concentrated, causing them to come into more intimate contact. Platinum and palladium act in this way for a number of gas reactions. Hydrogen and oxygen scarcely react at all at ordinary temperatures, but platinum and palladium have the power to absorb these gases, especially the hydrogen, and allow them to react with each other. Under suitable conditions the heat produced by this union may be sufficient to raise the temperature of the metal to a point where it can ignite the remaining gas mixture. Some gas and cigar lighters are constructed on this principle, and when the platinum or palladium is held in the stream of gas mixed with air, or in the escaping vapors of wood alcohol from a wick, the gas or vapor is ignited by the heat generated at first in the catalyst. Platinum finds extensive use in the *"contact process"* for the manufacture of sulfuric acid. As will be explained in Chapter XIV, the reaction

$$2\,SO_2 + O_2 = 2\,SO_3$$

occurs in the desired direction only at lower temperatures, where the reaction proceeds too slowly to be of use. When, however, the gases are passed over platinum at about 500° C. they react readily, so that the process has partly supplanted the older "lead-chamber process" for making sulfuric acid to a considerable extent (cf. paragraph 15).

Solid SO_3 unites vigorously with water to form H_2SO_4, but the vapor of SO_3 emerging from the contact process along with an excess of oxygen is not readily extracted by bubbling the gas through water, for it forms a mist with the water vapor not easily absorbed by the liquid. It is extracted far more easily by concentrated H_2SO_4, probably forming chiefly $H_2S_2O_7$, to which water is gradually added to form H_2SO_4 again.

12. When platinum is used to catalyze reactions its effectiveness may be increased by increasing the surface as much as possible, exposing atoms at edges and corners of the solid lattice, which, thus relieved of part of the attraction of their neighbors, are able to exert a stronger effect on the adsorbed substance. This is particularly important because of the high cost of platinum. The usual form in which it is used is "platinized asbestos," made by wetting asbestos fiber with a solution of a platinum salt and then heating it so as to decompose the salt and yield finely divided metallic platinum.

13. Haber Process. The union of nitrogen and hydrogen directly to give ammonia, developed by Haber, in Germany, referred to at the beginning of this chapter, is brought about by the aid of a similar catalyst, iron, to whose aid we owe this important means for the fixation of atmospheric nitrogen and its application as fertilizer.

14. Hydrogen peroxide is a very unstable substance, tending to decompose so as to give oxygen and water. This decomposition is aided by the presence of finely divided solids, such as manganese dioxide, MnO_2. This oxide likewise catalyzes other reactions where oxygen is evolved, notably

$$2 KClO_3 = 2 KCl + 3 O_2.$$

In making oxygen by heating potassium chlorate it is customary to add powdered manganese dioxide, so that the oxygen will be evolved more smoothly and at a lower temperature.

To prevent the decomposition of hydrogen peroxide, besides keeping it dilute and cool, as the kinetic theory would require, a negative or retarding catalyst is frequently added in the form of acetanilid, $C_6H_5NHOC_2H_3$.

15. Carriers. Many catalysts evidently act as "carriers," by the formation of an intermediate product which then decomposes readily. Such a catalyst is NO, as used in the "lead-chamber process" for the manufacture of sulfuric acid. The reaction

$$SO_2 + H_2O + \tfrac{1}{2} O_2 = H_2SO_4$$

does not occur with sufficient speed, but since the reaction

$$NO + \tfrac{1}{2} O_2 = NO_2$$

occurs readily in both directions, the oxides of nitrogen make the oxygen available in the following way,

$$SO_2 + H_2O + NO_2 = H_2SO_4 + NO.$$

The NO_2 is regenerated as shown above, so that a little of it suffices for the manufacture of an almost indefinite quantity of sulfuric acid.

16. Catalysis by Hydrogen Ion. An interesting reaction is the "inversion" of cane sugar, which consists in its splitting up, with the addition of a molecule of water, into two molecules of simpler sugars, fructose and glucose, containing the same atoms but in different arrangement. The reaction is

$$C_{12}H_{22}O_{11} + H_2O = C_6H_{12}O_6 \text{ (glucose)} + C_6H_{12}O_6$$
$$\text{(fructose)}.$$

The resulting mixture of sugars is often called invert sugar. This reaction is catalyzed by the hydrogen ion of acids and the speed of inversion is proportional to the concentration of hydrogen ion, which doubtless forms an intermediate product. Since the resulting invert sugar does not easily crystallize, it is important, in the refining of sugar, to avoid all acidity of the sugar solutions. When stewed fruit is sweetened the effect of the sugar will be greater if the fruit is sweetened while hot, causing the inversion of the sugar by the acid of the fruit. The altered taste of lemonade that has stood for some hours is due mainly to this inversion of its sugar. It is of interest to note that the sugar in honey is invert sugar. The inversion doubtless takes place in the body of the bee when it is gathered, and prevents subsequent crystallization in the comb.

By a process analogous to the inversion of sugar, starch may be made to take up water, becoming transformed into a mixture of various sugars to which is given the commercial name "glucose." Large quantities of syrup and sugar are made from cornstarch by digestion with acid, which acts as the catalyst.

17. Water is a catalyst for many reactions. Absolutely dry CO will not burn. Dry $AgNO_3$ and HCl dissolved in ether form no precipitate of AgCl. When ordinary NH_4Cl is heated it sublimes, dissociating into NH_3 and HCl gases. If, however, the salt is quite dry, it vaporizes without dissociation.

18. Enzymes. An important class of catalysts, known as enzymes, are produced by living organisms and catalyze many reactions. The ptyalin of saliva, whose function is to convert starch into sugar, the diastase of malt, which has a similar action, and the zymase of the yeast plant, which converts certain sugars into alcohol and carbon dioxide, are examples of important enzymes. Similar bodies are thought to play fundamental roles in the processes of growth and nutrition of plants and animals.

19. Activation. The slowness of reactions may be related to the stability of the reacting molecules, indicating that they must first be "opened up" in some way before their atoms can rearrange themselves in new molecules. It requires 103,000 cals. to dissociate one mole of hydrogen, 210,000 cals. to dissociate N_2. It is not strange, therefore, that these substances are slow to react at ordinary temperatures. It is not necessary in most cases, however, to split molecules into atoms in order for them to react. It suffices to "activate" them by bombarding them with electrons, by subjecting them to light of appropriate frequency, or by raising their temperature to a value where molecular collisions are sufficiently strong to introduce more energy into the molecule. Such activation may involve the temporary boosting of an electron to a higher orbit or energy state or it may make the molecule vibrate more vigorously thus giving it energy to aid in some subsequent reaction.

We may use a mechanical analogy to assist in understanding activation. Let us imagine a weight resting on a shelf provided with a rim, as in Fig. 1. It will be possible to let the weight do work while falling to the floor by attaching it by means of cord and pulley to a dynamo or other means of absorbing energy. If the rim were absent and the weight standing on a smooth, oiled shelf, very little energy would have to be

TABLE 1

Reaction	Energy of activation cals.
$N_2O_5 = 2\ NO_2 + \frac{1}{2}\ O_2$	23,900
$H_3CN_2CH_3 = N_2 + C_2H_6$	52,400
$2\ HI = H_2 + I_2$	38,900
$H_2 + I_2 = 2\ HI$	40,900

expended to push the weight over the edge and start the process, but in the arrangement shown, it is necessary to do work on the weight to lift it over the rim in order to start

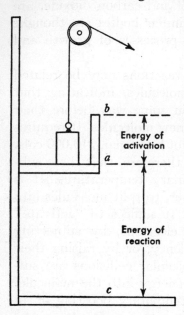

the process. This extra energy is then recovered by reason of the extra height through which the weight falls. We might call the energy required to lift the weight over the shelf, from a to b, the energy of activation, while the energy obtained from a to the floor, c, is the net energy of the reaction. These two amounts of energy evidently have no necessary connection.

20. Values for the energies of activation are given in Table 1 for several of the reactions considered above.

21. The magnitude of the heat of activation gives a clue to the temperature at which velocity becomes appreciable, also to the change in velocity with temperature. Thus the first reaction above

Fig. 1. Illustration of difference between energy of activation and energy of reaction.

proceeds with measurable speed at room temperatures while the second becomes appreciable only around 300° C.

22. The effect of temperature on the velocity constant, k, is given by the equation:

$$\log \frac{k_2}{k_1} = \frac{E}{4.58} \cdot \frac{T_2 - T_1}{T_1 T_2}$$

where k_1 and k_2 are the values of the velocity constant at T_1 and T_2, respectively, and E is the energy of activation. For the decomposition of N_2O_5, for example, we would have, for $T_2 = 303$ and $T_1 = 293$,

$$\log \frac{k_2}{k_1} = \frac{23,900}{4.58} \cdot \frac{10}{293 \times 303} = 0.588$$

and $k_2/k_1 = 3.87$, i.e., a nearly fourfold increase in velocity for a 10° increase in temperature from 20° to 30° C.

23. The rapid increase in reaction velocity with temperature corresponding to the above equation finds a physical explanation in considering the fact that the molecules of a gas have velocities both higher and lower than the mean velocity on which was based the simple discussions in Chapter III. The velocities are distributed among the molecules according to curves shown in Fig. 2, one curve for a lower temperature, T_1, the other for a higher temperature, T_2. Distribution curves of this shape are obtained in a great variety of connections, e.g., the heights or weights of persons; even, indeed, their marks in chemistry, if properly obtained. The curves show that most of the molecules vary but little from the mean of them

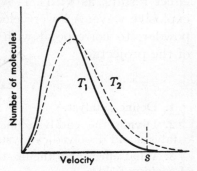

Fig. 2. Distribution of molecular velocities at lower temperature, T_1, and higher temperature, T_2.

all, but that there are a few with both very low and very high velocities. Let us suppose that the velocity u is required to activate molecules so that they can react in a given case. Evidently the proportion of molecules thus activated increases far more rapidly than the temperature, due to the shift of the whole curve to the right for the higher temperature.

24. Explosions. The heat liberated by a reaction may be dissipated so rapidly that the temperature does not rise appreciably. However, if the heat liberated leaks away more slowly than it is liberated the temperature of the mass rises, the reaction is accelerated and may finally become quite vigorous. This occurs in spontaneous combustion, say, of oily rags, where oxygen can diffuse into the pile but the heat leaks out only slowly. The combustion becomes more and more rapid until it is limited only by the rate of air access. If the oxygen is already present in some other form, as in gunpowder or dynamite, the reaction, once started, may proceed with explosive velocity. For an explosive to be "safe," there should be high energy of activation, so that it is hard to start. The safest explosives require higher energies than can be given by ordinary mechanical blows, responding only to "detonators" such as mercuric fulminate, $Hg(OCN)_2$, and lead azide, PbN_3. The power of an explosive depends on both the energy and the speed of the reaction. A shattering effect results, as with "T. N. T.", from high velocity of the explosive wave. A lower velocity is necessary for a propellant powder, to correspond with the more gradual acceleration of the projectile.

Exercises

1. Define catalyst.

2. Divide the catalysts mentioned in the text into surface catalysts and dissolved catalysts.

3. What effect may the use of a double boiler have on the speed of cooking food?

4. What means could you employ for rapidly washing photographic prints free from the "hypo" of the fixing bath?

5. How might you alter the time required for developing a photographic negative?

6. How might you endeavor to increase the speed of the reaction:

$$BrO_3^- + 6\,I^- + 6\,H^+ = 3\,H_2O + Br^- + 3\,I_2?$$

What effect would acetic acid have upon the speed as compared with hydrochloric acid of the same concentration?

7. The organism existing in "mother of vinegar" converts alcohol into acetic acid by the reaction

$$C_2H_5OH + O_2 = C_2H_4O_2 + H_2O.$$

By what means could the manufacture of vinegar be hastened?

CHAPTER XII

CHEMICAL EQUILIBRIUM. THE EFFECT OF CONCENTRATION

1. Reversibility of Chemical Reactions. The problem of the control of chemical reactions involves not only the speed, as discussed in Chapter XI, but also the fact that most reactions are reversible. We have, therefore, two problems as distinct from each other as are the speed and destination of a train. To reach a desired destination quickly it is not sufficient to get on a fast train; the train must also go in the right direction. With chemical reactions, similarly, the conditions accelerating the reaction often reverse the direction at the same time. For example, the velocity of formation of SO_3 from SO_2 and O_2 increases with the temperature, but the velocity of decomposition of SO_3 back into SO_2 and O_2 is likewise increased thereby, and more rapidly than the velocity of its formation, so that SO_3 becomes increasingly unstable at higher temperatures. Therefore, assuming that all the time necessary for them to take place is allowed, we will turn our attention to the problem of the direction of chemical reactions. Finally, in Chapter XIV, we will consider both effects together.

2. Most reactions are reversible, that is, the products of a reaction may usually be made to react with each other by suitable choice of conditions to produce the original substances. Many examples of this may be given. A liquid may be made to evaporate by raising the temperature or by reducing the pressure, and its vapor, conversely, may be recondensed to liquid by lowering the temperature or increasing the pressure. Solids may be liquefied by increasing the temperature, and liquids may be solidified by lowering the

175

temperature. Gases may either be dissolved in liquids or driven out of solution by suitable changes in pressure or temperature. The naturally occurring mineral, gypsum, $CaSO_4 \cdot 2 H_2O$, may be deprived of part of its water by moderate heating, giving plaster of Paris, which is approximately $CaSO_4 \cdot \frac{1}{2} H_2O$. When this is mixed with water the original dihydrate is re-formed, which causes the plaster to "set," due to the interlocking of the growing crystals of $CaSO_4 \cdot 2 H_2O$. Nitric oxide, NO, is decomposed by gentle heating into nitrogen and oxygen, and yet, at the high temperature of the electric arc a considerable amount of nitric oxide may be formed from the nitrogen and oxygen of air. Oxygen, O_2, is changed into ozone, O_3, by the silent electric discharge, and then gradually reverts to oxygen. When a lead storage battery is discharged, the lead dioxide of the positive plate, the lead of the negative plate and the sulfuric acid in the solution react as follows:

$$PbO_2 + Pb + 4 H^+ + 2 SO_4^{--} = 2 PbSO_4 + 2 H_2O,$$

and when the battery is recharged the reverse reaction takes place, corresponding to the equation as read from right to left. When water charged with carbon dioxide passes over limestone rock, the following reaction occurs:

$$CaCO_3 + H_2O + CO_2 = Ca^{++} + 2 HCO_3^-.$$

The calcium ion dissolved in the water produces what is called "hard water," and interferes with the cleansing power of soap by precipitating insoluble calcium soap. When this water is boiled, however, the CO_2 is driven off, and the calcium carbonate is reprecipitated, corresponding to the equation as read from right to left. When steam is passed through a tube containing iron filings or nails heated to dull redness, the following reaction occurs:

$$3 Fe + 4 H_2O = Fe_3O_4 + 4 H_2.$$

When an excess of hydrogen is passed over the iron oxide, Fe_3O_4, under similar conditions, some of it is changed to steam with the reduction of the oxide to iron, exactly the reverse of the above. Illustrations of reversibility might be multiplied *ad libitum*.

3. The experimental proof of reversibility consists simply in mixing each set of substances, as indicated by the two sides of the equation, and seeking conditions under which the other set will be formed. The disappearance of any of the substances taken, or the appearance of any of the products, is usually sufficient proof that a reaction has taken place. Which particular substance to test for is determined by the ease and decisiveness of the available tests. Thus the oxidation of mercury, represented by the equation

$$2 \, Hg + O_2 = 2 \, HgO,$$

could be proved if conditions could be found under which mercury in contact with oxygen would increase in weight. A change in appearance corresponding to the red color of the oxide, or a decrease in the amount of the gaseous oxygen would suffice equally well. The reverse reaction, the dissociation of mercuric oxide into mercury and oxygen, could be proved by taking the red mercuric oxide and discovering conditions of pressure and temperature under which there could be detected either the appearance of mercury or oxygen, or else a loss in weight.

4. It is frequently desirable to express in the equation for a reaction the fact that the reaction is reversible. This is done by substituting a double arrow, $\leftrightarrows$, for the equality sign. Written in this way, an equation such as the one above would appear as follows:

$$2 \, Hg + O_2 \leftrightarrows 2 \, HgO.$$

It must be remembered that the double arrow sign retains the full significance of the usual equality sign, merely adding further information, so that we would do well to regard it as an abbreviation for a fuller representation such as the following:

$$2 \, Hg + O_2 \overset{\rightarrow}{\underset{\leftarrow}{=}} 2 \, HgO.$$

Since nearly all reactions are reversible, however, the double arrow sign is somewhat superfluous, except, perhaps, where it is desired to emphasize the fact of reversibility. Its absence must never be construed as indicating irreversibility. In view of these facts we will not ordinarily use it in the following pages.

An irreversible reaction is frequently indicated by a single arrow, as illustrated by $C_6H_{12}O_6 \rightarrow 2\ C_2H_5OH + 2\ CO_2$ for the fermentation of one of the sugars, but the obligation to write a balanced equation often disappears when only a single arrow is used instead of the more explicit $\rightleftharpoons$.

5. It is Possible to Have All of the Substances Involved in Reversible Reactions Present Together in Chemical Equilibrium with Each Other. Instead of passing steam over heated iron in a tube, as in the experiment described above, we might simply heat them together in a closed vessel. We would expect, as before, the formation of some hydrogen and iron oxide, corresponding to the equation as read from left to right. Likewise, if we heat hydrogen and iron oxide together at the same temperature and in a similar vessel, we would expect the formation of iron and steam, corresponding to the equation as read from right to left. If we allow sufficient time for reaction in both cases, how will the final state of affairs in one vessel compare with that in the other? It is obviously absurd to expect either reaction to go to completion, just as it would be absurd to expect a ball placed on a certain table to roll all the way from a to b when we have previously found that, when placed at b, it rolls towards a. Obviously there must be some intermediate position on the table at which it tends to come to rest no matter at which end it is started. Again, if it is found that one body becomes cooler when brought into a certain room, and another becomes warmer when brought into the same room, it is evident that each body will come eventually to the same temperature, that of the room, which must lie somewhere between the initial temperatures of the two bodies.

6. By the same kind of reasoning, it should make no difference whether we start with $3 Fe + 4 H_2O$, or with $Fe_3O_4 + 4 H_2$, if we heat them to a temperature at which they are able to react, in identical vessels, we will eventually get a mixture of all four substances in **chemical equilibrium.** The term signifies that the concentrations of the substances involved in the opposing reactions have become so adjusted or balanced as to equalize their rates, making the rate at which each substance is produced equal to the rate at which it is used up, so that there is no further net change in the quantity. It is important to bear in mind that the constancy of these net quantities present does not mean that nothing is happening. The fact that the pressure of water vapor in a closed vessel containing some pure liquid is constant at any fixed temperature does not mean that the same molecules remain always in the vapor phase; individual molecules are continually escaping from the liquid and an equal number being recaptured by the liquid in the same time. When we start with iron and steam, at a sufficiently high temperature, they react with a velocity depending on the concentration of steam molecules and on the surface of the iron. As these are used up the reaction gradually becomes slower. At the same time, as more hydrogen and iron oxide are produced, they begin to react with each other to regenerate the iron and steam, with an increasing velocity, until the rate of one reaction just equals that of the other. This conception of equilibrium was used in connection with simpler phenomena in Chapter III, and has an important bearing on what is here to follow.

7. The Effect on Chemical Equilibrium of Changing the Concentration of the Reacting Substances. When chemical equilibrium has been attained, it is possible to disturb it by any means which changes the relative speeds of the two opposing reactions. These rates may be affected by changing the temperature, or the total pressure on the reacting system, or the concentration of the substances involved. The effect of changing the temperature or total pressure will be discussed in Chapter XIV, and we will turn our attention first to changes in concentration.

8. If we increase the concentration of one of the reacting substances, there are then more molecules of that substance present in a given space, so that their ability to find and react with other molecules is increased. This will cause a temporary gain in the rate of the reaction using up this kind of molecule, until more of the products of this reaction, represented on the other side of the equation, are produced, so as to equalize again the rates of the two reactions. The net result is that the reaction proceeds to some extent in the direction which will use up the substance whose concentration is thus increased.

9. For illustration let us consider a closed vessel containing SO_3, SO_2, and O_2 in chemical equilibrium, to attain which requires a sufficiently high temperature and perhaps a catalyst. When equilibrium is attained we must imagine that the two reactions, represented by the equation

$$2 SO_2 + O_2 = 2 SO_3,$$

read in both directions, are taking place with equal velocities, with a net result of no change in the relative amounts of the three gases present. Suppose, now, that more oxygen is introduced into the vessel. The increased number of oxygen molecules will render it easier for them to collide with sulfur dioxide molecules, resulting in a more rapid formation of sulfur trioxide molecules. As the number of the latter increase their own speed of decomposition will increase until the two reactions again take place at equal rates. The net effect of this increase in the amount of oxygen is to cause more of it to be used up, with a decrease in the amount of sulfur dioxide and an increase in the amount of sulfur trioxide. The effect of adding or removing any of the three substances present can be predicted on the above basis.

From a technical point of view, in making sulfur trioxide, the important thing is to use up the sulfur dioxide as completely as possible, since the latter costs money, whereas the supply of oxygen is free. To accomplish this the kinetic theory indicates that it is desirable to have the oxygen in excess, since otherwise considerable sulfur dioxide would remain uncombined when equilibrium has been reached.

10. In general, after equilibrium has been reached, **the effect of any change in the concentration of the reacting substances is to cause that reaction to take place which tends to neutralize the change;** that is, if the concentration of any substance is increased, that reaction tends to take place which uses up that substance, and where the concentration of any substance is decreased, that reaction tends to take place which will replace that substance. This conclusion is a special case of a more general one, called the **Theorem of Le Chatelier,** which states that when equilibrium has been reached a change in *any* of the factors affecting equilibrium tends to make that reaction take place which will neutralize the effect of the change. (The discussion of other factors will be taken up in Chapter XIV.)

11. The above conclusion, in so far as concentration alone is concerned, is called the "Law of Mass Action," or the **"Mass Law."** This name is slightly misleading, since it is not the masses of the substances present, but their concentrations, or masses per unit volume, which determine equilibrium. This point was discussed in Chapter III, where it was shown that the depth of the water in equilibrium with its vapor, or the extent of the surface between the two phases, has no effect upon the equilibrium. On the other hand, a change in the concentration of the vapor, as by changing its volume, or in the concentration of the liquid, as by adding some other substance to it, *would* cause some reaction to take place. Likewise, in the equilibrium discussed above, between iron, its oxide, steam, and hydrogen, the relative amounts of the solids have no more effect than would the addition of more salt to a saturated salt solution. The reactions occur at the place where the three phases, the two solids and the gas phase, are in contact, and these are not unbalanced by the excess of either solid.

12. Equilibrium in Solution. These same conclusions apply to reactions occurring in solution, including those between ionized substances. For example, that the reaction

$$HC_2H_3O_2 = H^+ + C_2H_3O_2^-$$

will take place as read from left to right may be shown by taking pure acetic acid (which is un-ionized, as shown by its being a nonconductor) and dissolving it in water, when the solution will have the properties of hydrogen ion. That the reaction will also take place as read from right to left, may be shown by mixing a solution of a strong acid, like hydrochloric acid, giving a large concentration of hydrogen ion, with one of sodium acetate, which gives a large concentration of acetate ion. We find that hydrogen ion disappears partly from the solution, and also that acetic acid appears, as is evident by its odor. It makes no difference, therefore, whether we start with a mole of acetic acid in a liter of water, or with a mole each of hydrogen and acetate ions in a liter of water, the final state of affairs is the same, which is that we will have present about 0.004 mole of each of the two ions and 0.996 mole of the undissociated molecules. If, subsequently, we add another mole of acetate ion (in solution with, say, sodium ion, which affects none of the substances present) some of the acetate ion will be able to use up more of the hydrogen ion, becoming acetic acid, resulting in a considerable decrease in the acidity (hydrogen ion concentration) of the solution.

13. The dilution of a solution of a weak electrolyte such as acetic acid results in an increase in the degree of dissociation (cf. page 140), as can readily be deduced by the aid of the kinetic picture of equilibrium. At equilibrium there are just as many molecules of acetic acid splitting into ions as are being reformed from the ions in a given time. If more water is added the rate of the ionization process can be little affected, since the acetic acid molecules in both solutions are surrounded entirely by water molecules. However, the H^+ and $C_2H_3O_2^-$ are farther apart, on the average, after the dilution, and cannot collide and reunite so frequently, so that the former reaction gains upon the latter, and the resulting increase in the number of ions increases the frequency of collision till the rate of recombination again equals the rate of dissociation. The net result of the dilution is, therefore, that more of the acid has ionized as expressed by the equation:

$$HC_2H_3O_2 = H^+ + C_2H_3O_2^-.$$

14. These conclusions are so important, and of such general validity, applying to gaseous as well as ionic equilibria, that we will emphasize them by the tabulation of the acetic acid equilibrium given in Table 1. The figures have been calculated by a method to be outlined later. Their relative, rather than their absolute, magnitudes should here receive attention. A comparison of cases A and B shows that the amounts of each of the three substances present at equilibrium are identical, regardless of the direction from which it has been reached. Case C shows the large diminution of H^+, and the consequent increase in $HC_2H_3O_2$, following an increase in the amount of $C_2H_3O_2^-$. Case D shows the corresponding diminution of $C_2H_3O_2^-$, following the addition of an excess of H^+. Case E shows the increase in the degree of dissociation caused by dilution. Chemists are accustomed to refer to the change from one condition of equilibrium to another, such as cases C, D, and E, as a **shift of equilibrium** to the left (Cases C and D) or to the right (E) as the case may be.

It is to be noted that the equation, read either to the right or the left, does not in itself tell how much material has reacted or what are the equilibrium concentrations, but only that if acetic acid is allowed to ionize, due to putting it into water, or by increasing the ionization by adding more water to a mixture in equilibrium, every molecule of acetic acid that ionizes forms one hydrogen ion and one acetate ion; again, if acetic acid molecules are formed, as by evaporation, or the processes stated in B, C, and D, the ions unite in the proportion one to one. In case C a large excess of $C_2H_3O_2^-$ had to be added to use up 0.0038 mole of H^+, but only 0.0038 mole of $C_2H_3O_2^-$ out of the 0.1 mole added combined with H^+. The presence of five hunters instead of one hunting for a rabbit in a certain tract of land greatly shortens the life expectation of the rabbit, but only one of the hunters bags the rabbit.

TABLE 1

	$HC_2H_3O_2$ =	H^+ +	$C_2H_3O_2^-$	Volume of solution, liters	Direction and moles of acid ionized or formed
A Take, moles	1	0	0	1	
Get, at equilibrium,	0.996	0.004	0.004	1	0.004 →
B Take, by mixing H^+ + Cl^- with Na^++$C_2H_3O_2^-$,	0	1	1	1	
Get, at equilibrium,	0.996	0.004	0.004	1	0.996 ←
C Take above equilib. mixture,	0.996	0.004	0.004	1	
Add 0.1 mole each Na^+ + $C_2H_3O_2^-$, get	1.00	0.0002	0.10	1	0.004 ←
D Take equilib. mixture,	0.996	0.004	0.004	1	
Add 0.1 mole each H^+ + Cl^-, get	1.00	0.10	0.0002	1	0.004 ←
E Take equilib. mixture,	0.996	0.004	0.004	1	
Dilute to 10 l., get	0.987	0.013	0.013	10	
Conc.	0.0987	0.0013	0.0013	1	0.009 →

15. Quantitative Expression of the Mass Law. In the above discussion of the effect of concentration on chemical equilibrium we have been content with predicting the direction of the effect of altering concentration, the qualitative effect, without inquiring how much a given equilibrium would be disturbed by a certain change in concentration of one or more of the reacting substances. This would be called the quantitative effect. Although the qualitative prediction suffices in most cases, it is nevertheless often desirable to make a quantitative prediction. This is possible by combining the quantitative expression for the speed of a chemical reaction, given in Chapter XI, with the idea introduced in this chapter, that at equilibrium the two opposite reactions are proceeding with equal velocity. For the sulfur trioxide reaction discussed above, we would have for the velocity of formation $v_1 = k_1 c_{SO_2}^2 \cdot c_{O_2}$, where k_1 is a constant. Similarly, for the decomposition of the trioxide back into the dioxide and oxygen, we would have for the velocity $v_2 = k_2 c_{SO_3}^2$. At equilibrium the two velocities are equal, so that $k_1 c_{SO_2}^2 \cdot c_{O_2} = k_2 c_{SO_3}^2$. Since k_1 and k_2 are constants their quotient is a constant, K, so that we may write

$$\frac{c_{SO_3}^2}{c_{SO_2}^2 c_{O_2}} = K.$$

It is customary to put the substances on the right-hand side of the chemical equation in the numerator, those on the left in the denominator. This makes a large value of K correspond to a large yield.

16. By means of this expression we are able to make qualitative as well as quantitative predictions. Since K is constant at a given temperature, the values of the three concentrations must always adjust themselves accordingly. For example, suppose that it were found by measurement, at a certain temperature, that when equilibrium was reached the concentrations were as follows: SO_2, 3 moles per liter, O_2, 1 mole per liter, SO_3, 2 moles per liter. By substituting these values in the above expression we obtain for the value of the constant $K = \frac{4}{9}$. From this we can calculate another set of equilibrium concentrations. Thus, if the concentration of O_2 were 5 moles per liter, and that of SO_3 2 moles per liter, we would have

$$\frac{4}{c_{SO_2}^2 \times 5} = \frac{4}{9}$$

from which we would find the concentration of SO_2 in equilibrium with sulfur trioxide and oxygen at the new concentrations to be 1.34 moles per liter.

17. It is also the custom to denote concentrations by the formula of the substance inclosed in brackets or parentheses. Using this notation we would write the above expression

$$\frac{(SO_3)^2}{(SO_2)^2(O_2)} = K,$$

which has exactly the same significance as before where c was used to denote concentration.

18. In the derivation of the equilibrium equation from the velocity equations in the manner just given we have ignored the fact, noted in the preceding chapter, that many reactions proceed in steps, one of which may be slower than the others and hence determines the rate. Such a state of affairs does not, as might be supposed at first sight, vitiate the equilibrium equation based on the total reaction, as can be seen from the following case: the equilibrium constant of the reaction $3\,HNO_2 = 2\,NO + H_2O + H^+ + NO_3^-$ is $K = \dfrac{(NO)^2(H^+)(NO_3^-)}{(HNO_2)_3}$. The concentration of the water remains practically constant in dilute solutions, therefore it does not need to appear in the equilibrium equation. The velocity equations, however, are not $v_1 = k_1(HNO_2)^3$ and $v_2 = k_2(NO)^2(H^+)(NO_3^-)$, for the reaction actually takes place in two stages, $4\,HNO_2 = N_2O_4 + 2\,NO + 2\,H_2O$, which is rapid and reversible, and $N_2O_4 + H_2O = HNO_2 + H^+ + NO_3^-$, which is slow, and determines the rate. There are, therefore, two rates from left to right, $v_1 = (k_1 HNO_2)^4$ and $v_1' = k_1'(N_2O_4)$, also two to the left, $v_2 = k_2(N_2O_4)(NO)^2$ and $v_2' = k_2'(HNO_2)(H^+)(NO_3^-)$. At equilibrium $v_1 = v_2$ and $v_1' = v_2'$, therefore

$$\frac{k_1}{k_2} = \frac{(N_2O_4)(NO)^2}{(HNO_2)^4} \text{ and } \frac{k_1'}{k_2'} = \frac{(HNO_2)(H^+)(NO_3^-)}{(N_2O_4)}$$

from which

$$\frac{k_1 k_1'}{k_2 k_2'} = \frac{(NO)^2(H^+)(NO_3^-)}{(HNO_2)^3},$$

which is a constant, since the small k's are all constants, identical with K, above.

19. It may be worth while to give examples of the equilibrium equation for several other reactions.

Reaction	*Equilibrium Equation*
$N_2 + O_2 = 2\,NO$	$\dfrac{(NO)^2}{(N_2)(O_2)} = K$
$N_2 + 3\,H_2 = 2\,NH_3$	$\dfrac{(NH_3)^2}{(N_2)(H_2)^3} = K$
$CO_2 + C\ (solid) = 2\,CO$	$\dfrac{(CO)^2}{(CO_2)} = K$

(Since carbon is solid its concentration is constant and need not be expressed in the equilibrium equation.)

Fe_3O_4 (solid) $+\ 4\,H_2 = 3\,Fe$ (solid) $+\ 4\,H_2O$ $\dfrac{(H_2O)^4}{(H_2)^4} = K'$

$$\text{or}\quad \frac{(H_2O)}{(H_2)} = K$$

$HC_2H_3O_2 = H^+ + C_2H_3O_2^-$ $\dfrac{(H^+)(C_2H_3O_2^-)}{(HC_2H_3O_2)} = K$

$H_2CO_3 = H^+ + HCO_3^-$ $\dfrac{(H^+)(HCO_3^-)}{(H_2CO_3)} = K$

$HCO_3^- = H^+ + CO_3^{--}$ $\dfrac{(H^+)(CO_3^{--})}{(HCO_3^-)} = K$

20. Since the partial pressure of a gas is proportional to the number of molecules in a given space, and hence to the concentration, it is possible, where gases are concerned, to write partial pressures instead of concentrations, and have constant a similar function of partial pressures. This constant is not necessarily the same as that where concentrations are used, so that we will express it as K_p. We would write, accordingly,

$$\frac{p_{NO}^2}{p_{N_2} \cdot p_{O_2}} = K_p, \qquad \frac{p_{NH_3}^2}{p_{N_2} \cdot p_{H_2}^3} = K_p, \text{ etc.}$$

21. When a gas reacts with substances in solution it is often convenient to let the equilibrium constant express the partial pressure of the gas along with the concentrations of the dissolved substances. Ammonia gas, passed into a solution containing Ag^+

gives $Ag(NH_3)_2{}^+$ (cf. Chapter XIII, paragraph 18) as well as dissolved NH_3 and NH_4OH. The reaction may be considered in two stages, NH_3 (gas) = NH_3 (aq.) (including NH_4OH) and $2 NH_3$ (aq.) $+ Ag^+ = Ag(NH_3)_2{}^+$. The equilibrium constants for these may be written, respectively, $p_{NH_3} = K_1$ (NH_3, aq.) and $(NH_3,$ aq.$)^2 + (Ag^+) = K_2[Ag(NH_3)_2{}^+]$. Combining these gives $p_{NH_3}^2(Ag^+) = K[Ag(NH_3)_2{}^+]$, where $K = K_1^2 K_2$.

22. In the case of carbonic acid we do not know very accurately what part of the CO_2 in solution is simply dissolved, as nitrogen dissolves, and what part is in the form of H_2CO_3. It is not necessary to make the distinction if we understand by (H_2CO_3) the sum of both forms. A similar convention should be understood for (NH_4OH) in spite of the fact that some of the dissolved ammonia doubtless consists of NH_3 (aq.).

In the former case it may be convenient to relate the dissociation constant to the partial pressure of CO_2, which is proportional to the dissolved CO_2, so that we may write $p_{CO_2}/(H_2CO_3) = K''$. Combining this with $(H^+)(HCO_3^-)/(H_2CO_3) = K$ we get (H^+) $(HCO_3^-)/p_{CO_2} = K'$.

23. Dissociation Constants of Weak Electrolytes. The equilibrium constants for the dissociation of a weak electrolyte, are called **dissociation constants** or **ionization constants,** and express the strength of an acid or base in the most general way. It is evident that the stronger the electrolyte the larger are the concentrations written in the numerator of the fraction, hence the larger the dissociation constant. Instead of stating the degree of dissociation for an electrolyte at a certain concentration, as was done in Chapter VIII, paragraph 13, it is more satisfactory to give the dissociation constant, from which the degree of dissociation at any concentration may be calculated. The values for certain familiar substances may be given as shown in Table 2 on page 189.

24. The concentration of hydrogen ion in a solution of acetic acid, for example, may be calculated from the dissociation constant of the acid as follows: If the acid alone is present in the solution, the hydrogen ion and the acetate ion are at the same concentration, hence $(H^+) = (C_2H_3O_2{}^-)$. Suppose that the total concentration of acetic acid is 0.1

molar. The amount ionizing is so slight that the un-ionized acid may be considered as 0.1 molar without appreciable error, i.e., $(HC_2H_3O_2) = 0.1$. Substituting these values in the equilibrium equation, we obtain

$$\frac{(H^+)^2}{0.1} = 1.8 \times 10^{-5} \text{ and hence } (H^+) = 0.0013.$$

Again, suppose that 0.05 molar acetate ion is present in the same solution, then $(C_2H_3O_2^-) = 0.05$, $(HC_2H_3O_2) = 0.1$ and $(H^+) = 0.000036$. It will be observed that the acidity of this solution is vastly less than that of the former.

TABLE 2

Substance	Reaction	Dissociation constant at room temperature*
Acetic acid	$HC_2H_3O_2 = H^+ + C_2H_3O_2^-$	1.8×10^{-5}
Dihydrogen phosphate ion	$H_2PO_4^- = H^+ + HPO_4^{--}$	6×10^{-8}
Carbonic acid†	$H_2CO_3 = H^+ + HCO_3^-$	4.3×10^{-7}
Hydrogen sulfide	$H_2S = H^+ + HS^-$	10^{-7}
Hydrocyanic acid	$HCN = H^+ + CN^-$	4×10^{-10}
Bicarbonate ion	$HCO_3^- = H^+ + CO_3^{--}$	4.7×10^{-11}
Hydrosulfide ion	$HS^- = H^+ + S^{--}$	10^{-15}
Ammonium hydroxide	$NH_4OH = NH_4^+ + OH^-$	1.8×10^{-5}
Bisulfate ion	$HSO_4^- = H^+ + SO_4^{--}$	1.2×10^{-2}

*All of these values have to be increased for solutions containing high concentrations of other ions, which aid in dissociating the weak electrolyte.

† The value of (H_2CO_3)—total dissolved CO_2—is $0.034\ M$ when the partial pressure of CO_2 is 1 atm. at 25° C.

25. The ionization of strong electrolytes does not obey the Mass Law, for reasons suggested in Chapter VIII, paragraph 13, therefore we cannot write for them simple dissociation constants like those given above for weak electrolytes. However, that need not disturb us greatly because most of them can be considered with approximate accuracy as completely ionized. It is well, however, to bear in mind the weak salts listed in Chapter VIII, paragraph 15.

26. Solubility Product. The Mass Law can be applied to the concentrations of the ions of a sparingly soluble salt.

Taking $PbSO_4$ as an example we write $(Pb^{++})(SO_4^{--}) = K$. The value of K at 25° C. is 1.8×10^{-8}. When pure $PbSO_4$ dissolves in water, no other ions are present to alter the concentrations of the two ions and $(Pb^{++}) = (SO_4^{--}) = \sqrt{K}$ or 1.3×10^{-4} moles per liter, which is therefore the value of the solubility of $PbSO_4$ in pure water. However, if $PbSO_4$ is shaken with, say, 0.01 M-K_2SO_4, which fixes $(SO_4^{--}) = 10^{-2}$, then $(Pb^{++}) = 1.8 \times 10^{-8}/10^{-2} = 1.8 \times 10^{-6}$, much less than it is in pure water.

TABLE 3

Solubility Products*

$PbBr_2$	6.3×10^{-6}	CdS	1.4×10^{-28}
AgBr	3.3×10^{-13}	CuS	4×10^{-38}
$CaCO_3$	4.8×10^{-9}	FeS	1×10^{-19}
Ag_2CO_3	8.2×10^{-12}	PbS	1.0×10^{-29}
$PbCl_2$	1.7×10^{-5}	HgS	3×10^{-53}
AgCi	1.7×10^{-10}	Ag_2S	1.0×10^{-51}
AgI	8.5×10^{-17}	SnS	8×10^{-29}
$PbCrO_4$	1.8×10^{-14}	ZnS	4.5×10^{-24}
CaF_2	3.4×10^{-11}	$CaC_2O_4 \cdot H_2O$	2.3×10^{-9}
$Ca(OH)_2$	7.9×10^{-6}	$Ag_2C_2O_4$	1.1×10^{-11}
$Fe(OH)_2$	1.6×10^{-15}	$BaSO_4$	1×10^{-10}
$Pb(OH)_2$	2.8×10^{-16}	$CaSO_4 \cdot 2 H_2O$	2.4×10^{-5}
$Mg(OH)_2$	5.5×10^{-12}	$PbSO_4$	1.8×10^{-8}
$Sn(OH)_2$	5×10^{-26}	Ag_2SO_4	1.2×10^{-5}
$Zn(OH)_2$	4.5×10^{-17}		

* The values for solubility products in Table 3 are selected from the extensive table in Appendix XI of *Reference Book of Inorganic Chemistry*, Latimer and Hildebrand, New York, The Macmillan Company, 1940.

The solubility product for $PbCl_2$ must be written $(Pb^{++})(Cl^-)^2 = K$, whose value is 1.7×10^{-5}. We see from the equation of solution, $PbCl_2(s) = Pb^{++} + 2 Cl^-$, that in pure water $(Cl^-) = 2 (Pb^{++})$, hence $(Cl^-)^2 = 4 (Pb^{++})^2$ and $4 (Pb^{++})^3 = 1.7 \times 10^{-5}$ or $(Pb^{++}) = (0.43 \times 10^{-5})^{1/3}$. To take a cube root of this kind of a number it is convenient to have an exponent divisible by 3, hence we will write $(4.3 \times 10^{-6})^{1/3}$ which is 1.63×10^{-2}. The value of Cl^- is then 3.26×10^{-2}.

Suppose that we wished to calculate (Pb^{++}) in the presence of 0.03 M-KCl. In that case the value of (Cl^-) would not be determined chiefly by the 0.03 M-Cl from the KCl, since enough $PbCl_2$ would dissolve to increase the total (Cl⁻) by an amount equal to 2 (Pb⁺⁺), whatever (Pb⁺⁺) turns out to be. The total (Cl⁻) in solution after it becomes saturated with Pb⁺⁺ is 0.03 + 2 (Pb⁺⁺) and therefore (Pb⁺⁺) [0.03 + 2 (Pb⁺⁺)]² = K = 1.7 × 10⁻⁵. To solve this for (Pb⁺⁺) is a little complicated and, unless a student comes fresh from algebra, the most feasible method is likely to be the "method of successive approximations." We know that (Pb⁺⁺) in this case is considerably less than 0.0163, the value calculated above for $PbCl_2$ in pure water. Let us assume several values as shown below and tabulate the corresponding values for the left side of the last equation above, which must be made to agree with the value on the right, 1.7 × 10⁻⁵. It is possible to approach the correct value as closely as desired.

(Pb⁺⁺)	K (calculated)
.005	8.0 × 10⁻⁵
.001	1.0 × 10⁻⁵
.002	2.3 × 10⁻⁵
.0015	1.64 × 10⁻⁵
.0016	1.76 × 10⁻⁵
.00155	1.7 × 10⁻⁵

27. There is a bothersome point that occurs to many students in handling the solubility product for such a salt as $PbCl_2$, considered above, or a base, such as $Ca(OH)_2$. If the concentration of Ca^{++} in the saturated solution is measured as c, then $K_s = c \times (2c)^2$. Why, it is often asked, does the number 2 occur twice in this expression? If we attempt to explain the 2 in the exponent by writing $Ca(OH)_2 = Ca^{++} + OH^- + OH^-$, then one might well ask why we do not write $K_s = c \times c \times c$? Now the coefficient, 2, occurs only in this particular case when the ions in solution all come from the solid which dissolves, and obviously 2 OH⁻ are liberated for every Ca^{++}. If we should disturb the equilibrium, e.g., by adding more OH⁻, then (OH⁻) would no longer equal 2 (Ca^{++}). But the exponent 2 always remains, and may be explained as follows:

Since dice are easier for most of our readers to visualize than ions, let us imagine a special game of dice in which we wish to throw triple sixes with one black and two white dice, from a total of N_b black and N_w white dice. The chance of throwing a black six is 1/6 if we use one die, 2/6 for 2, 3/6 for 3, etc.; hence, the probability of getting black sixes is proportional to the number of black dice used, N_b. But the probability of throwing 2 white sixes at the same time increases far more rapidly with the number of white dice thrown; as follows:

No. dice		2	3	4	5	N_w
No. of possible double sixes		1	3	6	10	$\frac{1}{2} N_w(N_w - 1)$

When N is very large, the number of doubles is therefore proportional to N_b^2, and since any of these black double sixes can be combined with any of the white sixes, the probability of throwing the desired triples is proportional to $N_b N_w^2$. We may apply similar reasoning to the reaction, $Ca^{++} + 2\,OH^-$. We should note, particularly, that one OH^- uniting with Ca^{++} still leaves OH^- of practically the same concentration. Since (Ca^{++}) in saturated $Ca(OH)_2$ at 20° C. is 0.022, (OH^-) *in this solution* is 0.044 and $K_s = 0.022\ (0.044)^2 = 4.3 \times 10^{-6}$. Any student who has put his mind to the problems of throwing dice should have no difficulty with a matter such as this.

28. Catalysts Do Not Shift Equilibrium. On page 167 we considered the catalyst as an agent for altering the speed of a reaction. We must now note that in the case of reactions which come to equilibrium the catalyst for the reaction in one direction must also be a catalyst for the reverse reaction, and that the catalyst can have no effect upon equilibrium, but only upon the speed with which it is attained. If a catalyst could shift equilibrium, we could use a gas reaction involving a change in the number of molecules, and by alternately putting in and taking out the catalyst, which would require little effort, we could produce an alternate increase and decrease in pressure which could do useful work at no expense, which is contrary to the evident morality of nature.

It is true that by the use of a catalyst we may reach equilibrium in a so much shorter time that we may be able to work at a lower temperature, where equilibrium is more favorable, but it is then the temperature not the catalyst which has shifted the equilibrium.

Exercises

See Appendix II for answers

1. Describe experiments which would prove whether or not the following reactions can be made to take place in both directions:

$$2 \text{ BaO (solid)} + O_2 = 2 \text{ BaO}_2 \text{ (solid)}; \quad \textit{HEAT,}$$

$$H_2 + S \text{ (liquid)} = H_2S;$$

$$Mg^{++} + 2 \text{ NH}_4OH = Mg(OH)_2 \text{ (precipitate)} + 2 \text{ NH}_4^+; \quad ADD \; NH_4^+$$

$$2 \text{ CrO}_4^{--} \text{ (yellow)} + 2 \text{ H}^+ = H_2O + Cr_2O_7^{--} \text{ (red)}; \quad ADD \; OH^-$$

$$NH_4^+ + Cl^- + H_2O = NH_4OH + H^+ + Cl^-. \quad ADD \quad HCl$$

2. Hard water may be softened by means of an insoluble substance called zeolite, $Na(H_6AlSiO_7)$, which exchanges the calcium (or magnesium) ion in the water for sodium ion as follows:

$$Ca^{++} + 2 \text{ Na}(H_6AlSiO_7) \text{ (solid)} = 2 \text{ Na}^+ + Ca(H_6AlSiO_7)_2 \text{ (solid)}.$$

Can you suggest a way of restoring the sodium zeolite after it has all been changed to calcium or magnesium zeolite? $ADD \quad Na^+$

3. Describe in words the effect of adding solid sodium acetate to a solution of acetic acid, and write an equation for the reaction.

4. The precipitation of manganese ion as manganese sulfide, according to the equation,

$$Mn^{++} + H_2S \text{ (gas)} = MnS + 2 \text{ H}^+, \quad ADD \quad Ac^-$$

is never complete. How would you make the amount precipitated as great as possible? How would you redissolve all of the precipitate?

5. Write equations showing what happens when (a) 2 moles of hydrogen are mixed with 4 moles of oxygen and an electric spark passed; (b) dilute solutions containing respectively 1 mole of hydrochloric acid and 2 moles of sodium acetate are mixed.

6. Using the equilibrium constants given in Table 2, calculate the (H^+) for the first five acids and the (OH^-) for ammonia when the substance is present in 0.05 molal solution.

7. N_2O_4 gas under certain conditions is dissociated to give $2 NO_2$. On the basis of kinetic theory predict the effect of volume change on this reaction.

8. 0.1 N anthranilic acid ($HC_7H_6NO_2$) is 1% dissociated. (*a*) What is its H^+ ion concentration? (*b*) What volume of 0.2 N-NaOH is necessary to neutralize 50 cc. of this solution? (*c*) When it is neutralized by NaOH what substances are present in the final solution?

9. Explain by the kinetic theory how the equilibrium $H^+ + C_6H_5COO^- = C_6H_5COOH$ should be shifted by dilution with water.

10. State in words what happens when a solution of NaAc is added to a saturated solution of AgAc.

11. Of the following factors, which influence the solubility and which the rate of solution of a salt: (*a*) size of particles; (*b*) temperature; (*c*) stirring; (*d*) excess of salt?

12. If the substances represented in the following equation are all present in equilibrium with each other,

$$Cu(OH)_2 + 4 NH_3 = Cu(NH_3)_4^{++} + 2 OH^-,$$

what will be the effect upon the amount of $Cu(OH)_2$ present (*a*) if the mixture is boiled, (*b*) if NaOH is added, (*c*) if K_2SO_4 is added, (*d*) if $(NH_4)_2SO_4$ is added? ~~TAKES OUT OH⁻ +moves it.~~

13. If H^+, Ac^- and HAc are present in a solution in equilibrium, explain, in terms of the kinetic theory, what will happen if you add (*a*) water, (*b*) NaAc solution, (*c*) HCl solution.

14. If NH_4^+, OH^-, NH_4OH and NH_3 are present in water in equilibrium with each other, explain in terms of the kinetic theory what will happen if you add (*a*) water, (*b*) NH_4Cl, (*c*) NaOH, (*d*) NaCl, (*e*) NH_3 gas.

15. State two ways of shifting the equilibrium $2 HCO_3^- = H_2CO_3 + CO_3^{--}$ so as to decrease the amount of HCO_3^-.

16. The amount of CO_2 formed per second from the reaction $MgCO_3 = MgO + CO_2$ increases if the CO_2 is pumped out but the amount of CO_2 formed by the fermentation of sugar is not so increased. Explain.

*17. The solubility of AgI is 10^{-8} moles/liter. What is the solubility of AgI in 0.001 M-KI solution?

*18. If the degree of ionization of the weak acid HX is 1% when its concentration is 0.1 M, what is the concentration of each sub-

---

* Questions of greater difficulty.

stance in this solution? What is the numerical value of the ionization constant?

*19. The solubility product for $\frac{1}{2} Ag_2O + \frac{1}{2} H_2O = Ag^+ + OH^-$ is 2.0×10^{-8}, and for $Ag_2CO_3 = 2 Ag^+ + CO_3^{--}$ it is 9.0×10^{-12}. What concentration of OH^- would be sufficient to transpose Ag_2CO_3 into Ag_2O in the presence of $0.5\ M\text{-}CO_3^{--}$? Is the natural concentration of OH^- in $0.5\ M\text{-}CO_3^{--}$ enough to do this?

$$\uparrow 4.4 \times 10^{-2} \qquad x$$

$$19. \quad (Ag^+)(OH^-) = 2 \times 10^{-8}$$

$$.5m$$

$$(Ag^+)^2(CO_3^{--}) = 9 \times 10^{-12}$$

$$\left(.5x^2 = 9 \times 10^{-12} \right) = (Ag)$$

CHAPTER XIII

TYPES OF EQUILIBRIA

1. We have seen, in Chapter XII, that it is possible to control reactions which come to equilibrium by changing the concentrations of the reacting substances. A reaction may be made more complete by using the reacting substances at greater concentration, or by removing one or more of the products of the reaction. We may now ask the questions: In what ways may substances be added to or taken away from reacting mixtures, and what properties of substances determine whether a reaction proceeds more completely in one direction or another? The ability to answer these questions enables one, without previous experiment, to predict and control reactions in a large number of cases. It is important that the amount of experimental material to be memorized should be the minimum necessary to deal with the vast number of reactions likely to be encountered. How this material may be arranged and applied will be shown in the following pages.

2. **Volatility.** One of the properties of substances that may be utilized in bringing about reactions is volatility. If a certain reacting mixture is in an inclosed space, equilibrium may be reached long before all of the desired products are obtained; but if one of the substances produced is volatile at the temperature of the reaction, it may be allowed to escape, or be pumped off, and its removal will allow more of it to be formed, according to the principle set forth in the last chapter. If this removal is continued, it may be possible to make the reaction go to completion. For example, if solutions of sodium chloride and sulfuric acid are mixed, there is only a small tendency to form hydrochloric acid, since the

latter is a little stronger than the former. However, since hydrogen chloride, in the absence of water, is a gas, it is possible to produce it by the reaction between *solid* sodium chloride and *concentrated* sulfuric acid, as follows:

$$NaCl + H_2SO_4 = NaHSO_4 + HCl.$$

If this were done in a closed vessel, equilibrium would be reached before much of the salt and sulfuric acid had reacted in this way; but if the vessel is open, so that the HCl gas can escape, then it can all be removed, and the reaction may go to completion. Further heating, if enough salt is present, will give neutral sodium sulfate, Na_2SO_4, the second step being

$$NaCl + NaHSO_4 = Na_2SO_4 + HCl.$$

The more volatile acid is thus driven out of its salt by the less volatile one. This principle is used in the manufacture of hydrochloric acid, where the gas is caught and dissolved in water. A number of other acids are obtained commercially from their salts by heating them with sulfuric acid in the same way, among them nitric acid, HNO_3, from the naturally occurring $NaNO_3$; hydrofluoric acid, HF, from fluorspar, CaF_2; acetic acid from calcium acetate,[1] etc.

3. Sodium sulfate, on the other hand, may be changed to sodium phosphate by using P_2O_5, which is less volatile than SO_3. The reaction is

$$3 Na_2SO_4 + P_2O_5 = 2 Na_3PO_4 + 3 SO_3.$$

This is a case where it may be more satisfactory to consider the salts as combinations of the metallic and nonmetallic oxides, as explained in Chapter V. The equation is

$$3 Na_2O \cdot SO_3 + P_2O_5 = (Na_2O)_3 \cdot P_2O_5 + 3 SO_3.$$

Again, since SiO_2 is still less volatile than P_2O_5, a phosphate may be changed to a silicate by heating it to a sufficiently high temperature with SiO_2, as follows:

$$(Na_2O)_3 \cdot P_2O_5 + 3 SiO_2 = 3 Na_2O \cdot SiO_2 + P_2O_5.$$

---

[1] When wood is distilled the acetic acid is separated from the wood alcohol, acetone, etc., occurring in the distillate, by using slaked lime. $Ca(OH)_2$, in order to convert it into the nonvolatile calcium atcetae.

In solution, where the difference in volatility of the above substances would not be evident, the reverse changes only would take place, since silicic, phosphoric, and sulfuric acids are successively stronger, as will be explained presently.

It is well to remember that ammonium salts are easily volatilized, and that many chlorides are rather volatile, especially $HgCl_2$, $FeCl_3$, $AlCl_3$, $SbCl_3$, $SbCl_5$, $AsCl_3$, $SnCl_4$.

4. Solubility. The solubilities of substances have an important bearing on the course of reactions. When a rather insoluble salt is put into water a little of it dissolves, for almost no salts are so insoluble that the amount going into solution cannot be measured. The small quantity which does dissolve will be ionized, since nearly all salts are ionized insofar as they will go into solution. The equation expressing the reaction when such a salt is put into water should express this ionization, as exemplified by the following:

$$BaSO_4 \text{ (solid)} = Ba^{++} + SO_4^{--},$$
$$AgCl \text{ (solid)} = Ag^+ + Cl^-,$$
$$CaCO_3 \text{ (solid)} = Ca^{++} + CO_3^{--},$$
$$PbCrO_4 \text{ (solid)} = Pb^{++} + CrO_4^{--}.$$

When the solution is saturated there will be equilibrium between the solid salt, represented on the left side of each equation, and its ions in solution, represented on the right. The observed fact that all the above salts are only very slightly soluble means that the solutions will contain but very little of their ions. It also enables us to predict that if we mix the ions of any of the salts at any considerable concentration, they will react almost completely to form a **precipitate** (from a Latin word meaning to throw down) of the corresponding salt. A knowledge of the solubilities of salts, therefore, enables us to tell what ions will precipitate each other from solution. No matter what other ions are present, no matter from what compounds they are obtained, Ba^{++} and SO_4^{--} in any appreciable concentration will always form a precipitate of $BaSO_4$. Moreover, if it is desired to remove Ba^{++} from solution most completely, our knowledge of equilibrium indicates that we should add an excess of SO_4^{--}. This effect is constantly sought in quantitative analysis.

5. Solution of Precipitates. Conversely, if we wish to dissolve a precipitate, we must endeavor to remove from the solution one of its ions. This removal, in the case of ions, is not so simple as is the removal of a gas, but requires a knowledge of other combinations the ion is capable of forming, as we will see later.

6. Comparative Insolubility. Which of the two salts of a common ion will be precipitated depends on their relative solubility and the relative concentrations of the ions in question. If to a mixture of chloride and iodide ions is added a solution of silver ion, silver iodide, yellow, is formed before silver chloride, white. This shows that AgI is less soluble than AgCl, or, in other words, I^- removes Ag^+ from solution more completely than does Cl^- at the same concentration. This would also enable us to predict that if we start with AgCl we might bring about the following transformation quite readily:

$$AgCl + I^- = AgI + Cl^-,$$

whereas the reverse reaction could only be brought about by keeping the concentration of I^- extremely small and that of Cl^- very large, as would be the case in continual washing of the AgI precipitate on a filter with a solution of Cl^-. If, subsequently, we find that Ag_2CO_3, silver carbonate, is readily transposed into AgCl by allowing Cl^- to act upon it, then we know that Ag_2CO_3 is more soluble than either of the others, or, in other words, carbonate ion, CO_3^{--}, removes Ag^+ from solution less completely than either Cl^- or I^-, and without trying it, we could predict with assurance that the following reaction would take place very readily as read from left to right, but not in the reverse direction:

$$Ag_2CO_3 + 2 I^- = 2 AgI + CO_3^{--}.$$

Again, on finding by experiment that AgI is readily changed

into Ag_2S by SH^-, we could conclude that both of the other precipitates could be transposed into Ag_2S still more easily. It will be seen that with the aid of the ideas of equilibrium we are able to predict a large number of reactions on the basis of a few well-chosen experiments, and thus utilize our experimental knowledge to the best advantage.

The solubility products for AgI and AgCl, 8.5×10^{-17} and 1.7×10^{-10}, enable us to calculate the equilibrium constant of the reaction $AgI + Cl^- = AgCl + I^-$ to be $8.5 \times 10^{-17}/1.7 \times 10^{-10}$ or 5×10^{-7}. If AgI were washed with 1 M-KCl, the maximum concentration of I^- obtainable would be 5×10^{-7}; i.e., it would require at least 2,000,000 liters of 1 M-KCl to transform 1 mole of AgI to AgCl.

7. The same considerations apply to relatively insoluble acids and bases. Magnesium hydroxide, $Mg(OH)_2$, when put into water, dissolves slightly, forming its ions as follows:

$$Mg(OH)_2 = Mg^{++} + 2 OH^-.$$

Therefore if solutions of, say, magnesium chloride and sodium hydroxide are mixed, a precipitate of $Mg(OH)_2$ will be formed.

8. Since knowledge of the solubilities of salts, acids, and bases in water is evidently extremely important in enabling one to predict and control reactions, some useful generalizations are given below.

As far as the relation between solubility and other properties is concerned, we may note that, other things being equal, **the higher the melting point of the compound the less soluble it will be,** not only in water, but in any solvent. Also, where the melting points are approximately the same, **the compounds most soluble in water will be those in which there is the greatest difference in the positive and negative character of the constituent parts** (cf. Chapter V), so that the salts of a metal like silver will be less soluble than those of a metal like potassium. These rough conclusions are illustrated by the values in Table 1.

9. Generalizations Regarding Solubility. A number of statements may be made regarding the compounds of particular ions such as the following. It must be understood, however, that only the commoner compounds are considered:

All nitrates are soluble.

All acetates are soluble ($AgC_2H_3O_2$ only moderately).

All chlorides are soluble, except $AgCl$, $HgCl$, $PbCl_2$ (the last is sparingly soluble in cold water, moderately soluble in hot).

TABLE 1

Substance	Melting point	Solubility at 20°, in moles per 1000 grams of solution
$CaCl_2 \cdot 6H_2O$	30°	1.9
H_3BO_3	185°	0.077
$AgNO_3$	218°	4.3
$NaNO_3$	333°	5.5
$AgCl$	455°	0.00001
KCl	722°	3.3
$BaCO_3$	795°	0.0001
$PbSO_4$	1100°	0.00015
CaF_2	1400°	0.0002
$CaSiO_3$	1510°	0+
$BaSO_4$	1580°	0.00001

All sulfates are soluble, except $BaSO_4$, $PbSO_4$ ($CaSO_4$, Hg_2SO_4, and Ag_2SO_4 are sparingly soluble).

All carbonates and phosphates are insoluble, except those of sodium, potassium, and ammonium. [Many dihydrogen phosphates are soluble, e.g., $Mg(H_2PO_4)_2$, $Ca(H_2PO_4)_2$, and $Ba(H_2PO_4)_2$.]

All hydroxides are insoluble, except $NaOH$, KOH, NH_4OH, and $Ba(OH)_2$; $Ca(OH)_2$ is sparingly soluble.

All sulfides are insoluble, except those of sodium, potassium, and ammonium. Those of magnesium, calcium, barium, and aluminum are not precipitated from solution because they are decomposed by water.

All salts of sodium, ammonium, and potassium are soluble, except $Na_4Sb_2O_7$, $(K$ or $NH_4)_2PtCl_6$, and $(K$ or $NH_4)_3Co(NO_2)_6$.

All silver salts are insoluble, except $AgNO_3$, $AgNO_2$, $AgClO_4$, $AgC_2H_3O_2$, Ag_2SO_4 (the last two are moderately soluble).

10. Separations. It is upon the basis of solubilities that different ions present in the same solution may be separated. Suppose, for example, that a solution contained the nitrates of silver, barium, zinc, and potassium. The addition of chloride ion, using, say, a solution of ammonium chloride, would precipitate the silver ion as AgCl, which could be filtered out. The addition, then, of sulfate ion, as by using ammonium sulfate solution, would precipitate the barium ion as $BaSO_4$. After this is filtered out, the zinc ion could be precipitated as sulfide, using ammonium sulfide. The excess of ammonium salts in the solution could finally be removed by evaporating the solution to dryness and heating the residue, which would volatilize the ammonium salts, leaving only the potassium salts.

11. Ionization of Water. It was shown in Chapter VIII, paragraphs 19 and 20, that water is an extremely weak electrolyte, dissociating to a minute extent as follows:

$$H_2O = H^+ + OH^-.$$

In pure water we have $(H^+) = (OH^-) = 10^{-7}$ moles per liter. This is very slight indeed, but we shall see that it is very important. If an excess of either of the ions H^+ or OH^- is added to water, as in dissolving an acid or base in it, the result is a diminution in the concentration of the other. If, for example, 0.001 M-HCl is present, the concentration of the hydrogen ion is increased 10,000 times, which will cause that of the hydroxide ion to decrease 10,000 times, becoming 10^{-11}. This inverse relationship is shown in the first two columns of Table 2.

12. Neutralization. We may conclude, from the slightness of the ionization of water that the reverse reaction will take place almost completely, so that whenever an acid and a base are mixed they will react almost completely to form water, leaving the other ions in solution, unless they happen to form an insoluble substance. We must therefore regard neutralization of acids and bases as taking place because of the fact that water is almost entirely undissociated. In connection with the neutralization of weak acids and bases we will return later to this topic.

13. Indicators. The concentration of H^+ and OH^- in a solution may be estimated approximately by the aid of indicators (cf. page 108). Table 2 gives the concentrations of

TABLE 2
Approximate Indicator Colors

Conc. of H^+	Conc. of OH^-	pH*	Methyl violet	Methyl orange	Bromphenol blue	Bromcresol green	Litmus	Bromthymol blue	Thymol blue	Phenolphthalein	Alizarin yellow R	Indigo carmine	Solutions of certain common substances giving the corresponding pH
1	10^{-14}	0	y	r	y	y	r	y	r	c	y	b	1 M-HCl
10^{-1}	10^{-13}	1	g	r	y	y	r	y	o	c	y	b	0.1 M-HCl
10^{-2}	10^{-12}	2	b	r	y	y	r	y	y	c	y	b	
10^{-3}	10^{-11}	3	v	r	y	y	r	y	y	c	y	b	0.05 M-HC$_2$H$_3$O$_2$
10^{-4}	10^{-10}	4	v	o	g	y	r	y	y	c	y	b	H$_2$CO$_3$(CO$_2$ at 1 atm.)
10^{-5}	10^{-9}	5	v	y	b	g	r	y	y	c	y	b	0.2 M-NH$_4$Cl
10^{-6}	10^{-8}	6	v	y	b	b	r	y	y	c	y	b	
10^{-7}	10^{-7}	7	v	y	b	b	t	g	y	c	y	b	"Neutral point"
10^{-8}	10^{-6}	8	v	y	b	b	b	b	y	c	y	b	1 M-NaHCO$_3$
10^{-9}	10^{-5}	9	v	y	b	h	b	b	g	t	y	b	0.2 M-NaC$_2$H$_3$O$_2$
10^{-10}	10^{-4}	10	v	y	b	b	b	b	b	r	y	b	
10^{-11}	10^{-3}	11	v	y	b	b	b	b	b	r	o	b	0.05 M-NH$_4$OH;
10^{-12}	10^{-2}	12	v	y	b	b	b	b	b	r	r	b	0.4 M-Na$_2$CO$_3$
10^{-13}	10^{-1}	13	v	y	b	b	b	b	b	r	r	g	0.1 M-NaOH
10^{-14}	1	14	v	y	b	b	b	b	b	r	r	y	1 M-NaOH

(Abbreviations: b = blue, c = colorless, g = green, o = orange, r = red, y = yellow, v = violet, t = transition.)

* pH is an abbreviated designation of the concentration of H^+ much used in biological work. Its meaning is obvious from the table.

H^+ and OH^- between normal H^+ and normal OH^-, together with the corresponding colors shown by several of the common indicators. The colors given are approximate only, depending not only on hydrogen ion concentration, but also on indicator concentration, other ions, vessel size, illumination, and visual peculiarities. Where accuracy is desired, the indicator should be used only to compare an unknown solution with one of known hydrogen ion concentration under identical conditions of the above factors.

14. Ionization of Weak Acids, Bases, and Salts. The fact that many acids, bases, and a few salts are but slightly ionized, as set forth in Chapter VIII, furnishes other reasons for expecting certain reactions to take place, for the principles of equilibrium tell us that in such cases the corresponding ions will unite, when brought together, to an extent depending on the ionization of the substance. For example, because we know that acetic acid is weak, that is, but slightly ionized, we know that when hydrochloric acid, which gives a high concentration of H^+, is mixed with sodium acetate, which gives a high concentration of $C_2H_3O_2^-$, these ions will combine till one or both are almost used up. Although sodium acetate is not a base, but a salt, we see that it has the effect of reducing high acidity. Similarly, because NH_4OH is a weak base it can be prepared from any ammonium salt by the action of any strong base, since NH_4^+ and OH^- unite rather completely. This property is used as a test for NH_4^+, and also in the manufacture of NH_3. Considerable ammonia is given off when coal is distilled, as in making gas and coke. This is extracted from the gas by washing in sulfuric acid, forming $(NH_4)_2SO_4$. When this salt is acted upon by slaked lime, $Ca(OH)_2$, which gives a sufficiently high concentration of OH^-, there is set free NH_4OH, which breaks up at the temperature applied into NH_3 gas and H_2O. (We have no experimental way of distinguishing NH_4OH from hydrated NH_3.) It is evident, in general, that weak acids should be liberated from their salts in solution by the action of stronger acids, and that weak bases should be liberated in like manner by strong bases.

15. An important application of this principle is in making "superphosphate" for fertilizer. Tricalcium phosphate (normal calcium phosphate), $Ca_3(PO_4)_2$, occurs in bones and mineral deposits, but is so insoluble that even though finely ground it does not furnish plants at all freely with the phosphate necessary for their growth. Accordingly the soluble calcium dihydrogen phosphate is produced by the action of concentrated sulfuric acid, as represented by the equation,

$$Ca_3(PO_4)_2 + 2\ H_2SO_4 = Ca(H_2PO_4)_2 + 2\ CaSO_4.$$

Enough lime is then added to change the dihydrogen to the monohydrogen phosphate, $CaHPO_4$.

16. Successive Neutralizations. Where the ions of several weak acids are competing for an insufficient amount of hydrogen ion, it is evident that the weakest acid will be formed first, the next weakest second, etc. In a mixture of $C_2H_3O_2^-$ and CO_3^{--}, the values on page 189, Table 2, make it evident that if H^+ is added to the solution gradually, the first reaction to take place will be

$$H^+ + CO_3^{--} = HCO_3^-,$$

followed by $H^+ + HCO_3^- = H_2CO_3$,

followed by $H^+ + C_2H_3O_2^- = HC_2H_3O_2$.

17. Complex Ions. As a rule the positive ions in solution are very simple, consisting nearly always only of a metallic atom, with its ionic charge or charges. There are, however, some cases where these simple ions can unite with other ions or neutral molecules and still remain in solution as a more **complex ion.** They may best be considered in groups, according to the substances which are prone to form them.

18. Ammonia Complexes. A solution of ammonia in water yields all of the substances denoted in the equation,

$$NH_3 + H_2O = NH_4OH = NH_4^+ + OH^-.$$

Ordinarily, when this solution is added to one containing an ion of a heavy metal, there is enough OH^- present to precipitate the metallic hydroxide. If, however, more of the ammonia solution is added, the concentration of NH_3 will increase faster than that of OH^-, and there results, in the case of certain metallic ions, notably Cu^{++}, Ni^{++}, Co^{++}, Cd^{++}, Zn^{++}, Ag^+, and Cu^+, a solution which contains a complex positive ion containing both metal and ammonia. With the divalent cations the complex ions seem all to contain $4 NH_3$, while those of the monovalent ions contain $2 NH_3$, so that the formulas are as follows: $Cu(NH_3)_4^{++}$, $Ni(NH_3)_4^{++}$, $Cd(NH_3)_4^{++}$, $Ag(NH_3)_2^+$, $Cu(NH_3)_2^+$. Since the NH_3 is a neutral molecule its presence does not alter the original ionic charge. In the cases of copper and nickel, these ammonia complexes are a deep blue in color, furnishing rather delicate tests for the presence of these metals. On account of this behavior the effect of an excess of ammonia is always to use up most of the free ions of these metals, with corresponding effects upon other equilibria, as will be explained later.

The number of NH_3 molecules in the complex ion can be discovered by varying the equilibrium concentrations and determining which value of the exponent in Chapter XII, paragraph 22 gives uniform values of K.

19. Cyanide Complexes. Cyanide ion has the power to form complexes with a large number of metallic ions. In this case the metals are contained in the anion as illustrated by the equation for the formation of the silver cyanide complex ion:

$$Ag^+ + 2 CN^- = Ag(CN)_2^-.$$

(When Ag^+ is present in any considerable amount, $AgCN$ is first precipitated, dissolving in excess of CN^-.)

Among these complexes may be mentioned the following: $Cu(CN)_2^-$, $Zn(CN)_4^{--}$, $Au(CN)_2^-$, $Au(CN)_4^-$, $Pt(CN)_4^{--}$, $Pt(CN)_6^{--}$, $Fe(CN)_6^{----}$, $Fe(CN)_6^{---}$, $Ni(CN)_4^{--}$, $Co(CN)_6^{----}$, $Co(CN)_6^{---}$.

20. Complex Halides. Many metallic ions, especially those of the noble metals, have a tendency to form complex halides. This is particularly strong in the case of gold, platinum, and the other "platinum metals," as shown in the following: $AuCl_2^-$, $AuCl_4^-$, $PtCl_6^{--}$.

21. Complex Oxalates. Certain metallic ions form complex oxalates with oxalate ion, $C_2O_4^{--}$, as exemplified by $Fe(C_2O_4)_3^{---}$.

22. Competition between the Foregoing Factors. We have seen, in a few instances, how reactions are determined by competition between the various ions of weak acids, or the relative solubilities of various salts of the same ion. We are now prepared to discuss competition between the different factors, volatility, solubility, ionization of water, weak acids, bases and salts, complex ions, and to consider general examples of the control of reactions.

23. Hydrolysis. When the salt of a weak acid is dissolved in water we have present in the solution an ion that has a great tendency to combine with hydrogen ion. Now water, though it is such a weak electrolyte, yields some hydrogen ion. Consequently, there is a slight formation of the weak acid, with a resulting decrease in the concentration of the hydrogen ion and a corresponding increase in the concentration of the hydroxide ion. To say this concretely, let us consider a solution of sodium acetate, which gives a large concentration of Na^+ and $C_2H_3O_2^-$. Now, since the water yields a trace of H^+ and OH^-, and since $HC_2H_3O_2$ is a weak acid, there will be some union of H^+ and $C_2H_3O_2^-$ to form the acid, liberating an excess of OH^-, so that the solution will be slightly alkaline. This may be expressed by an equation as follows:

$$C_2H_3O_2^- + H_2O \rightleftharpoons HC_2H_3O_2 + OH^-.$$

It will be observed that this reaction is the reverse of the neutralization of acetic acid with a strong base, and since the latter reaction is nearly complete, of course the former can take place but slightly under similar conditions.

In writing the equation we show the net effect of what has happened, as expressed previously in words. We must guard against the error of thinking that the formulas on the right-hand side of the equation tell what is in the solution after equilibrium is reached. The solution still contains mostly $C_2H_3O_2^-$ and H_2O, which fact is expressed by saying that the above substances react only slightly before equilibrium is reached, not by writing their formulas on both sides of the equation. Moreover, in a single equation like this, we should not write water as ionized, for the bulk of it is un-ionized. As a matter of fact, there are two simultaneous reactions occurring, as follows:

$$C_2H_3O_2^- + H^+ = HC_2H_3O_2, \text{ and } H_2O = H^+ + OH^-.$$

The sum of these two gives the former.

Obviously there is a competition between $C_2H_3O_2^-$ and OH^- for the H^+, as might be represented in this way:

$$HC_2H_3O_2 = C_2H_3O_2^- + H^+$$
$$+$$
$$OH^-$$
$$\|$$
$$H_2O.$$

That the OH^- should get or keep most of the H^+ is to be expected from the fact that water is vastly less ionized than is acetic acid. It is this disparity between the ionization of the two substances that enables $C_2H_3O_2^-$ to set free but a slight amount of OH^- from water, on the one hand, and which causes neutralization of $HC_2H_3O_2$ by OH^- to be nearly complete, on the other hand.

24. If, instead of an acetate, we dissolve in the water the salt of some weaker acid, like sodium phenolate, $NaOC_6H_5$, we have in phenolate ion, $OC_6H_5^-$, one which will unite with the hydrogen ion of water more completely than will acetate ion, forming HOC_6H_5, the acid known as phenol, or carbolic acid, and setting free from the water more OH^- than in the case of sodium acetate. The competition for H^+ is here between OH^- and $OC_6H_5^-$, and though the latter gets but little of it, since carbolic acid is much more ionized than water, it nevertheless gets more than does acetate ion. We may express this competition in the same manner as before,

$$HOC_6H_5 = OC_6H_5^- + H^+$$
$$+$$
$$OH^-$$
$$\|$$
$$H_2O.$$

The net result we may write, as before,

$$OC_6H_5^- + H_2O = HOC_6H_5 + OH^-.$$

A process such as this is called hydrolysis. The idea underlying the name is that a salt is split up by water into free acid and base. We see that salts of weak acids always hydrolize in aqueous solution on account of the possibility of forming the free weak acid. Of course, the ions giving weak bases also take part in hydrolysis. All ammonium salts are hydrolyzed, because of the formation of the weak base, ammonium hydroxide, as illustrated by the equation,

$$NH_4^+ + H_2O = NH_4OH + H^+,$$

where the solution becomes slightly acid. If the salt is one of both a weak acid and a weak base, like ammonium acetate, $NH_4C_2H_3O_2$, both of its ions take part in hydrolysis, as shown by the equation,

$$NH_4^+ + C_2H_3O_2^- + H_2O = NH_4OH + HC_2H_3O_2.$$

In a case like this the acidity or alkalinity of the resulting solution depends upon whether the acid or the base is weaker. In this particular case they are of almost identical strength, as may be seen from the values in Table 2, page 189, so that the solution is almost neutral, though it does contain more NH_4OH than a solution of NH_4Cl, and more free $HC_2H_3O_2$ than one of $NaC_2H_3O_2$, since both of the ions present aid in splitting up the water.

An alternate point of view regarding NH_4^+ is to consider it, itself, as a weak acid, dissociating as follows: $NH_4^+ = NH_3 + H^+$. This has certain advantages in simplicity of representation, although it is not essentially different from $NH_4^+ + H_2O = NH_4OH + H^+$, for both NH_3 and H^+ are "hydrated."

25. Applications of Hydrolysis. Hydrolysis plays an important part in many reactions, a few examples of which will be given. It is desirable that solutions to be used for household cleaning should have a slightly alkaline reaction, since this aids in emulsifying grease and removing dirt, and also tends to soften hard water, as will be explained later. It is not desirable, however, to use a strong base like sodium hydroxide, because this gives too great a concentration of OH^-, which has injurious effects on the hands and on some fabrics, unless used in very dilute solution, where the slight amount of OH^- would soon be used up. What is wanted is a solution containing but little free OH^-, but which is able to yield more should this be used up. Such is the case with ammonia, so that it finds large use in the home. We see also that salts of weak acids fulfill these conditions, and several of them find extensive application as cleansing agents. Sodium carbonate, Na_2CO_3, is the salt of a very weak acid, and its solutions give a very marked alkaline reaction, as follows:

$$CO_3^{--} + H_2O = HCO_3^- + OH^-.$$

On this account it is extensively known and used as "washing soda." There are two sodium carbonates, this one and $NaHCO_3$, sodium acid carbonate. The solution of the latter also undergoes hydrolysis,

$$HCO_3^- + H_2O = H_2CO_3 + OH^-.$$

However, since H_2CO_3 is considerably more dissociated than HCO_3^-, according to the figures given on page 189, the former will be formed from HCO_3^- and H^+ less completely than the latter will be from CO_3^{--} and H^+. Hence the solution of Na_2CO_3 is much more alkaline than one of $NaHCO_3$, and is used as "washing soda," whereas the latter is used only where a much less alkaline reaction is desired, as for internal use. The $NaHCO_3$, on the other hand, is "baking soda," because it can yield much more CO_2 for the same weight both of itself and acid.

26. Borax, sodium borate, is the salt of the very weak boric acid, and has the same effect in cleansing as sodium carbonate. Sodium silicate, the salt of weak silicic acid, behaves in the same way, and is a constituent of laundry soaps.

27. Aluminum hydroxide, $Al(OH)_3$, is not only insoluble, but is a weak base as well, so that aluminum ion, Al^{+++}, in water forms some of the hydroxide, liberating the hydrogen ion and causing the solution to become distinctly acid. On this account aluminum salts can be used to liberate carbon dioxide from carbonates, as is done in the alum baking powders. A similar reaction is used by oil companies in a scheme for extinguishing gasoline or petroleum fires on oil tanks. The sodium carbonate solution and one of aluminum sulfate, containing glue to produce a froth which retains the CO_2 gas, are projected from adjacent pipes over the burning tank, when the froth produced spreads over the fire and quenches it.

28. Al^{+++} hydrolyzes to give so high a concentration of H^+ that if the ion of a very weak acid is added, the hydrolysis is complete, yielding $Al(OH)_3$ and the weak acid. For example, if CO_3^{--} is added to Al^{+++}, $Al(OH)_3$ is precipitated instead of a carbonate; and aluminum sulfide, prepared directly from the elements, when put into water, decomposes completely as follows:

$$Al_2S_3 + 6\,H_2O = 2\,Al(OH)_3 + 3\,H_2S.$$

29. There are a number of other compounds, such as the chlorides of the nonmetals, that undergo complete hydrolysis. When PCl_3, phosphorus trichloride, is put into water the following reaction takes place:

$$PCl_3 + 3\,H_2O = P(OH)_3 + 3\,H^+ + 3\,Cl^-.$$

The hydroxide of phosphorus is so completely an acid rather than a base that the above reaction is complete.

30. Choice of Indicator. In titrating a weak acid with a strong base, or vice versa, it is necessary to determine, not when the solution is neutral, but when it contains equivalent amounts of acid and base, a minute proportion of which will be free, giving an alkaline or acid reaction, as the case may be. If sodium acetate, for example, is dissolved in water, the solution is slightly alkaline, although equivalent amounts of acid and base are present. To reproduce this condition, when acetic acid is titrated with sodium hydroxide, one should use an indicator like phenolphthalein, which, as shown on page 203, changes color in a solution which is faintly alkaline, so that a slight excess of either acid or base would affect the indicator. Similarly, in titrating ammonia with hydrochloric acid, we wish to end with the solution not really neutral but slightly acid, since a solution of ammonium chloride reacts slightly acid. Hence an indicator like methyl orange, according to the table on page 203, would be suitable for this purpose. In general, the proper indicator to use in a titration may be found by taking the normal salt which will result from the titration, dissolving it in water and determining what indicator will change color when a drop of solution of the free acid or base is added in excess.

31. The Solution of Hydroxides. We have seen that when a more or less insoluble metallic hydroxide is in contact with water it gives to the water a certain amount of its ions, equilibrium being reached the sooner the less soluble the hydroxide. As an example we may consider magnesium hydroxide, $Mg(OH)_2$, which gives a small concentration of ions as follows:

$$Mg(OH)_2 = Mg^{++} + 2\,OH^-.$$

We have seen also that hydrogen ion has a very great tendency to unite with hydroxide ion. If, therefore, H^+ is added to the precipitate of magnesium hydroxide suspended in water, there will be a competition between the H^+ and the Mg^{++} for the OH^-, which may be represented, as before, by the double equation,

$$Mg(OH)_2 = Mg^{++} + 2\,OH^-$$
$$+$$
$$2\,H^+$$
$$\parallel$$
$$2\,H_2O.$$

Now, since water is so extremely undissociated we might

expect that the H^+ added would be successful in stealing the OH^- away from the magnesium ion, liberating the latter, which would thus go into solution so that the effect of the acid would be to dissolve the precipitate. The total reaction is therefore

$$Mg(OH)_2 + 2\,H^+ = Mg^{++} + 2\,H_2O.$$

As a matter of fact, water is formed so completely from its ions that it takes but a moderate concentration of acid to dissolve practically all hydroxides.

Our principles of equilibrium would lead us to expect that any substance that would unite with OH^- would have the effect of dissolving insoluble bases. Besides H^+, we have found that NH_4^+ is a substance which has a tendency to unite with OH^- to form the weak base NH_4OH. We know, however, that these two ions do not unite nearly so completely as do H^+ and OH^-, therefore we should not expect NH_4^+ to be nearly as effective as H^+ in dissolving bases. It is true that the solubility of any base will be increased by the presence of NH_4^+, but if the base is very insoluble to begin with, the increase may not be sufficient to bring the amount in solution up to a value such that we would call it soluble. Suppose, for example, that the solubilities of two bases in water are 0.001 and 0.000,001 molal respectively, and that the addition of a certain amount of NH_4^+ is enough to increase each 1000 times. The effect would be to make the solubilities of the two bases now 1 molal and 0.001 molal, respectively. We would then call the first soluble in NH_4^+, but the second, insoluble. Among the insoluble bases which may be thus dissolved in NH_4^+ are $Mg(OH)_2$, $Ca(OH)_2$, $Zn(OH)_2$, $Fe(OH)_2$, $Mn(OH)_2$, $Ni(OH)_2$, $Co(OH)_2$.

32. The Solution of Oxides. Oxides of metals are much like the corresponding hydroxides, and may either be converted into hydroxides, in some cases, or produced from them by heating. The solubility of hydroxides in H^+ leads us to expect that oxides will likewise dissolve in acids. We may think here of the formation of water from the H^+ of the acid and the oxygen of the oxide. (Most oxides, indeed, are easily dissolved in acids, though more difficultly than are the corresponding hydroxides.) This difficulty may be largely a matter of the speed of the reaction. In a few instances, notably Fe_2O_3, Cr_2O_3, and Al_2O_3, if they have been heated to a very high temperature they become practically insoluble in acids.

33. Amphoterics. There are several metallic hydroxides that are capable of acting either as weak bases or weak acids. Any substances that behave in this way are called amphoteric. Such a substance may give to water not only the metallic cation and the OH^- of a base, but also H^+ and a corresponding anion. Taking $Al(OH)_3$ as an example, we may express this double power of dissociating as follows:

$$Al^{+++} + 3\,OH^- = Al(OH)_3 = H^+ + H_2AlO_3{}^-.$$

As is the case with most weak polybasic acids, the various hydrogen ions dissociate in steps, and since H_3AlO_3 is an exceedingly weak acid, even the first H^+ is ionized with difficulty, and the second and third are practically unionized unless a large excess of OH^- is added. From the double equilibrium that we have represented it will be seen that the precipitate can be dissolved not only by the addition of H^+, which would act as follows:

$$Al(OH)_3 + 3\,H^+ = Al^{+++} + 3\,H_2O,$$

but also by the addition of OH^-, which would act in the following way,

$$H_3AlO_3 + OH^- = H_2O + H_2AlO_3{}^-.$$

It is possible, therefore, to have aluminum present either in an alkaline or in an acid solution, while in a solution approximately neutral it cannot exist, but will be precipitated as $Al(OH)_3$.

Other hydroxides behaving in this way are those of zinc, chromium, lead, and tin (both stannous and stannic). This amphoteric character may be made use of in separating from each other metallic ions existing in the same solution. Thus Fe^{+++} is commonly separated from Al^{+++} and Cr^{+++} by adding concentrated OH^- in excess, which leaves the first precipitated as $Fe(OH)_3$, but dissolves the others as aluminate and chromite ions respectively.

34. There are many substances in addition to the hydroxides mentioned above which are amphoteric. The most important are the amino acids, which are the units out of which proteins are built (cf. Chapter XVIII, paragraph 21). One of these is glycine, amino-acetic acid, NH_2CH_2COOH. The $-NH_2$ group, at one end of the molecule, can react like NH_3 towards water, liberating OH^-, while the H^+ can split off from the other end. This substance can accordingly neutralize either H^+ or OH^-.

35. The isoelectric point is the hydrogen ion concentration at which an amphoteric substance is least ionized in both directions. If it is a relatively insoluble substance, its solubility would be at a minimum at that point. If its acid and basic strengths are equal, then the isoelectric point is at $(H^+) = (OH^-) = 10^{-7}$. If its acid strength is greater than its basic strength, a higher concentration of H^+ is necessary to repress the acid ionization and the isoelectric point will be at $(H^+) > 10^{-7}$.

In the case of glycine, paragraph 34, the isoelectric point is at pH 6.1, or $(H^+) = 7.5 \times 10^{-7}$. The proteins, built up of amino acids, have their characteristic isoelectric points, at which they do not migrate in an electric field, where they show the least swelling or, if in colloidal solution, the maximum viscosity. The following isoelectric points are illustrations: gelatin, 4.7; egg albumen, 4.8; insulin, 5.4; hemoglobin, 6.8; pepsin, 3; wool, 4.

36. The Solution of Sulfides in Hydrogen Ion. The similarity between oxides and sulfides has been previously pointed out, also the fact that hydrogen sulfide is a very weak electrolyte, like water. It is but a slight transition, therefore, from the consideration of oxides to that of sulfides. The chief difference to be noted is that whereas reactions like the following are very numerous,

$$Zn^{++} + 2\,OH^- = Zn(OH)_2,$$

the corresponding reaction, when sulfur is substituted for oxygen, is the formation of a sulfide, rather than a hydrosulfide, as shown by the reaction:

$$Zn^{++} + 2\,SH^- = ZnS + H_2S.$$

This is analogous to what takes place with OH^- in the case of Ag^+, and, when the solution is boiled, with Cu^{++}, as shown by

$$2\,Ag^+ + 2\,OH^- = Ag_2O + H_2O,$$

and

$$Cu^{++} + 2\,OH^- = CuO + H_2O.$$

The solution of a sulfide in an acid depends upon the removal of the sulfide ion by the hydrogen ion of the acid to form hydrogen sulfide, H_2S, and its precipitation depends upon the presence of sufficient sulfide ion. This competition between the metallic ion and the hydrogen ion for the sulfide ion may be represented by the scheme used before,

$$ZnS = Zn^{++} + S^{--}$$
$$+$$
$$2\,H^+$$
$$\|$$
$$H_2S.$$

37. Some sulfides are so insoluble that the metallic ion finds enough sulfide ion to be precipitated even when the solution contains a moderately concentrated acid. These sulfides, conversely, will not be dissolved by hydrogen ion in moderate concentrations. The sulfides which behave in this way include Ag_2S, HgS, PbS, Bi_2S_3, CuS, As_2S_3, As_2S_5. Next, we have several, including CdS, Sb_2S_3, Sb_2S_5, SnS, SnS_2, that will dissolve if the H^+ is concentrated but not if it is dilute. Then follow ZnS, MnS, FeS, NiS, CoS, which are so soluble that dilute H^+ is sufficient to prevent their precipitation. The cases of NiS and CoS are peculiar in that they are not precipitated in acid solution, but nevertheless will not dissolve at all rapidly in dilute acid if first precipitated from an alkaline solution. This may be due to the existence of two modifications of the solids, so that when the more soluble modification is once precipitated it changes over into the insoluble modification; or it may be an example of slow rate of reaction, similar to the slow reaction between certain acids and oxides, referred to in paragraph 32. In order to precipitate this group of sulfides it is necessary to have a neutral or slightly alkaline solution so that sufficient sulfide ion can be present. The usual reagent is a solution of "ammonium sulfide," made by passing H_2S into NH_4OH solution. If acetic acid is used, it is possible, by adding acetate ion, to reduce the concentration of H^+ sufficiently to allow the precipitation of ZnS.

38. Another factor that may be used to assist the solution of a sulfide is the volatility of H_2S. If the solution is boiled, the H_2S is more readily removed, so that more can form, resulting in an easier and more rapid solution of the sulfide. To dissolve the less soluble sulfides the use of concentrated H^+, together with boiling the solution, is insufficient, and we shall see in Chapter XV that it is necessary to destroy the H_2S by an oxidizing agent.

The order of solubility of the above sulfides in water is roughly as follows, beginning with the most soluble: MnS, FeS, ZnS, NiS, CoS, SnS_2, SnS, Sb_2S_3, CdS, PbS, Bi_2S_3, CuS, Ag_2S, As_2S_5, HgS.

39. Amphoteric and Acid Sulfides. We have seen how several hydroxides are able to dissolve in OH^-. There are, likewise, five sulfides which can dissolve in either OH^- or SH^-, namely, As_2S_3, As_2S_5, Sb_2S_3, Sb_2S_5, SnS_2.

The analogy between the oxides and sulfides may be brought out in the following parallel reactions:

$$As_2O_5 + 2\,OH^- = 2\,AsO_3^- + H_2O;$$
$$As_2S_5 + 2\,SH^- = 2\,AsS_3^- + H_2S.$$

The oxide may be dissolved in SH^- and the sulfide in OH^- to produce mixtures of the above products or else intermediate ions.

The compounds in which the metals have the lower oxidation number are always less acidic, both in the case of the oxides and the sulfides, hence Sb_2S_3 dissolves with some difficulty in ammonium sulfide, and SnS is practically insoluble in the same. In dissolving both of these sulfides yellow ammonium sulfide is used, which contains polysulfide ions, such as S_2^{--}, S_3^{--}, etc. Although these ions are usually written in this way for the sake of simplicity, they are actually ions of weak acids and it would be doubtless more accurate to write: HS_2^-, HS_3^-, etc. They are capable of dissolving the lower sulfides of all three metals, changing them to the sulfo-ion of the higher oxidation number, thus,

$$Sb_2S_3 + S_3^{--} = 2\ SbS_3^-,$$
$$SnS + S_2^{--} = SnS_3^{--}.$$

40. The extremely insoluble HgS will dissolve in a solution of Na_2S, according to the reaction:

$$HgS + S^{--} = HgS_2^{--},$$

but will not dissolve in "ammonium sulfide," which contains chiefly NH_4^+ and SH^-, because NH_4^+ shifts the equilibrium $S^{--} + H_2O = SH^- + OH^-$ so far to the right, by forming NH_4OH, that very little S^{--} exists in the latter solution.

When acid is added to the solutions of the above sulfo-ions the weak acid, H_2S, is produced, reprecipitating the sulfides, just as the addition of acid to stannate ion reprecipitates the stannic hydroxide. This reprecipitation consists simply in the reversal of the reactions whereby these sulfo-ions are produced.

41. Separations. The different behaviors of sulfides towards the H^+ and SH^- or S_2^{--} is made the basis of important separations in both qualitative and quantitative analysis. If a solution contains the following ions, Pb^{++}, Bi^{+++}, Cu^{++}, As^{+++}, Sb^{+++}, Sn^{++}, Zn^{++}, Mn^{++}, Mg^{++}, they can be divided into groups by controlling the concentrations of the substances in the equilibrium,

$$H_2S = H^+ + SH^- = 2 H^+ + S^{--}.$$

This separation can best be outlined by the aid of a diagram.

Have dilute H^+ (0.3 M-HCl) present, and pass in H_2S				
Precipitate insoluble PbS, Bi_2S_3, CuS, As_2S_3, Sb_2S_3, SnS. Treat with S_2^{--} (yellow ammonium sulfide)			In solution Zn^{++}, Mn^{++}, Mg^{++}. Make alkaline, add $S^{--}(SH^-)$ (ammonium sulfide)	
Left insoluble, PbS, Bi_2S_3, CuS.	In solution AsS_3^-, SbS_3^-, SnS_3^{--}. Reprecipitate the sulfides and heat with 12 N-HCl		Precipitate ZnS, MnS	In solution Mg^{++}
	Left insoluble, As_2S_5	In solution Sn^{++++}, Sb^{+++}, dilute to 2 N-H^+, pass in H_2S cold, ppt. Sb_2S_3		

42. Salts of Other Weak Acids. Salts of all weak acids are made more soluble by the addition of H^+. This increase in solubility, in the case of carbonates, is enough to bring all insoluble carbonates into solution in dilute H^+. A very interesting case of the solution of a carbonate was alluded to in Chapter XII, paragraph 2. It is the reaction whereby hard water is produced from limestone rock. If very dilute H^+, as is present in very dilute HCl, is allowed to act upon $CaCO_3$, the CO_3^{--} which the latter gives to the solution in very slight amount is converted into HCO_3^- only, and not into H_2CO_3, as would be the case if more concentrated acid were used. The equation for this reaction is as follows:

$$CaCO_3 + H^+ + Cl^- = Ca^{++} + HCO_3^- + Cl^-.$$

If H_2CO_3 is used instead of HCl, it also can furnish sufficient H^+ to bring about essentially the same reaction,

$$CaCO_3 + H_2CO_3 = Ca^{++} + 2\,HCO_3^-.$$

Since most surface water contains some dissolved carbon dioxide, the above reaction takes place whenever such water flows over limestone. A quite analogous reaction occurs with $MgCO_3$. The reaction can be reversed by removing the H_2CO_3, either by boiling the solution, as occurs in a tea-kettle, whence the name "temporary hardness," or else by neutralizing it with some alkali, or some substance giving OH^- by hydrolysis, like sodium carbonate or borax. When this is done on a large scale, the water is analyzed and just the right amount of $Ca(OH)_2$ is added. Although more Ca^{++} is added in this way, there is produced enough CO_3^{--} to precipitate all of it; the total reaction is represented by the equation:

$$2\,Ca^{++} + 2\,HCO_3^- + 2\,OH^- = 2\,CaCO_3 + 2\,H_2O.$$

When the hardness in water is produced by dissolving a salt like $CaSO_4$, it is necessary to add CO_3^{--} (as Na_2CO_3) to precipitate the Ca^{++}.

43. Basic Salts. When the solubility of the hydroxide of a metal is about as small as the solubility of its carbonate, the latter will hydrolyze partly to give a basic carbonate. This is the case with the carbonates of copper, lead, and mercury, as illustrated by $Pb(OH)_2 \cdot 2\,PbCO_3$, the "white lead" of the painter. Mercurous and mercuric nitrates readily form basic nitrates.

44. Solution of Phosphates. There are no phosphates so insoluble in water but that they are dissolved by moderately concentrated H^+. Although PO_4^{---} is the ion of the very weak acid, HPO_4^{--}, nevertheless dilute H^+ is not sufficient to dissolve all of the normal phosphates, both because some are so insoluble to begin with that the increase is not sufficient to make them soluble in the usual sense, and also because some monohydrogen phosphates, like $CaHPO_4$, are rather insoluble, and even though $Ca_3(PO_4)_2$ be converted into the former, solution does not result.

As a rule the acid salts are more soluble than the normal salts, as exemplified by the series of calcium phosphates. $Ca(H_2PO_4)_2$ is soluble, $CaHPO_4$ is insoluble, and $Ca_3(PO_4)_2$ is very insoluble in water. The chief exception to this rule is furnished by the sodium carbonates, where the acid salt is the less soluble.

45. The industrial preparation of sodium carbonate by the **Solvay process** furnishes an interesting application of the principles here discussed. The normal salt, Na_2CO_3, is very soluble, but the acid salt, $NaHCO_3$, is not very soluble in the cold. The latter can therefore be precipitated by bringing together the ions Na^+ and HCO_3^- in sufficient concentration. To do this, NH_3 gas and CO_2 gas are led into a cold concentrated solution of NaCl. The acid and base produced by the solution of the gases in water react to give NH_4^+ and HCO_3^-, provided they are used in the right proportion, and when the concentration of HCO_3^- reaches a sufficient value it begins to precipitate the Na^+ as $NaHCO_3$ (cf. Chapter XXI, paragraph 17).

46. Solution by Forming Weak Salts. In the previous cases we have treated compounds which could be brought into solution by adding some substance, especially H^+, which would use up the anion of the precipitate. It is likewise possible to dissolve a compound by adding some reagent that will use up the free cation. CdI_2, for example, is a moderately weak salt, consequently the following reaction can be made to proceed to some extent by using a sufficient concentration of I^-:

$$CdS + 2 I^- = CdI_2 + S^{--}.$$

47. Solution by Forming Complex Ions. Wherever the cation is capable of forming a complex ion, a precipitate can be rendered more soluble than it is in water. Thus, a salt like $ZnCO_3$ can be dissolved, not only by using up the anion, as in adding H^+, but also by using up the cation, as when $Zn(NH_3)_4^{++}$ is formed by the addition of ammonia solution. The competition between the CO_3^{--} and the NH_3 may be represented as before:

$$ZnCO_3 = Zn^{++} + CO_3^{--}$$
$$+$$
$$4\,NH_3$$
$$\shortparallel$$
$$Zn(NH_3)_4^{++}.$$

If the concentration of the ammonia is sufficient, the complex ion is formed at the expense of the insoluble carbonate, resulting in the net reaction,

$$ZnCO_3 + 4\,NH_3 = Zn(NH_3)_4^{++} + CO_3^{--}.$$

It is worth noting that the solution of $Zn(OH)_2$ in NH_3 (aq.), by the reaction:

$$Zn(OH)_2 + 4\,NH_3 = Zn(NH_3)_4^{++} + 2\,OH^-,$$

would be assisted by NH_4^+, if present, reacting with the OH^-, giving a net reaction of:

$$Zn(OH)_2 + 2\,NH_3 + 2\,NH_4^+ = Zn(NH_3)_4^{++} + 2\,H_2O.$$

In the case of ZnS, which is much less soluble, the formation of the complex ion cannot take place to an appreciable extent, so that ZnS is not dissolved by ammonia. The copper ammonia complex ion seems to be formed more completely than the corresponding zinc ion, so that traces of $Cu(NH_3)_4^{++}$ can be formed from CuS if concentrated ammonia is used, in spite of the smaller solubility of CuS.

48. Solution by Forming Ions of Amphoteric Hydroxides. The effect of a considerable concentration of OH^- may be to dissolve the relatively insoluble salts of certain metals, in a fashion similar to that whereby complex ions are formed. In fact, these ions may be considered as complex ions. Most of the lead salts, for example, are dissolved by OH^-, as exemplified by the reaction,

$$PbSO_4 + 3\,OH^- = H_2O + HPbO_2^- + SO_4^{--}.$$

Even ZnS is not so insoluble but that it can be dissolved by concentrated OH^-.

49. Systematizing the Reactions of a Given Ion. It is not necessary to perform and remember all of the reactions of a certain ion with a set of reagents in order to tell what they will be. It suffices to make an intelligent selection of a few of the possible reactions and arrange the resulting information systematically. As an example of what is meant let us consider a number of the reactions of silver ion, Ag^+, with the following: CO_3^{--}, OH^-, CN^-, Cl^-, Br^-, I^-, S^{--}, NH_3, $S_2O_3^{--}$. Let us assume that we have performed experiments which show that the reactions take place which are represented by the following equations as read from left to right:

$$AgCl + Br^- = AgBr + Cl^-,$$
$$AgCl + 2\,NH_3 = Ag(NH_3)_2^+ + Cl^-,$$
$$Ag(NH_3)_2^+ + I^- = AgI + 2\,NH_3,$$
$$Ag_2O + H_2O + 2\,Cl^- = 2\,AgCl + 2\,OH^-,$$
$$AgI + 2\,CN^- = Ag(CN)_2^- + I^-,$$
$$Ag_2CO_3 + 2\,OH^- = Ag_2O + H_2O + CO_3^{--} \quad \text{(easily reversed)}$$
$$AgBr + 2\,S_2O_3^{--} = Ag(S_2O_3)_2^{---} + Br^-,$$
$$Ag(S_2O_3)_2^{---} + I^- = AgI + 2\,S_2O_3^{--},$$
$$AgCl + CN^- = AgCN + Cl^-,$$
$$Ag(NH_3)_2^+ + Br^- = AgBr + 2\,NH_3 \quad \text{(easily reversed)}$$
$$2\,Ag(CN)_2^- + S^{--} = Ag_2S + 4\,CN^-,$$
$$Ag_2CO_3 + 2\,Cl^- = 2\,AgCl + CO_3^{--},$$
$$AgCN + 2\,NH_3 = Ag(NH_3)_2^+ + CN^-.$$

From these observations it is possible to arrange the following list of substances in the order showing the completeness with which they unite with Ag^+ to form a precipitate or a complex ion as the case may be. It must be understood that the reagents forming complexes are taken in moderate excess:

Reagent	To form
CO_3^{--}	Ag_2CO_3
OH^-	Ag_2O
Cl^-	$AgCl$
CN^-	$AgCN$
NH_3	$Ag(NH_3)_2^+$
Br^-	$AgBr$
$S_2O_3^{--}$	$Ag(S_2O_3)_2^{---}$
I^-	AgI
CN^-	$Ag(CN)_2^-$
S^{--}	Ag_2S

50. In order to make this list it is necessary to make a minimum of nine observations, and from them it is possible to predict the direction of forty-five reactions. The list was made in such a way that each substance in the first column will steal Ag^+ away from its combinations with any substance above it, because less Ag^+ can exist in the same solution with substances farther down the column than with those higher up at the same concentration. Thus $AgBr$ gives to the solution more Ag^+ than can exist together with I^-, hence the following reaction will readily take place:

$$AgBr + I^- = AgI + Br^-.$$

For the same reason, AgI will dissolve in CN^-, and also any precipitate in the above list can be transposed into AgI by I^- except Ag_2S. Where two substances have about the same power to combine with Ag^+, as is the case with NH_3 and Br^-, it is possible to reverse the reaction easily by altering the concentrations. Thus the reaction,

$$AgBr + 2 NH_3 = Ag(NH_3)_2^+ + Br^-,$$

can be made to take place as read from left to right or from right to left, according as the concentration of NH_3 or that of Br^-, respectively, is taken in sufficient excess.

By adding to the information given by the above list a few facts about the other reactions of the substances, we are able to predict a very large number of reactions. For example, HCN is a very weak acid, hence AgCN can be dissolved by H⁺. For the same reason, H⁺ will liberate Ag⁺ from a solution of $Ag(CN)_2^-$, and if Cl⁻ is present along with the H⁺, then AgCl will be precipitated as follows:

$$Ag(CN)_2^- + 2 H^+ + Cl^- = AgCl + 2 HCN.$$

In similar fashion, AgCl will be dissolved by NH_3, according to the reaction represented earlier, but will be reprecipitated on the addition of H⁺, which takes up the NH_3 to form NH_4^+, allowing the Ag⁺ to recombine with the Cl⁻ left from the previous reaction, as shown by the equation:

$$Ag(NH_3)_2^+ + 2 H^+ + Cl^- = AgCl + 2 NH_4^+.$$

Again, since Ag_2SO_4 is moderately soluble (cf. paragraph 9), we see that it can be readily transposed to AgCl by dissolving it in water and adding Cl⁻, for AgCl is insoluble. In order to reverse this transposition we see that some other principle besides solubility must be invoked. If water is absent, we can take advantage of the greater volatility of HCl as compared with H_2SO_4, so that the reaction,

$$2 AgCl + H_2SO_4 = Ag_2SO_4 + 2 HCl,$$

can be brought about by heating AgCl with concentrated H_2SO_4.

51. Miscellaneous Transformations. The general application of the above principles and information can be illustrated by further miscellaneous examples.

To change $CaSO_4$ to $CaCO_3$ we can take advantage of the greater solubility of the former (cf. paragraph 9) and treat it with a solution of a soluble carbonate, like Na_2CO_3, which gives CO_3^{--}, when the insoluble $CaCO_3$ would be precipitated. The manner of expressing this in an equation would depend upon whether the amount of water present is such that the $CaSO_4$ is mainly present as solid or as dissolved ions. These cases would be represented respectively as follows:

$$CaSO_4 + CO_3^{--} = CaCO_3 + SO_4^{--},$$
$$Ca^{++} + SO_4^{--} + CO_3^{--} = CaCO_3 + SO_4^{--}.$$

To bring about the reverse transformation we would have to make up for the greater solubility of $CaSO_4$, which shifts the equilibrium towards $CaCO_3$, by adding H^+, which would use up CO_3^{--} and reverse the reaction.

52. To change $CuSO_4$ to $CuCl_2$ it is necessary to replace SO_4^{--} by Cl^-. This might be done by adding $BaCl_2$ to a solution of the $CuSO_4$, giving the reaction,

$$Cu^{++} + SO_4^{--} + Ba^{++} + 2\ Cl^- = BaSO_4 + Cu^{++} + 2\ Cl^-.$$

If exactly the right amount of $BaCl_2$ were used, all of the Ba^{++} and SO_4^{--} present would precipitate each other, leaving in solution Cu^{++} and Cl^-, and if the precipitate were filtered out and the solution evaporated, these ions would combine to give solid $CuCl_2$, as desired. However, it is difficult to add just the equivalent amount of $BaCl_2$, and it is accordingly better to use a different method, with reagents an excess of which can be easily removed. Since $Cu(OH)_2$ is insoluble, it can be precipitated by adding OH^- (e.g., NaOH solution) to the solution of $CuSO_4$. If the precipitate is now filtered out, the SO_4^{--} is disposed of. The precipitate of $Cu(OH)_2$ can now be dissolved by HCl solution, since the H^+ of the acid unites so strongly with the OH^- of the base, giving a solution containing Cu^{++}, with H^+ and Cl^- in excess. If, now, this solution is evaporated, the excess of H^+ and Cl^- go off along with the water as HCl gas, leaving finally solid $CuCl_2$. By precipitating the carbonate, instead of the hydroxide, the same transformation can be made, since this is equally soluble in the stronger acids. In fact, a soluble salt of any metal which has an insoluble hydroxide or carbonate can be transposed to another soluble salt of the same metal by precipitation of one of these and dissolving it in the acid corresponding to the desired salt.

53. Aluminum chloride, $AlCl_3$, can be changed to aluminum oxide, Al_2O_3, by first precipitating $Al(OH)_3$, using a soluble hydroxide, e.g., NaOH, NH_4OH, and then heating, which aids the decomposition of the hydroxide into the oxide and the volatile substance steam. The two processes are represented by the equations,

$$Al^{+++} + 3\,OH^- = Al(OH)_3,$$

and

$$2\,Al(OH)_3 = Al_2O_3 + 3\,H_2O.$$

54. To change sodium acid carbonate, $NaHCO_3$, into sodium carbonate, Na_2CO_3, two methods are available. The salt can be dissolved in water and treated with 1 equivalent of NaOH, when the HCO_3^- will be neutralized by the added OH^-, as shown by the equation

$$Na^+ + HCO_3^- + Na^+ + OH^- = 2\,Na^+ + CO_3^{--} + H_2O.$$

The resulting solution yields solid Na_2CO_3 on evaporation. Again, the acid carbonate is capable of another kind of decomposition, represented by the equation,

$$2\,NaHCO_3 = Na_2CO_3 + H_2O + CO_2.$$

Since two of the substances produced by this reaction are volatile, the reaction can be made to proceed so as to produce them by heating the mixture in an open vessel so that they can escape.

55. To change Na_2CO_3 to NaOH, it is necessary to remove the CO_3^{--} and supply OH^-. Since both sodium compounds are soluble, the insolubility of some other substances must be invoked. We need a hydroxide of some metal which is more soluble than the corresponding carbonate. The best one for this purpose is $Ca(OH)_2$, which is itself scarcely soluble, especially in a solution of NaOH. The insolubility of $CaCO_3$ causes the following reaction to take place, whereas any excess of $Ca(OH)_2$, together with the $CaCO_3$ produced, can be filtered off:

$$Ca(OH)_2 + 2\,Na^+ + CO_3^{--} = CaCO_3 + 2\,Na^+ + 2\,OH^-.$$

56. Iron rust can be dissolved by moderately dilute hydrochloric acid, as shown by the equation:

$$Fe_2O_3 + 6\,H^+ = 2\,Fe^{+++} + 3\,H_2O.$$

In dissolving a rust or ink stain off a delicate fabric it is not desirable, however, to use such concentrated acid. More dilute H^+ can be used if the reaction is aided by the removal of one of the products. This is accomplished by using oxalic acid, which furnishes both dilute H^+, since it is a rather weak acid, and also oxalate ion, $C_2O_4^{--}$, which unites with the free ferric ion to form a complex ion (cf. paragraph 21). The reaction is

$$Fe_2O_3 + 6 H_2C_2O_4 = 2 Fe(C_2O_4)_3^{---} + 3 H_2O + 6 H^+.$$

57. Buffers. It is often highly desirable to keep the hydrogen ion concentration of a solution as nearly constant as possible,

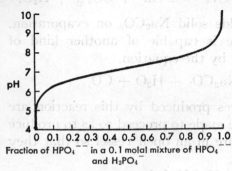

Fraction of HPO_4^{--} in a 0.1 molal mixture of HPO_4^{--} and $H_2PO_4^-$

Fig. 1. Phosphate buffer.

as when measuring the velocity of a reaction or studying the growth of bacteria or plants, each species of which thrives only through a certain range. This can be accomplished by using an approximately equal mixture of a weak acid or base and its salt. Let us consider mixtures of NaH_2PO_4 and Na_2HPO_4. The ionization constant of the reaction, $H_2PO_4^- = H^+ + HPO_4^{--}$, is 6×10^{-8}, i.e. $(H^+)(HPO_4^{--}) = 6 \times 10^{-8} (H_2PO_4^-)$. If we mix the two salts to give a series of ratios (HPO_4^{--}) to $(H_2PO_4^-)$ whose sum is 0.1 molal and calculate the corresponding values of (H^+), we get the curve shown in Fig. 1 where $- \log (H^+)$ or pH is plotted against the value of (HPO_4^{--}) in a solution in which $(HPO_4^{--}) + (H_2PO_4^-) = 0.1$. It is evident that the curve is rather flat in the region of an equimolal mixture of HPO_4^{--} and HPO_4^-, hence the addition of a moderate amount of H^+ or OH^- to such a solution would cause but little change in pH; the mixture of the two phosphate ions thus serves as a "buffer" against changes in the acidity of the solution, and a process such as bacterial culture could be carried out in such a solution under controlled conditions. The above mixture could evidently be used for values of pH between about 6.5 and 8.0. Other mixtures can be selected for other ranges.[1]

58. Hydrolysis: Quantitative Calculations. Since hydrolysis represents competition for H^+ between the OH^- of water and the anion of a weak acid, such as $C_2H_3O_2^-$, as explained in paragraphs 23 and 24, it is obvious that the concentration of the products of hydrolysis can be calculated from the dissociation constants of water and of the particular weak acid or base formed. Using the hydrolysis of $C_2H_3O_2^-$ as an example, $C_2H_3O_2^- + H_2O = HC_2H_3O_2 + OH^-$, we note first, that every molecule of $HC_2H_3O_2$ formed results in the liberation of one of OH^-, therefore their concentrations are identical, so we write, $(HC_2H_3O_2) = (OH^-)$. We choose the concentration of $NaC_2H_3O_2$ in the solution, say 0.1 molal, and since we know that the amount hydrolyzed is very slight, we can set $(C_2H_3O_2^-) = 0.1$. We have, accordingly, four equations:

$$(HC_2H_3O_2) = (OH^-) \quad (1) \qquad\qquad (H^+)(OH^-) = 10^{-14} \quad (3)$$

$$(C_2H_3O_2^-) = 0.1 \quad (2) \qquad\qquad \frac{(H^+)(C_2H_3O_2^-)}{(HC_2H_3O_2)} = 1.8 \times 10^{-5} \quad (4)$$

which are simultaneous, and can be solved by the ordinary methods of algebra. Substituting (1) and (2) in (4) gives $\frac{(H^+)10^{-1}}{(OH^-)} = 1.8 \times 10^{-5}$. Writing $(H^+) = 10^{-14} (OH^-)$, from (3) gives $(OH^-)^2 = \frac{10^{-15}}{1.8 \times 10^{-5}} = \frac{10 \times 10^{-16}}{1.8 \times 10^{-5}} = 5.6 \times 10^{-11}$. To take the square root of an exponential, we want an even exponent, therefore we write $(OH^-)^2 = 56 \times 10^{-12}$, whence $(OH^-) = 7.5 \times 10^{-6}$. Since, furthermore, $(HC_2H_3O_2) = (OH^-)$, we see that so little $C_2H_3O_2^-$ was hydrolyzed that we were quite justified in setting its concentration at equilibrium equal to the amount per liter put into the solution.

In titrating acetic acid with alkali, we wish an end-point not when the solution is neutral but when the acid and base are present in equivalent amounts, when $(OH^-) = 7.5 \times 10^{-6}$ and $(H^+) = 1.3 \times 10^{-9}$, or pH ≈ 9 (cf. paragraph 25). Thymol blue or phenolphthalein would serve the purpose.

Hydrocyanic acid, HCN, is much weaker than acetic, its ioniza-

---

[1] Latimer and Hildebrand, Reference Book of Inorganic Chemistry, Appendix III.

tion constant is 4×10^{-10} (cf. Chapter XII, Table 2) therefore the degree of hydrolysis of CN^-,

$$CN^- + H_2O = HCN + OH^-$$

must be much greater than that of $C_2H_3O_2^-$. Let us choose 0.5 M-KCN, assume that $(CN^-) = 0.5$, and see whether this must be corrected. Setting up the four equations as in the previous case,

$$(HCN) = (OH^-)$$
$$(CN^-) = 0.5$$
$$(H^+)(OH^-) = 10^{-14}$$
$$(H^+)(CN^-) = 4 \times 10^{-10} \text{ (HCN)}$$

Solving for (OH^-) gives, first, $10^{-14} \times 0.5 = 4 \times 10^{-10} (OH^-)^2$, then $(OH^-)^2 = 1.25 \times 10^{-5} = 12.5 \times 10^{-6}$ and $(OH^-) = 3.5 \times 10^{-3}$. But $(HCN) = 3.5 \times 10^{-3}$, also, and the true (CN^-) has not been reduced below 0.5 sufficiently to require any correction. In a case where the degree of hydrolysis is large, one must either use the method of successive approximation (cf. Chapter XII, paragraph 27) or else write, for a weak acid, HX, and its ion, X^-, $(HX) + (X^-) =$ concentration of salt taken, M, and $(H^+)[M - (HX)] = (HX)K_a$ or $(H^1)[M - (OH^-)] = (OH^-)K_a$ or $M - (OH^-) = (OH^-)^2 K_a/K_w$. To solve this quadratic equation requires the troublesome operation of completing the square.

The hydrolysis of the ion of a weak base, of course, is dealt with by essentially the same method. If the weak base is MOH, its ion, M^+, and its ionization constant, K_b, the equation for the hydrolysis is $M^+ + H_2O = MOH + H^+$ and the four equations are,

$$(MOH) = (H^+)$$
$$(M^+) = \text{molality of salt, unless}$$
$$\text{hydrolysis is very large.}$$
$$(H^+)(OH^-) = 10^{-14}$$
$$(M^+)(OH^-) = K_b(MOH)$$

Exercises

See Appendix II for Answers

1. Which of the following substances, when added to water, will give an acid reaction, which alkaline, and which neutral: (a) $NaCl$, (b) CO_2, (c) $NaAc$,* (d) $NaNO_3$, (e) CaO, (f) K_2CO_3, (g) $(NH_4)_2SO_4$, (h) Ca, (i) sodium borate, (j) $BaCl_2$?

2. Can you give a way for demonstrating the hydrolysis of $Al_2(SO_4)_3$ without an indicator?

3. Write in order of decreasing acidities: 1 M-H_2SO_4, 1 M-HAc, 1 M-NH_4Ac, 1 M-NaAc, 1 M-NH_4OH, 1 M-HCl, 1 M-NH_4Cl, 0.1 M-$Ba(OH)_2$.

4. Arrange the following solutions in order of decreasing concentration of OH^-: (a) 0.5 M-NaAc, (b) 0.1 M-Na_2CO_3, (c) 0.1 M-NH_4Cl, (d) 0.1 M-NH_4Ac, (e) 0.1 M-NaOH, (f) 0.1 M-$Ba(OH)_2$, (g) a solution made by dissolving 0.112 g. of CaO in 200 cc. of water.

5. Why may it be necessary to use different indicators for titrating different acids and bases?

6. What indicator could you use to distinguish between (a) distilled water and 0.001 M-NaOH; (b) 0.001 M-NaOH and 0.1 M-NaOH? State the distinguishing colors in each case.

7. Which of the two salts, NaH_2PO_4 and Na_2HPO_4, would be more hydrolyzed when dissolved in water?

8. What is the effect on a water glass (sodium silicate) solution of (a) exposure to the CO_2 in the air; (b) the addition of a solution of ammonium chloride?

9. (a) How can you determine by experiment which of the following reactions goes farther in pure water:

$$HCO_3^- = H^+ + CO_3^{--};$$

$$HCO_3^- + H_2O = H_2CO_3 + OH^-?$$

(b) What is the net result of both reactions?

10. Point out the relation between the strengths of bases and acids and the hydrolysis of the corresponding ions.

11. How would you prepare (a) pure solid $CuSO_4$ from $CuCl_2$, (b) pure solid $CuCl_2$ from $CuSO_4$, (c) $CaCO_3$ from $CaSO_4$, (d) $CaSO_4$ from $CaCO_3$, (e) solid $NaCl$ from NH_4Cl?

12. How could you determine by experiment whether $CaCO_3$ or $CaSO_4$ is more soluble in water?

* Ac^- is a convenient abbreviation for the acetate ion, $C_2H_3O_2^-$.

13. Describe a simple experiment that would enable you to decide whether CaC_2O_4 is more or less soluble than $CaCO_3$.

14. What substances would remain as solids and would be evolved as gases when solutions of the following are evaporated: (a) Zn^{++}, Cl^- and excess of H^+ and SO_4^{--}; (b) Zn^{++}, Cl^- and excess of H^+ and NO_3?

15. (a) Explain briefly why solid $BaCO_3$ and solid $BaAc_2$ are soluble in dilute HCl solution while solid $BaSO_4$ is not. (b) Write equations.

16. What is the effect of (a) NH_4Cl solution, (b) HNO_3 solution, (c) H_2CO_3 solution, upon a precipitate of $Ca(OH)_2$? Explain in each case.

17. If, when 2 moles of NaCl and 1 mole of H_2SO_4 are brought together, the reaction ceases when the HCl gas produced exerts a pressure of 10 atmospheres at 77° C. in a volume of 2 liters, (a) how many moles each of NaCl and H_2SO_4 have reacted; (b) what fraction of each has reacted; (c) how might the quantities reacting be increased?

18. Write the formulas of the various molecules or ions present and state the approximate concentration of each when the following are put into 1 liter of water: (a) 0.02 mole of $CaCl_2$, (b) 0.02 mole of $CaCl_2$ and 0.03 mole of NaCl, (c) 0.02 mole $CaCl_2$ and 0.05 mole Na_2CO_3, (d) 0.01 mole of $CuCl_2$, (e) 0.02 mole $CaCl_2$, 0.02 mole Na_2SO_4, and 0.02 mole Na_2CO_3, (f) 1 mole NH_3, (g) 1 mole NH_3 and 0.5 mole NaOH, (h) 1 mole NH_3 and 1 mole HCl, (i) 1 mole NH_4OH, (j) 1 mole NH_3, 0.1 mole $AgNO_3$, and 0.1 mole NaCl, (k) 0.01 mole $AgNO_3$, 0.05 mole KCl, and 0.05 mole KI.

19. How could you determine experimentally whether the NH_3, the NH_4^+, or the OH^- of an ammonium hydroxide solution is responsible for the formation of a complex ion with a nickel ion?

20. The following can exist together in equilibrium at suitable concentrations: $Ag_2O + H_2O + 4 NH_3 = 2 Ag(NH_3)_2^+ + 2 OH^-$. Explain how the equilibrium would be affected (a) by boiling, (b) by adding NaOH, (c) by adding NH_4NO_3, (d) by adding Ag_2O, (e) by adding KNO_3.

21. What would be present and approximately at what concentration when the following substances are mixed: (a) 0.1 mole $HgNO_3$, 0.1 mole KOH, 1 liter of water; (b) 0.1 mole $ZnSO_4$, 22.4 liters of NH_3 gas at standard conditions, 1 liter of water; (c) 1 mole $BaCl_2$, 1 mole $CaCl_2$, 1 mole H_2SO_4, 10 liters of water; (d) 1 mole Zn, 0.5 mole HgCl, 500 cc. of water?

22. How would you prepare a pure silver compound and a pure copper compound from a mixture of solid silver chloride and cupric hydroxide? Write equations.

23. In the following list of ions: H^+, Ba^{++}, Ag^+, NH_4^+, SO_4^{--}, Ac^-, Cl^-, CO_3^{--}, CN^-, OH^-, state each pair that would tend to combine largely if brought together in dilute solution. In each case give reason for your answer and write equation.

24. What is an amphoteric substance?

25. Can the following substances be present in moderate concentration in the same solution? If not, what is formed? H^+ and NO_3^-, H^+ and OH^-, H^+ and SO_4^{--}, H^+ and CO_3^{--}, H^+ and $C_2O_4^{--}$, Ca^{++} and CO_3^{--}, Ca^{++} and H_2CO_3, OH^- and H_2CO_3, H_2CO_3 and CO_3^{--}, HAc and CO_3^{--}, Al^{+++} and OH^-, Cu^{++} and NO_3^-, Ag^+ and NH_3, Hg^{++} and Cl^-.

26. Given the following reactions, arrange the compounds of copper involved so far as you can in a list according to increasing ability to hold Cu^{++}. (a) H_2S gives no precipitate in a cyanide solution of copper; (b) copper sulfide is insoluble in ammonia; (c) ferrocyanide ion added to copper ammonia complex solution precipitates copper ferrocyanide; (d) copper hydroxide is soluble in ammonia.

27. Given the following reactions, arrange the compounds of lead involved so far as you can in a list according to increasing ability to hold Pb^{++}.

$$PbI_2 + SO_4^{--} = PbSO_4 + 2\ I^-,$$
$$PbI_2 + 3\ OH^- = HPbO_2^- + H_2O + 2\ I^-,$$
$$PbCrO_4 + 3\ OH^- = HPbO_2^- + H_2O + CrO_4^{--},$$
$$PbCl_2 + 2\ I^- = PbI_2 + 2\ Cl^-,$$
$$HPbO_2^- + S^{--} + H_2O = PbS + 3\ OH^-,$$
$$PbI_2 + CrO_4^{--} = PbCrO_4 + 2\ I^-.$$

*28. Derive the expression for the concentration of OH^- in a solution of the salt, NaX, of molar concentration, M. The acid, HX, is a weak acid, with ionization constant, K_a. Assume that the amount of X^- hydrolyzed is not sufficient to reduce its concentration appreciably below the amount taken, M.

*29. Use the formula derived in the preceding exercise to calculate (OH^-) in 0.4 M-KCN. Take for HCN $K_a = 4 \times 10^{-10}$.

*30. Calculate, as in Exercise 29, the (OH^-) in 0.1 M-Na_3PO_4. K_a for HPO_4^{--} is 10^{-12}. Note that enough HPO_4^{--} is formed to indicate that (PO_4^{---}) at equilibrium is appreciably less than 0.1 M, therefore the formula derived in Exercise 28 is not sufficiently

---

* Questions of greater difficulty.

accurate for so large a degree of hydrolysis. There are two procedures for obtaining a better value of (OH^-). What are they? Use one of them to obtain (OH^-) to within 10 per cent.

*31. Calculate the dissociation constant of HClO from the value $(OH^-) = 3 \times 10^{-4}$ in 0.5 M-NaClO.

CHAPTER XIV

THE EFFECT OF PRESSURE AND TEMPERATURE UPON EQUILIBRIUM

1. We have seen in the last two chapters that it is possible, by altering the concentration of one of the reactants in a system at chemical equilibrium, to cause the equilibrium to shift in such a manner as would tend to restore the initial concentrations, or, as we may say, to neutralize the imposed change. It is likewise possible to affect an equilibrium by changing the total pressure to which the system is subject, or by changing its temperature. We shall now inquire into the direction in which a reaction must proceed in order to restore equilibrium when subjected to such changes in pressure and temperature.

2. Effect of Changing Total Pressure upon a System in Equilibrium. If we have an equilibrium between a liquid and its vapor, as discussed in Chapter III, we have seen that an increase in pressure tends to cause vapor to condense, since the number of molecules in the gaseous state is thereby reduced, relieving the pressure. We have seen also that this is in harmony with the kinetic theory, and have stated, in Chapter XII, the general Theorem of Le Chatelier which demands that any equilibrium system, no matter how complex, subjected to such an increase in pressure must likewise tend to neutralize the change. Thus, an increase in pressure always tends to produce the system having the smallest volume, a decrease in volume tending to relieve the increase in applied pressure. If an applied pressure may be minimized not only by the contraction of the substances composing the system but also by a reaction between them, the increase in pressure will tend to cause that reaction to proceed which results in a diminution of the volume of the system. This effect of pressure on equilibria will, of course, be greatest in the case of reactions involving the largest change in volume, e.g., in reactions involving a change in the number of gaseous molecules.

3. Suppose, for example, that we have a closed vessel containing SO_3, SO_2, and O_2 in equilibrium, which has been reached by the substances reacting in one direction or the other, as represented by the equation, $2 SO_2 + O_2 = 2 SO_3$. We see from the equation that when SO_3 is formed there is a change in the number of molecules in the proportion 3 to 2. If pressure is applied to the three gases in equilibrium, it will compress them, resulting in a decrease in volume. A further decrease is possible, however, by the union of some of the SO_2 with some of the O_2, the consequent diminution in the number of molecules relieving somewhat the pressure applied. Starting, in two experiments, with identical amounts of SO_2 and O_2 at the same temperature, we find that more SO_3 will be produced when equilibrium is finally attained if the pressure is high than if it is low.

The same conclusion may be drawn with respect to the reaction for the synthesis of ammonia, whose equation is $N_2 + 3 H_2 = 2 NH_3$, which shows that ammonia is formed with a dimution in the number of molecules. A high pressure would favor that reaction which would yield the smaller volume, thus relieving, as far as possible, the high pressure applied.

On the other hand, with the equilibria, $N_2 + O_2 = 2 NO$, and $H_2 + Cl_2 = 2 HCl$, with no change in the number of gaseous molecules during reaction, pressure will be without effect on the amounts formed.

4. In predicting the effect of pressure we must have regard to the physical states of the substances involved under the conditions of the experiment. It is possible, for instance, by using either liquid sulfur or sulfur vapor to make H_2S directly from its elements. The respective reactions may be represented by the equations,

$$H_2 + S \text{ (liquid)} = H_2S,$$
$$2 H_2 + S_2 \text{ (vapor)} = 2 H_2S.$$

In the first reaction there is practically no change in volume, if the reaction is carried out at constant pressure, since the volume of the liquid sulfur is negligible. Therefore, the relative amounts of H_2 and H_2S present at equilibrium will be practically independent of the pressure applied, or of the volume of the vessel in which the reaction takes place. In the second process, where the conditions are such that the sulfur is in the vapor state, the formation of H_2S at constant pressure results in a decrease in volume, hence the higher the pressure the greater the amount of H_2S formed.

5. Not only is the effect on the direction indicated by the above discussion, but its magnitude also depends upon the magnitude of the volume change during the reaction. Thus a tenfold increase in total pressure will produce a much greater increase in the amount of NH_3 produced from N_2 and H_2 than in the amount of SO_3 produced from SO_2 and O_2, since the decreases in volume in the two reactions are respectively from 4 to 2 and from 3 to 2. For the same reason, very great changes in pressure have to be applied in order to have much effect on equilibria involving liquids and solids only, where only small changes in volume occur.

6. The influence of pressure on a gas phase equilibrium may be calculated quantitatively by noting that the effect of the pressure is exerted solely upon the concentration of the reagents and not at all on the molecules themselves. Accordingly, the equilibrium constants derived in Chapter XII are independent of total pressure. In terms of kinetic theory, it is clear that any increase in pressure increases the concentration of all the reactants and hence speeds up both the forward and back reactions in each equilibrium. Therefore if the two reactions involve no change in the number of molecules, as in $N_2 + O_2 = 2 NO$, a change in the total pressure causes no change in equilibrium concentrations; but if, as in $N_2 + 3 H_2 = 2 NH_3$, the reactions involve different numbers of molecules, the equilibrium will shift toward the side with the smaller number in harmony with the kinetic theory. This is clear from the quantitative expressions for the equilibrium constants for these two reactions, expressed in number of moles in the volume, V.

	$N_2 + O_2 = 2 NO$			$N_2 + 3 H_2 = 2 NH_3$		
Take, moles	1	1	0	1	3	0
Amount reacting	x	x		x	$3x$	
Amount present at equilibrium	$1-x$	$1-x$	$2x$	$1-x$	$3-3x$	$2x$
Equilibrium concentrations	$\dfrac{1-x}{V}$	$\dfrac{1-x}{V}$	$\dfrac{2x}{V}$	$\dfrac{1-x}{V}$	$\dfrac{3-3x}{V}$	$\dfrac{2x}{V}$
Equilibrium constants	$K = \dfrac{(1-x)^2}{4x^2}$			$K = \dfrac{(1-x)(3-3x)^3}{4x^2 V^2}$		

The volume has canceled out for the first reaction but not for the second, where the smaller we make V by increasing pressure the larger x must become to compensate. If, for example, for the latter equilibrium $x = 0.1$ when $V = 100$ l., $K = 0.0443$, then, if pressure is applied to increase x to 0.2, the corresponding volume would be 39.5 l.

7. Effect on Equilibrium of Changing the Temperature.

In order to appreciate the effect of changing temperature upon a system at equilibrium, we must realize (1) that the immediate effect of any difference in temperature is to determine the direction of flow of heat and (2) that energy in general, and heat in particular, is as much a reagent as any atomic or molecular species. If we have a tank of water at 20° C., and put into it a piece of iron at a temperature of 30°, heat will flow from the iron to the water in the tank, tending to equalize the temperature. If on the other hand, the piece of iron is at a temperature of 10°, when it is put into the water, heat will flow from the water into the iron. Suppose, now, that we have a closed vessel containing SO_2, O_2, and SO_3, in equilibrium, in an oven at a temperature of 500°, and we transfer it to another oven in which the temperature is 550°. Just as with the piece of iron in the former case, so in this case heat will flow into the vessel and its reacting mixture. The immediate effect of the heat will be to increase the temperature, the heat content, of the inclosed gases.

Energy is, however, as much a reactant in this system as SO_2, O_2, or SO_3 as shown by the equation

$$2\,SO_2 + O_2 = 2\,SO_3 + 45{,}000 \text{ cal.}$$

which means that for every two moles of SO_3 formed 45,000 calories of energy are liberated from the system. Since heat is evolved by the formation of SO_3, it will be absorbed by the reverse reaction, in which SO_3 is dissociated into SO_2 and O_2. Hence, the effect of bringing the reacting mixture to the higher temperature, i.e., of supplying heat to the system, is to shift the equilibrium so as to form less SO_3.

If, on the contrary, the vessel with its equilibrium mixture is transferred from the oven at 500° into an oven at 450°, the heat will flow out of it. This heat will be furnished not only by the cooling of the contained gases, but also by their reacting to some extent to give off heat; accordingly, more SO_3 is present at equilibrium at the lower temperature.

8. In the formation of NO from its elements heat is absorbed, as indicated by the equation,

$$N_2 + O_2 = 2\,NO - 44{,}000 \text{ cal.}$$

Consequently, if we have these gases in equilibrium, a rise in temperature will favor the absorption of heat in every possible way, which will not only cause the temperature of the gases to increase, but will also tend to form more NO. We see here that the higher the temperature the more NO will be obtained at equilibrium, while with SO_3 the reverse is true, the higher the temperature the less SO_3 is obtained at equilibrium.

9. Considerations of this sort apply to every sort of equilibrium and enable us either to predict the effect of changing the temperature from the sign (and magnitude) of the heat of reaction, or, conversely, to predict the latter from the former. As an illustration of this reverse process, let us consider a saturated solution of a salt whose solubility is greater the higher the temperature, and ask ourselves whether this salt evolves or absorbs heat when more dissolves under

approximately equilibrium conditions. Since raising the temperature causes more salt to dissolve, and since also, raising the temperature favors any process that can take place with absorption of heat, we conclude that this particular salt absorbs heat while dissolving. By similar reasoning, any salt that becomes less soluble as the temperature increases must have positive heat of solution, that is, it must evolve heat on dissolving.

10. The temperature effect on an equilibrium is, in the main, due to the variations with temperature in the kind and intensity of the internal molecular vibrations. As temperature rises all molecules tend to undergo more numerous and more violent vibrations (cf. Chapter III, paragraph 24) which render them more and more unstable. This tendency will differ in degree with different molecules so that, while all molecules become less stable with respect to decomposition into their constituent atoms as the temperature rises, their relative stabilities may vary considerably. In most cases it may be said that the more complex the molecule the more rapidly it becomes unstable. Thus both the SO_3 and NH_3 syntheses reverse more and more at high temperatures to give the simpler molecules. Since this effect is dependent on molecular structure and not on concentration it is not surprising that the equilibrium constant varies with temperature as contrasted to its nonvariance with pressure. The qualitative variance may be predicted as outlined above. Quantitatively it is found that the logarithm of the equilibrium constant is roughly proportional to the reciprocal of the absolute temperature. The ratio of the value of an equilibrium constant, K, at a temperature T to its value, K', at T' is given fairly accurately by the equation,

$$\log_{10} \frac{K}{K'} = \frac{\Delta H}{4.58}\left(\frac{1}{T} - \frac{1}{T'}\right),$$

where ΔH is the heat in calories absorbed during the reaction.

11. Simultaneous Consideration of All Factors Governing Reactions. In Chapter XI we considered the velocity of chemical reactions, as it is affected by concentration, temperature, and the presence of catalysts. We have also considered separately the effect of concentration, pressure, and tempera-

ture upon chemical equilibrium and are now prepared to consider the simlutaneous effect of these factors in controlling chemical reactions. We must again emphasize the fact that the question of velocity is quite distinct from that of equilibrium. If we should put some calcium fluoride, CaF_2, and some calcium sulfide, CaS, into separate beakers of water, we might conclude from a hasty examination that both are very insoluble. As a matter of fact, the small amount of the solid going into solution is due to very different reasons in the two cases. Calcium fluoride is truly insoluble, and no amount of time or stirring would cause more than a very small amount of it to dissolve. Calcium sulfide, on the other hand, is insoluble because, in order to dissolve, it must hydrolyze, giving $Ca(OH)_2$ and $Ca(SH)_2$, a process which takes place very slowly. Again, calcium chromate, $CaCrO_4$, is more soluble in cold water than in hot, if sufficient time is allowed for the solution to become saturated, but it will dissolve much faster in hot water than in cold, so that after a given time more might be found in a hot than in a cold solution, although eventually the latter would contain more of the salt. It is thus very important, in attempting to realize difficult reactions, to remember that speed and equilibrium require independent considerations, and that conditions which favor the desired equilibrium may not favor its rapid attainment, and vice versa. A discussion of the complete conditions for realizing certain important reactions will make this clearer.

12. The "Contact Process" for Making Sulfuric Acid. We have seen above that to make SO_3 from SO_2 and O_2 a low temperature is desirable in order to give the most complete yield of SO_3. By recalling the discussion in Chapter XI, however, we will see that the lower the temperature the more slowly will the desired equilibrium be reached. We must therefore distinguish between the amount of SO_3 which would be produced at equilibrium and the amount that would be produced in a given time. The time necessary for reaching equilibrium grows enormously as the temperature

is lowered, with the result that it is practically impossible to reach equilibrium except at high temperatures, where the amount of SO_2 converted into SO_3 is so small that it would not be profitable to use the reaction.

In order to work at a temperature at which the equilibrium is favorable a new factor must be introduced to increase the velocity. This is accomplished in practice by passing the gases over a solid catalyst of either finely divided platinum or some form of vanadic oxide, V_2O_5. (Hence the name "contact process.")

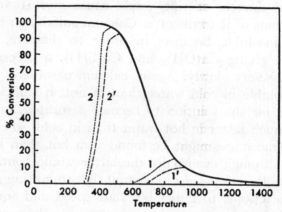

Fig. 1. Approach to equilibrium in the conversion of SO_2 and O_2 into SO_3; curves 1, without catalyst; curves 2, with catalyst; at two different rates of flow, 1 and 2 slower than 1' and 2'.

These effects may be brought out by the curves in the accompanying figure (Fig. 1) where the solid line indicates the per cent of the total possible amount of SO_3 which would be obtained at various temperatures if sufficient time were allowed for equilibrium to be reached as a function of the temperature at equilibrium. The dotted lines in Fig. 1 indicate the actual nearness of approach to equilibrium with no catalyst present (curve 1) and with a catalyst present (curve 2) for the same rate of flow of the gases through the heated chamber. The dashed curves, 1' and 2', show the corresponding nearness of approach to equilibrium if the rate of flow is increased in each case, i.e., the time allowed for reaction is less. These data are for a gas mixture at one atmosphere total pressure containing 7% SO_2, 14% O_2, and 79% N_2 by volume.

In commercial practice it is not desired to get maximum conversion but rather optimum conversion. A low rate of flow gives maximum conversion but the rate at which product is produced may be too low for economy. A rapid rate of flow may give a higher rate of production but does not give a close approach to equilibrium at a favorable temperature and requires more expensive plant outlays. A balance must be struck at which the cost per ton of product is a minimum. The product, sulfuric acid, is obtained by dissolving the fog of SO_3 in concentrated sulfuric acid (it is not readily absorbed by water), and then diluting with water to give the desired concentration.

13. The speed of the reaction, and also the desired equilibrium, might be influenced in the right direction by having the reaction take place under high pressure, but this would involve difficulties in the way of more complicated construction and operation that are not required for adequate yields. Since the SO_2 must be paid for, while the O_2 is obtained free from the air, it is more important to use up the SO_2 completely than the O_2. This is done by taking the air in considerable excess, 3- or 4-fold, of the equivalent amount required. We may summarize in tabular form our conclusions concerning the best conditions for realizing this reaction.

	To favor large amount of SO_3 at equilibrium	To favor high speed either of formation or decomposition	Conditions used commercially
Total pressure	High	High	1 atm.
Temperature	Low	High	400–450° C.
Other factors	Excess of O_2	Catalyst	3- or 4-fold O_2 excess, Pt or V_2O_5 catalyst.

14. The Synthesis of Ammonia. If we compare the reaction for the synthesis of ammonia,

$$N_2 + 3 H_2 = 2 NH_3 + 24,000 \text{ cal.},$$

with the above reaction for making SO_3, we see that the same conditions are indicated for realizing this reaction as for the former. This reaction, however, is exceedingly slow, so that even with iron, the best catalyst that has been discovered after extensive search, advantage must be taken of high pressure in aiding both the speed and the equilibrium at the temperatures at which the reaction will take place with measurable velocity.

The effect of both temperature and pressure on the yield of NH_3 at equilibrium is indicated in the following figures:

| | Yield of NH_3 in per cent | |
Temperature, ° C.	At 1 atmosphere	At 100 atmospheres
800°	0.011	1.1
700°	0.021	2.1
600°	0.048	4.5
500°	0.13	10.8

A further lowering of temperature below 500° C. to improve the yield would give too slow a reaction, so that the process is worked at about this temperature, and under pressures up to 1000 atmospheres. As the N_2 and H_2 pass over the catalyst they unite partially to form NH_3. The gases are then passed through a cooling coil in which the NH_3 is condensed to liquid and removed, or the NH_3 may be removed by bubbling the gas mixture through water to give aqua ammonia. The N_2 and H_2 again pass over the heated catalyst, again forming the equilibrium amount of NH_3, and so on. The removal of NH_3 is compensated for by pumping in fresh H_2 and N_2.

It is of interest to note that this process enabled Germany to prolong the First World War by several years after being cut off from the natural sources of "fixed nitrogen" from Chile saltpeter, $NaNO_3$. Both fertilizer and explosives require combined nitrogen in their preparation and this process gives an inexhaustible supply from the nitrogen in the air and the hydrogen in water. Before 1913 no nitrogen was fixed in this manner, while in 1940 over 50 per cent of all manufactured nitrogen compounds stemmed from synthetic ammonia.

15. The Synthesis of Nitric Oxide. We have already referred briefly to the reaction,

$$N_2 + O_2 = 2\,NO - 44{,}000 \text{ cal.}$$

We see that the formation of NO would be aided by the following conditions, which we will tabulate as before.

Pressure, Temperature, and Equilibrium

	To favor large amount of NO at equilibrium	To favor high speed either of formation or decomposition
Total pressure	No effect	High
Temperature	High	High

As a consequence of these conclusions, we see that NO should be formed more rapidly and also more completely at high temperatures. That this is true is seen from the following figures on the basis of experiments:

Temperature, ° C.	1540	1920	2930	3930
Per cent NO at equilibrium, starting with air	0.37	0.97	5.0	10

Obviously NO is stable, in a true sense, only at extremely high temperatures, and both a favorable equilibrium and high speed in attaining it are aided by high temperatures such as those given by an electric arc. The problem is then to lower it to ordinary temperature without letting the equilibrium shift back to N_2 and O_2 as it cools. This is done by cooling it sufficiently rapidly as the gas mixture leaves the arc. There is also an electrical effect, due to the arc, tending to give a greater yield than is indicated by the above conditions of ordinary equilibrium.

At ordinary temperatures NO unites readily with more O_2 to form N_2O_4, which will dissolve in water forming a mixture of nitric and nitrous acids. The N_2O_4 may also be passed over slaked lime, giving a mixture of calcium nitrite and nitrate, which is used as fertilizer to supply nitrogen to the soil. This process was once used successfully on a commercial scale in Norway, but is now of only academic interest.

16. The "Cracking" of Petroleum. The principles above set forth have been of great aid in "cracking" the heavier molecules of petroleum so as to produce lighter molecules of more volatile substances, such as benzene, C_6H_6; toluene, $C_6H_5CH_3$; and paraffins like C_5H_{12}, C_6H_{14}, C_7H_{16}, etc., which are contained in gasoline. However it must be realized that equilibrium is not usually attained, although for certain reactions it may be approached. Thus our reasoning is not exact, but indicates only which reactions will be favored by certain conditions.

Let us take a typical molecule too heavy for gasoline, $C_{14}H_{30}$, and see how it might break up at high temperatures. Several typical reactions follow, arranged in order of increase in volume.

$$C_{14}H_{30} \text{ (gas)} = CH_4 \text{ (gas)} + C_{13}H_{26} \text{ (gas)} - 16{,}000 \text{ cal.}$$

$$C_{14}H_{30} \text{ (gas)} = C_7H_{14} \text{ (gas)} + C_7H_{16} \text{ (gas)} - 18{,}000 \text{ cal.}$$

$$C_{14}H_{30} \text{ (gas)} = 2\,C_4H_8 \text{ (gas)} + C_3H_6 \text{ (gas)} + C_3H_8 \text{ (gas)}$$
$$- 55{,}000 \text{ cal.}$$

$$C_{14}H_{30} \text{ (gas)} = 2\,C_7H_8 \text{ (toluene)} + 7\,H_2 \text{ (gas)} - 105{,}600 \text{ cal.}$$

$$C_{14}H_{30} \text{ (gas)} = 14\,C \text{ (solid)} + 15\,H_2 \text{ (gas)} - 79{,}400 \text{ cal.}$$

In the older "thermal cracking," the hydrocarbons were heated to a temperature at which a variety of reactions take place simultaneously. It is evident from the above equations that at low pressure coke (C), aromatics (toluene, etc.), and low molecular weight olefins (C_3H_5, etc.) are favored. At higher pressures more products in the gasoline range (C_7H_{16}, etc.) can be expected. Very high temperatures likewise favor the last set of products, particularly the aromatics, while very low temperatures shift all the equilibria to the left, i.e., give no reaction. Thus intermediate temperatures and high pressures favor gasoline components. More recent cracking processes involve the use of selected catalysts to speed up certain desired reactions at lower temperatures. The influence of pressure and temperature is still present but is now of limited effect.

Butadiene, C_4H_6, important for the production of synthetic rubber (Chapter XVIII, paragraph 25), is formed by splitting hydrogen out of butane (C_4H_{10}) and butene (C_4H_8).

$$C_4H_{10} = C_4H_8 + H_2 - 29,000 \text{ cal.}$$

$$C_4H_8 = C_4H_6 + H_2 - 29,000 \text{ cal.}$$

However, at moderate temperatures these reactions proceed from right to left rather than in the desired direction. Only at about 900° K. are these equilibria shifted far enough to the right to make this process practical.

Exercises

1. If the volume of a solution is greater than that of the salt and water from which it is made, how will the solubility of the salt change when pressure is applied to the saturated solution?

2. In which direction would each of the following equilibria be displaced by decreasing the total pressure? (Explain.)

$$N_2O_4 = 2 NO_2,$$

$$2 HCl = H_2 + Cl_2,$$

$$C \text{ (solid)} + S_2 \text{ (vapor)} = CS_2 \text{ (vapor)}.$$

3. Ammonium chloride dissolves with considerable absorption of heat. How is its solubility affected by the temperature?

4. The solubility of sodium chloride increases very slightly with temperature. What can be concluded concerning its heat of solution?

5. When AgCl is prepared by mixing its ions heat is evolved. Is the precipitate more soluble in hot or in cold water? (Explain.)

6. Explain how temperature would affect the production of H_2S according to the reaction: $H_2 + S = H_2S + $ heat.

7. The formation of benzene from acetylene according to the reaction $3 C_2H_2 = C_6H_6 + 137,700$ cal. takes place slowly at a high temperature (benzene being a vapor) and is reversible.

(*a*) What weight of benzene could be made by the complete

conversion of 49.3 liters of acetylene, measured at 27° C. and 1 atmosphere?

(b) State and explain the experimental conditions you would adopt to secure the maximum yield of benzene from acetylene in a given time.

8. Knowing that the neutralization of strong acids by strong bases evolves much heat, it is possible to decide how the ionization of water varies with the temperature. Trace the connection.

9. Acetic acid is more highly ionized at higher than at lower temperatures. Which of the following reactions, consequently, will evolve more heat?

$$H^+ + OH^- = H_2O;$$

$$HAc + OH^- = H_2O + Ac^-.$$

10. Equilibrium at 1000° C. and 1 atm. is reached when the gas phase of the reaction

$$CO_2 \text{ (gas)} + C \text{ (solid)} = 2 CO \text{ (gas)} - 95,000 \text{ cals.}$$

consists of about 99 per cent CO. What changes in conditions might you make to obtain a gas phase consisting chiefly of CO_2?

11. Comparing equilibria between the substances involved in the following reactions:

(a) $H_2 + I_2$ (gas) $= 2 HI$ (gas) $- 2800$ cals.

(b) $CO_2 + C$ (charcoal) $= 2 CO - 95,000$ cals.

(c) $CaCO_3 = CaO + CO_2 - 23,200$ cals.

(d) $2 SO_2 + O_2 = 2 SO_3$ (gas) $+ 44,000$ cals.

(e) $3 H_2 + N_2 = 2 NH_3 + 24,000$ cals.

Designate by letter the equilibrium (1) for which an increase in total pressure, with temperature kept constant would cause (a) the least effect, (b) the greatest shift to the right; (2) for which an increase in temperature, at constant volume, would cause the greatest shift (a) to the right, (b) to the left.

*12. When H_2 is burned against ice, small amounts of H_2O_2 are produced. Two explanations for this have been offered: one, that the H_2O_2 is produced by shifting the equilibrium, $2 H_2O + O_2 = 2 H_2O_2 -$ heat, towards H_2O_2 at high temperatures; the other, that two reactions occur, $H_2 + O_2 = H_2O_2$, followed by $2 H_2O_2 = 2 H_2O + O_2$, the latter being incomplete due to the rapid cooling of the flame. Can you suggest any experimental study that might serve to decide between these explanations?

* Question of greater difficulty.

CHAPTER XV

OXIDATION AND REDUCTION

1. In the previous chapters our attention has been largely confined to reactions in which there are no changes in oxidation number. In Chapter IX, however, brief mention was made of reactions in which such changes do occur, and it was there pointed out that oxidation consists essentially of an increase in oxidation number, or loss of electrons, and reduction of a decrease in oxidation number or gain of electrons. We are now prepared to give fuller attention to such reactions, considering, first, the writing of equations representing them, and, second, the oxidizing and reducing powers of the substances involved.

2. Whenever an element is oxidized some element must be reduced. The substance containing the element which is oxidized is called the **reducing agent,** since it is responsible for the reduction of the other element. Conversely, the substance which causes an increase in oxidation number is the **oxidizing agent,** and contains an element which is reduced. The following table illustrates these terms:

$$Cu + 2 H_2SO_4 = CuSO_4 + SO_2 + 2 H_2O.$$

Oxid. No. 0   6   2,6   4

Element oxidized, Cu.   Oxidizing agent, H_2SO_4.
Element reduced, S.   Reducing agent, Cu.

$$H_2S + I_2 = S + 2 H^+ + 2 I^-.$$

Oxid. No. -2 0   0 -1

Element oxidized, S.   Oxidizing agent, I_2.
Element reduced, I.   Reducing agent, H_2S.

$$2 \, Fe^{+++} + H_2SO_3 + H_2O = 2 \, Fe^{++} + SO_4^{--} + 4 \, H^+.$$

Oxid. No. 3   4   2   6

     Element oxidized, S.   Oxidizing agent, Fe^{+++}.

     Element reduced, Fe.   Reducing agent, H_2SO_3.

$$MnO_4^- + 5 \, Fe^{++} + 8 \, H^+ = Mn^{++} + 5 \, Fe^{+++} + 4 \, H_2O.$$

Oxid. No.   7   2   2   3

     Element oxidized, Fe.   Oxidizing agent, MnO_4^-.

     Element reduced, Mn.   Reducing agent, Fe^{++}.

3. Writing Equations for Reactions Involving Oxidation and Reduction. The Substance Produced. Before an equation can be written for any reaction it is necessary to know what substances are produced. This may be determined by experiment or predicted, in most cases, from a knowledge of the reacting substances. For example, when hot concentrated sulfuric acid reacts with copper it is possible to detect the evolution of sulfur dioxide by its odor, and the production of copper sulfate by the blue color it gives on the addition of water. When sulfurous acid acts upon ferric ion, the ferrous ion produced shows its presence by its faint green color, or by other characteristic tests, and the formation of sulfate ion can be proved by adding barium ion. One sufficiently familiar with the chemistry of iron and of sulfur would not need these tests, for he knows that when ferric ion decreases in oxidation number in acid solution it usually becomes ferrous ion, and that the corresponding increase of odixation numbers on the part of sulfurous acid would give sulfate ion. It is therefore important to know the oxidation numbers the elements are capable of assuming and the compounds characteristic of each oxidation number.

4. For example, many of the metals, including the alkali and alkaline earth metals, silver, zinc, cadmium, and aluminum, exhibit only one oxidation state in addition to that of the free metal, which is zero. Therefore a substance like aluminum ion, Al^{+++}, cannot be oxidized farther, nor can it be reduced to metal in water solution. Hence we would not expect it to take part in any oxidation or reduction process in aqueous solution. Chlorine shows the following oxidation states, -1, 0, $+1$, $+3$, $+5$, $+7$, which correspond to the compounds tabulated in Chapter X, paragraph 9. Consequently, we would never find the chlorine in chloride ion, Cl^-, acting as an oxidizing agent, because it is already as completely reduced as it is capable of being. Likewise, if chlorine, Cl_2, acts as an oxidizing agent it must be reduced, and the only probable product would be chloride ion or one of its compounds. Again, knowing that chlorine reacts with hydroxide ion as follows:

$$Cl_2 + 2\,OH^- = Cl^- + ClO^- + H_2O,$$

we know that when ClO^- acts as an oxidizing agent in alkaline solution, the chlorine could not be reduced to the next lower oxidation number, zero, corresponding to Cl_2, but would be reduced all the way to chloride ion.

5. The following table represents the substances characteristic of chromium in the oxidation numbers of three and six respectively, and in acid, neutral, or alkaline solution:

Oxidation number	Acid	Neutral	Alkaline
3	Cr^{+++}	$Cr(OH)_3$	CrO_2^-
6	$Cr_2O_7^{--}$	CrO_4^{--}	CrO_4^{--}

In accordance with the knowledge thus summarized, we would expect Cr^{+++} to be produced when a reducing agent acts upon $Cr_2O_7^{--}$. Similar information should be remembered for the other common elements giving compounds in which they show more than one oxidation number.

6. **The Assignment of Oxidation Numbers to the Elements Oxidized and Reduced.** Having decided upon the substances produced by the reaction, the first step is to write their formulas, together with those of the substances reacting, upon the appropriate side of the equation, and to assign an oxidation number to the elements oxidized and reduced, as explained in Chapter V.

7. Let us illustrate the process by balancing the equation for the oxidation of Fe^{++} by MnO_4^-. The following scheme thus gives the various steps involved:

(*a*) Substances in which oxidation numbers change

$$Fe^{++} + MnO_4^- = Fe^{+++} + Mn^{++}.$$

(*b*) Oxidation numbers   2   7   3   2
(*c*) Changes per atom $+1$ -5
(*d*) Atoms required   5   1
(*e*) Molecules required

$$5\,Fe^{++} + MnO_4^- = 5\,Fe^{+++} + Mn^{++}$$

(*f*) Other molecules added to balance

$$5\,Fe^{++} + MnO_4^- + 8\,H^+ = 5\,Fe^{+++} + Mn^{++} + 4\,H_2O.$$

Step (*c*), the change in oxidation number per atom, is found by noting that the iron changes from 2 to 3, while the manganese changes downward, from 7 to 2. To balance the reduction of 1 atom of manganese thus requires 5 atoms of iron, as shown in step (*e*). The oxidation and reduction are now balanced, and the **coefficients assigned must not be disturbed in the final balancing of the other elements and charges.** To do this one may consider, first, either the discrepancy in oxygen atoms, or the discrepancy in charges. It will usually be found somewhat simpler to begin with the latter. In step (*e*) we have on the left $+10 - 1$ or $+9$, and on the right $+15 + 2$ or $+17$. We must, therefore, either add $8\,H^+$ on the left or $8\,OH^-$ on the right. Since the metallic ions given in the equation could not exist as such in an alkaline solution the solution is acidic, and we should add $8\,H^+$ on the left. It will then be found that these 8 hydrogen atoms and the 4 oxygen atoms of the MnO_4^- will be balanced by adding finally $4\,H_2O$ on the right, giving step (*f*) as the completed equation.

8. Let us next consider a reaction occurring in alkaline solution. We will indicate the steps used in balancing it just as in the preceding example.

(*a*) Substances in which oxidation numbers change

$$CrO_2^- + ClO^- = CrO_4^{--} + Cl^-.$$

(*b*) Oxidation numbers	3	1	6	−1
(*c*) Changes per atom	3	−2		
(*d*) Atoms required	2	3		
(*e*) Molecules required				

$$2\,CrO_2^- + 3\,ClO^- = 2\,CrO_4^{--} + 3\,Cl^-.$$

(*f*) To balance charges, add 2 OH⁻ on left, and to balance oxygen and hydrogen, H₂O on right, getting

$$2\,CrO_2^- + 3\,ClO^- + 2\,OH^- = 2\,CrO_4^{--} + 3\,Cl^- + H_2O.$$

9. There is sometimes confusion due to the presence in the same molecule of more than 1 atom of an element oxidized or reduced. As an example we will consider the oxidation of SO_2 to SO_4^{--} by $Cr_2O_7^{--}$ (in acid solution, since $Cr_2O_7^{--}$ exists only in acid solution). Using the same steps as before, we have,

(*a*) Substances in which oxidation numbers change

$$SO_2 + Cr_2O_7^{--} = Cr^{+++} + SO_4^{--}.$$

(*b*) Oxidation numbers (of 1 *atom*)	4	6	3	6
(*c*) Changes per atom	2	−3		
(*d*) Atoms required	3	2		
(*e*) Molecules required				

$$3\,SO_2 + Cr_2O_7^{--} = 2\,Cr^{+++} + 3\,SO_4^{--}.$$

(*f*) To balance charges add 2 H⁺ on left, and to balance H and O add H₂O on right, getting

$$3\,SO_2 + Cr_2O_7^{--} + 2\,H^+ = 2\,Cr^{+++} + 3\,SO_4^{--} + H_2O.$$

The point to notice is that the required 2 atoms of Cr are already taken in the molecule of $Cr_2O_7^{--}$, whereas the co-efficient 2 is required before the Cr^{+++} on the right.

10. We will take next a reaction in which the same element is both oxidized and reduced, viz., the reaction of active phosphorus with concentrated NaOH solution to form phosphine, PH_3, and hypophosphite ion, $H_2PO_2^-$.

(a) Substance in which oxidation number changes

$$P_4 = H_2PO_2^- + PH_3.$$

(b) Oxidation numbers   0 $+1$ -3
(c) Changes per atom   1 -3
(d) Atoms required   4   3   1
(e) Molecules required $P_4 = 3\ H_2PO_2^- + PH_3.$
(f) To balance charges add 3 OH^- on left, and to balance H and O add 3 H_2O on left, getting

$$P_4 + 3\ OH^- + 3\ H_2O = 3\ H_2PO_2^- + PH_3.$$

11. Equations involving peroxides are sometimes troublesome, and we will therefore include one illustration.

(a) Substances in which oxidation numbers change

$$H_2O_2 + MnO_4^- = Mn^{++} + O_2.$$

(b) Oxidation numbers -1 7   2   0
(c) Changes per atom   1 -5
(d) Atoms required   5   1
(e) Molecules required

$$5\ H_2O_2 + 2\ MnO_4^- = 2\ Mn^{++} + 5\ O_2.$$

(f) To balance charges, add 6 H^+ on left, etc., getting

$$6\ H^+ + 5\ H_2O_2 + 2\ MnO_4^- = 2\ Mn^{++} + 5\ O_2 + 8\ H_2O.$$

12. An Alternative Method. Since an element is oxidized when it gives up electrons and reduced when it takes on electrons, the number of electrons transferred may be made the basis for balancing an equation. For example, whenever MnO_4^- is reduced in acid solution it becomes Mn^{++}. To take care of the oxygen atoms in the MnO_4^- there will obviously be required 8 H^+, giving 4 H_2O and to balance the charges will require 5 electrons, giving for the oxidizing half of the reaction the half-equation,

$$MnO_4^- + 8\ H^+ + 5\ e^- = Mn^{++} + 4\ H_2O.$$

The same result is achieved by writing in first the 5 electrons necessary to change the manganese from oxidation number 7 to oxidation number 2, and then adding the 8 H^+ to produce 4 H_2O. If the substance oxidized is Fe^{++}, the reducing half of the reaction is $Fe^{++} = Fe^{+++} + e^-$. Obviously the former process can take the electrons from 5 times the latter, so that multiplying the latter half-equation by 5 and adding to the former gives

$$MnO_4^- + 5\ Fe^{++} + 8\ H^+ = Mn^{++} + 5\ Fe^{+++} + 4\ H_2O,$$

the same result as was previously obtained by the other method.

13. Let us give an illustration of the balancing of a reaction in alkaline solution by this method. To oxidize CrO_2^- to CrO_4^{--} requires 4 OH^-, giving

$$CrO_2^- + 4\ OH^- = CrO_4^{--} + 2\ H_2O + 3\ e^-,$$

the 3 electrons being obviously necessary to make the equation balance.

To reduce ClO^- to Cl^- requires H_2O, giving 2 OH^-, so that

$$ClO^- + H_2O + 2\ e^- = Cl^- + 2\ OH^-.$$

Multiplying this half-reaction by 3 and the former by 2 and adding cancels out the electrons, giving

$$2\ CrO_2^- + 3\ ClO^- + 2\ OH^- = 3\ Cl^- + 2\ CrO_4^{--} + H_2O.$$

14. Although these methods may appear to be superficially different they rest upon the same theoretical foundation and will give identical results. It should be evident that gain in oxidation number is arithmetically equivalent to loss of electrons, so that there is no essential difference between the two methods where complete equations are involved. When dealing with the half-reactions occurring at electrodes, in electric cells, it is, of course, important to have the electrons appear in the equations.

Thinking in terms of electrons avoids the necessity of assigning oxidation numbers in cases where their location in a complex molecule or ion is not clearly evident, as in the case of $S_2O_3^{--}$, (cf. Chapter IX, paragraph 7) where 8 electrons are given off when $S_2O_3^{--}$ is oxidized to $2\ SO_4^{--}$. It should be understood, however, that oxidation numbers do not need to be theoretically correct in order to permit the correct balancing of equations, they need only to be arithmetically consistent.

15. The Relative Oxidizing and Reducing Powers of Various Substances. The Metals and Their Ions. It was pointed out in Chapter V that a metal having a smaller affinity for its electrons can give them up to an ion whose affinity for electrons is greater. This is illustrated by the following reactions, all of which take place quite readily:

$$2\ Na + Zn^{++} = Zn + 2\ Na^+,$$
$$Zn + Fe^{++} = Fe + Zn^{++},$$
$$Fe + Pb^{++} = Pb + Fe^{++},$$
$$Pb + Cu^{++} = Cu + Pb^{++},$$
$$Cu + 2\ Hg^+ = 2\ Hg + Cu^{++},$$
$$Hg + Ag^+ = Ag + Hg^+.$$

In each of these cases the baser metal is oxidized by the ion of the nobler one, and it is evident that zinc will reduce not only ferrous ion, but lead, copper, and silver ions as well. Likewise, silver ion can act as an oxidizing agent, not only to copper, but to all of the other metals represented. In all cases the metals act as the reducing agents, their reducing power decreasing as we descend the list, while the ions act as oxidizing agents, their oxidizing power increasing as we descend the list. This behavior may be summarized in Table 1.

TABLE 1

	Weak		Oxidizing Agents			Strong	
	Na^+	Zn^{++}	Fe^{++}	Pb^{++}	Cu^{++}	Hg^+ Ag^+	
	Na	Zn	Fe	Pb	Cu	Hg Ag	
	Strong		Reducing Agents			Weak	

Oxidation ↑ (left margin) · Reduction ↓ (right margin)

This table has been arranged so that any ion will be reduced if brought in contact with a metal to the left in the table. In order, however, for this arrangement to hold, the ions must all be in approximately equal concentration. If this is not the case, the positions of some may be reversed. Thus Hg^+ and Ag^+ have about the same oxidizing power, hence the reaction,

$$Hg^+ + Ag = Ag^+ + Hg,$$

is easily reversible by changing the relative concentrations. The principles of equilibrium set forth in Chapter XII apply here also, so that a high concentration of Hg^+ and a low concentration of Ag^+ favor the reaction as read from left to right, whereas the reverse reaction is favored by reversing the relative concentrations. With most pairs of metals the corresponding reversal requires greater differences in concentration.

16. Galvanized Iron. Many interesting applications of this oxidation-reduction series are possible. For example, it is evident that if a piece of zinc is put into a solution of ferrous ion there is a tendency for the latter to be reduced. Accordingly, if zinc and iron are in contact in an oxidizing solution, the former will be dissolved before the latter. This is the reason for the protective action of the zinc coating on "galvanized" iron.

17. Electric Batteries. When a piece of zinc is dropped into a solution of one of the ions to the right of it in the table, a reaction takes place such as the following:

$$Zn + Cu^{++} = Cu + Zn^{++}.$$

Now this may be regarded as a transfer of positive electricity from the copper ion to the zinc, or, better, as the transfer of negative electrons from the zinc to the copper ion. If this transfer of electricity can be made to take place through a wire we will have an electric current, and the reaction can be made to do work. To do this the zinc must not be put directly into the solution of copper ion, but electrodes of the two metals must dip into solutions of their own ions, the solutions being separated by a porous partition or by the aid of their difference in density, as in the case in the "gravity cell," illustrated in Fig. 1. At the zinc electrode the following process tends to take place:

$$Zn = Zn^{++} + 2\,e^-,$$

while at the copper electrode the reaction is

$$Cu^{++} + 2\,e^- = Cu.$$

Each of these processes can continue only if the stream of negative electrons, or atoms of electricity, can flow from the zinc to the copper, while the positive and negative ions in the solution migrate towards their respective poles. For

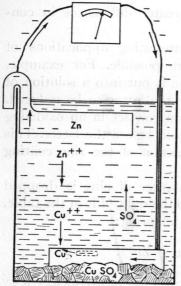

every mole of zinc that dissolves one mole of copper will be deposited and two faradays of electricity (cf. page 132) will travel through the wire. The electromotive force (e.m.f.) between the electrodes depends upon the difference between the tendencies of the metals to become ions, and also upon the relative concentration of the ions in the solution. If the concentration of zinc ion is diminished, or that of copper ion is increased, the reaction,

$$Zn + Cu^{++} = Cu + Zn^{++},$$

Fig. 1.   Electric cell utilizing the reaction, $Zn + Cu^{++} \rightleftharpoons Zn^{++} + Cu$.

will have a greater tendency to take place, and will give a larger electromotive force when occurring in an electric battery. If silver ion and silver are substituted for copper ion and copper, we will have a stronger oxidizing agent, a greater tendency to take up the electrons given off by the zinc and a battery of higher electromotive force.

18. It is customary to represent the sequence of the component parts of an electric cell or battery by a simple, formal scheme. The cell just described could be written:

$$Zn \mid Zn^{++} \vdots Cu^{++} \mid Cu$$

but, since the electromotive force depends upon the concentrations, it is often desirable to be more explicit, for example, as follows:

$$Zn \mid 0.1 \ M\text{-}Zn^{++}, \ 0.1 \ M\text{-}SO_4^{--} \vdots 0.1 \ M\text{-}SO_4^{--}, \ 0.1 M\text{-}Cu^{++} \mid Cu.$$

Again, suppose that we wish to obtain electric energy from the oxidation-reduction reaction,

$$2 \ Fe^{++} + Cl_2 = 2 \ Fe^{+++} + 2 \ Cl^-.$$

The main point to remember is that the oxidizing and reducing agents must not come into direct contact, but the electrons derived from the reducing part of the reaction, the "reducing couple," in this case $Fe^{++} = Fe^{+++} + e^-$, must flow out of the solution and through an external circuit, where they can do electric work for us, on their way to the oxidizing agent which unites with them, in this case by the reaction: $Cl_2 + 2 \ e^- = 2 \ Cl^-$. This can be accomplished by inclosing the solution containing the Fe^{+++} in a porous cup which would permit the migration of ions while preventing gross diffusion or convection.

19. In the preceding case, the reducing agent, Zn, is a metal and the electrons can escape directly from it into the wire of the external circuit; but when using Fe^{++} as the reducing agent, it is necessary to supply an inert, conducting electrode which can receive the electrons without undergoing any chemical reaction. Any metal not oxidized by Fe^{+++} could be used, but platinum, Pt, is usually preferred. The electrons coming through the external circuit to react with the Cl_2 can be led into the solution through a similar inert electrode, e.g., platinum or graphite, surrounded by chlorine gas. The construction of the cell is illustrated in Fig. 2 and can be formally represented, with sample concentrations, by

$$Pt \mid 0.01 \ M\text{-}Fe^{+++}, \quad 0.01 \ M\text{-}Fe^{++}, \quad 0.05 \ M\text{-}Cl^- \vdots 0.05 \ M\text{-}K^+,$$
$$0.05 M\text{-}Cl^- \mid Pt, Cl_2 \ (1 \text{ atmos.})$$

20. The e.m.f. of the cell depends upon the concentrations of all the participating ions as well as upon the pressure of the Cl_2 gas. The effect can be correlated qualitatively, with the effect of changing concentrations upon shifting an equilibrium. Just as equilibrium for the reaction

$$2\ Fe^{++} + Cl_2 = 2\ Fe^{+++} + 2\ Cl^-$$

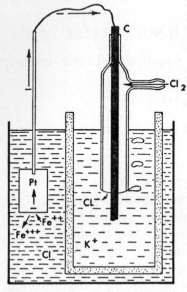

would be driven to the right by increasing the concentration of Fe^{++} or the concentration or pressure of Cl_2 gas, or by decreasing the concentration of Fe^{+++} or of Cl^-, so the driving force and hence the e.m.f. of the reaction when not at equilibrium would be increased by the same changes in concentration.

Fig. 2. Electric cell utilizing the reaction, $2\ Fe^{++} + Cl_2 = 2\ Fe^{+++} + 2\ Cl^-$.

21. The quantitative effect of changing concentration is given approximately by the formula $\Delta E = \dfrac{0.059}{n} \log_{10} \dfrac{C_1}{C_2}$, where ΔE is the change in e.m.f. produced by changing the concentration of the ion from C_1 to C_2. The charge of the ion is n. A cell made by having 2 zinc electrodes dipping respectively into 0.01 and 0.001 molal Zn^{++} solutions would have an e.m.f. of $\Delta E = \dfrac{0.059}{2} \log \dfrac{0.01}{0.001}$ = 0.0295 volts. The cell discussed in the preceding paragraph has an e.m.f. of 1.107 volts for molal concentrations of Zn^{++} and Cu^{++}. Changing the concentration of Zn^{++} to 0.001 molal would increase this e.m.f. to

$$1.107 + \frac{0.059}{2} \log \frac{1}{0.001} = 1.107 + 0.089 = 1.196 \text{ volts.}$$

22. The hydrogen electrode can be used to measure the hydrogen ion concentration of a solution. This consists of a small plate of platinum, made rough by depositing fine "platinum black" by electrolysis, and dipping partly into the solution and projecting above into an atmosphere of hydrogen. The gas dissolves sufficiently in the platinum to be capable of the reaction, $\frac{1}{2} H_2 = H^+ + e^-$, and set up a definite e.m.f. If two such electrodes were used, one dipping into 1 M-H^+, the other into H^+ of unknown concentration, the e.m.f. between the two electrodes could be used to calculate C_2 in

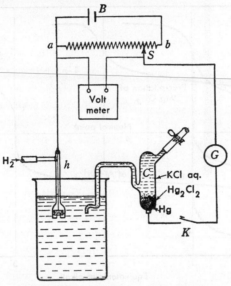

Fig. 3. Hydrogen electrode apparatus.

the above formula. It is more convenient, actually, to use a standard calomel electrode, mercury, covered with Hg_2Cl_2 in 1 M-KCl, in place of the known hydrogen electrode, since we already know the relation between these two. The apparatus is illustrated in Fig. 3. Figure 4 shows several curve types resulting from following the hydrogen ion concentration, plotted as pH (cf. Chapter XIII, Table 2) against equivalents of alkali added. Such curves throw much light on the processes taking place. HCl, being a strong acid, keeps the solution at high acidity as long as any of it is present. The concentration of H ion drops only one power of ten when the acid is nine-tenths neutralized, two powers of ten when it is 0.99 neutralized, etc. There is a sudden rise in pH through the neutral point to strong alkalinity. Acetic acid is a moderately weak acid and hence the curve begins for a 0.1 molal solution at H ion concentration of 0.0013. As neutralization proceeds the accumulating acetate ion causes a rapid decrease in acidity, the H ion concentration becoming 1.8×10^{-5} when it is half neutralized, that is $(Ac^-) = (HAc)$. The steep portion of the curve extends through a much smaller range than was the case for hydrochloric acid. This illustrates clearly why there is a much narrower choice of

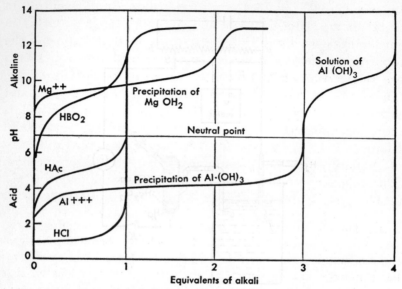

Fig. 4. Neutralization followed by means of a hydrogen electrode.

indicators for this titration than for the other and that the best results would be obtained for an indicator changing in the neighborhood of $pH = 9$. Boric acid is a very weak acid and can be neutralized only in a rather alkaline solution. Furthermore, the steepness of the curve at the end of the titration is not very great and even though an indicator were carefully chosen the color change could not be sharp. The precipitation of $Mg(OH)_2$ from Mg^{++} requires a rather alkaline solution and is practically complete on addition of two equivalents of alkali. To precipitate $Al(OH)_3$, of course, requires three equivalents of alkali, but on account of the great insolubility of this substance it takes place in acid solution. The beginning of the curve shows an acidity due to the hydrolysis of Al^{+++}. Aluminum hydroxide dissolves in approximately one equivalent of alkali showing that it acts as a monobasic acid and that the principal ion present in the solution is AlO_2^- or $H_2AlO_3^-$.

23. Ionization of water from e.m.f. of hydrogen electrode in alkaline solution. The e.m.f. of a cell with two hydrogen electrodes, one in acid of known concentration, the other in alkali of known concentration, the two solutions separated by one of KCl, enables one to calculate the concentration of H^+ in the latter solution, and the product $(H^+)(OH^-)$ in this solution is, by aid of the formula in paragraph 21, the ionization constant of water. In practice, the measurements are made somewhat differently to avoid potentials at the boundaries of the solutions, but the procedure does not differ from the above in principle. This e.m.f. method is more accurate than the conductivity method outlined in Chapter VIII, paragraph 20, because of the great difficulty of preparing absolutely pure water for the latter method. The following values of K_w have been obtained: $0°$ C., 0.114×10^{-14}; $18°$ C., 0.58×10^{-14}; $25°$ C., 1.005×10^{-14}.

24. The electromotive force of a battery is a measure of the tendency of the reaction to take place, of the **chemical affinity** of the reaction, a term much used in the development of chemistry, but also much abused, for it has often been used very loosely. It is only in comparatively recent years that it has been given an exact

TABLE 2

Reaction	ΔH	ΔF
$\frac{1}{2} H_2 + \frac{1}{2} Cl_2 (g) = H^+ + Cl^-$	$- 39,940$	$- 31,370$
$H^+ + OH^- = H_2O$	$- 13,330$	$- 19,120$
$Zn + 2 H^+ = Zn^{++} + H_2$	$- 36,720$	$- 34,980$
$Ca^{++} + CO_3^{--} = CaCO_3$	$+ 2,780$	$- 10,920$
$Pb + Cl_2 (g) = PbCl_2$	$- 85,390$	$- 75,050$
$Fe^{+++} + Ag = Ag^+ + Fe^{++}$	$+ 14,300$	$+ 1,220$

definition. On this account it is desirable to substitute the term **free energy** for affinity. The electromotive force of the copper-zinc cell when normal solutions of copper and zinc sulfates are used is about 1.09 volts. The free energy of the reaction at these concentrations is the work it can do, which would be $1.09 \times 2 \times 96,540$ volt-coulombs, or joules, per mole of reacting substances.

Table 2 shown on page 263 illustrates the degree of correspondence between free energies, ΔF, and heats of reaction, ΔH.

25. Cleaning Silver. The reaction between zinc and silver ion may be utilized in cleaning the tarnish from silverware. The tarnish consists of silver sulfide, Ag_2S, and though this gives but a small concentration of silver ion, the free energy of the reaction is still sufficient for it to take place quite readily. If, therefore, a piece of zinc (aluminum will also serve) is placed in electrical contact with a piece of tarnished silver, both dipping into water containing a little salt to render it conducting, and hot to increase the speed of reaction, the following reaction takes place over the surface of the silver:

$$Ag_2S + 2\,e^- = 2\,Ag + S^{--},$$

the electrons being furnished by the zinc. The sulfide ion liberated would, of course, undergo hydrolysis. The silver is thus restored instead of being rubbed off as in ordinary polishing.

26. If a solution containing the ions of two metals is electrolyzed, it is possible to reduce at the cathode, first the ion of the nobler metal, and afterwards that of the baser metal, by proper regulation of the electromotive force. It is possible thus to make an **electrolytic separation** of different metals, which is to be preferred, in many cases, to the ordinary methods of separation based upon the precipitation of insoluble compounds. The metal is deposited upon a weighed platinum cathode, then washed, first with water, then with methyl alcohol, or with ethyl alcohol followed by ether, dried and reweighed.

27. Electrolytic Refining. An impure metal can often be refined very cheaply by making it the anode in a solution of one of its own salts and transferring it to a cathode of pure metal. Any nobler metals present in the anode remain behind unoxidized as a "sludge" in a bag around the anode, while any particles of baser metals coming to the surface as the

anode dissolves go into solution as ions but are not deposited
at the cathode since there are enough ions of the metal
being refined to unite with
the electrons coming to the
cathode. The diagram in Fig.
5 illustrates this process for
copper supposed to contain
the nobler silver and the baser
zinc. The silver remains in
the anode sludge, the zinc remains in solution, and pure
copper deposits at the cathode. The e.m.f. is practically
the same at the two electrodes,
so that only a very low voltage is necessary, and hence the
energy cost is low. High purity
is particularly important for

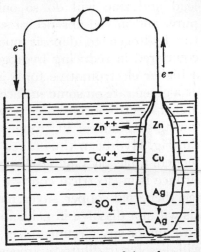

Fig. 5.   Electrolytic refining of copper.

copper to be used for electric wiring since certain impurities
greatly increase its resistance.

28. The Solution of Metals in Water and Acids. When a
metal dissolves in water, in alkali, or in dilute acids the
substance reduced is usually hydrogen ion. Accordingly, it
is desirable to introduce H^+ and H_2 into the table previously
given. In attempting to do this we find an apparent discrepancy in the reactions of the metals with hydrogen ion,
for iron will dissolve in dilute hydrogen ion, whereas zinc,
if very pure, and especially if wet with mercury, will not.
We find, however, that this is due to the difficulty which
hydrogen has in depositing on a surface of pure zinc or
mercury, for if a piece of platinum is dipped into the acid
and brought into contact with the zinc, we find that the
latter dissolves quite readily. The hydrogen is then deposited
on the platinum, the electrons left behind when zinc is converted to zinc ion traveling through the metals to the platinum, where they neutralize the hydrogen ions, changing
them into hydrogen gas. If we test the solubility of the

various metals in dilute acids in this way, we find that all those to the left of copper in the table will dissolve, although lead and zinc will do so only with great difficulty, when pure, and in the absence of some more favorable surface for the hydrogen to deposit upon. The same difficulty is encountered in reducing hydrogen ion at certain cathodes, for a higher electromotive force is required to deposit hydrogen at a given rate on some surfaces than on others. A successively higher electromotive force is required with cathodes of the following substances: Pt (rough), Pt (smooth), Ag, Cu, Sn, Pb, Zn, Hg. Hydrogen thus takes the place given in the more extended table on page 269, provided that a rough platinum surface is in electrical contact with the metal dissolving. We see, then, that copper, silver, mercury, and the other noble metals will not dissolve in acids like dilute hydrochloric and sulfuric under any circumstances, while lead and the baser metals will dissolve in dilute hydrogen ion, provided that platinum is in contact with the metal, but that lead and zinc, or other base metals if amalgamated with mercury, may dissolve very slowly, or practically not at all. When impure zinc is used, the particles of foreign substances, like iron and carbon, furnish nuclei upon which the hydrogen can deposit with more ease, hence such zinc will dissolve at a reasonable rate.

29. As we approach the top of the table, where the metals become baser, and better reducing agents, the hydrogen ion does not need to be so concentrated in order to act upon the metal, and even the extremely dilute hydrogen ion of water is able to oxidize and dissolve metals like calcium and sodium.

Aluminum dissolves easily in dilute hydrogen ion, the reaction being

$$Al + 3\,H^+ = Al^{+++} + \tfrac{3}{2}\,H_2.$$

If hydroxide ion is used instead of hydrogen ion, although the decrease in the concentration of the latter would tend, by itself, to stop the solution of the aluminum, at the same time the concentration of aluminum ion is decreased very greatly on account of the formation of the aluminate ion, a fact which aids the reaction, and compensates for the reduction in the hydrogen ion concentration. Hence aluminum will dissolve in alkali as well as in acid. The same is true of zinc. The equation for the former is

$$Al + OH^- + H_2O = AlO_2^- + \tfrac{3}{2} H_2.$$

30. Solution of Noble Metals. For the metals to the right of hydrogen in the table a stronger oxidizing agent than hydrogen ion is necessary. This is found, for some, in nitric acid, whose oxidizing action is due to the reduction of nitrogen rather than of hydrogen. Copper, silver, and mercury can accordingly be dissolved in nitric acid. A typical reaction is the following:

$$3\,Cu + 2\,NO_3^- + 8\,H^+ = 3\,Cu^{++} + 2\,NO + 4\,H_2O.$$

Sulfuric acid, if hot and concentrated, can oxidize copper, silver, and mercury, its sulfur being reduced to SO_2.

31. When we come to the noblest metals, like gold and platinum, even the oxidizing power of nitric acid becomes insufficient. Instead, however, of seeking a stronger oxidizing agent, another principle is invoked. The following reaction will not take place with nitric acid alone:

$$3\,Pt + 4\,NO_3^- + 16\,H^+ = 3\,Pt^{++++} + 4\,NO + 8\,H_2O.$$

Platinic ion, however, is prone to form a complex acid with hydrochloric acid, H_2PtCl_6, chloroplatinic acid (cf. Chapter XIII, paragraph 20), and hence, if a mixture of hydrochloric and nitric acids, known as "aqua regia," is used instead of the nitric acid alone, the platinic ion, one of the products of the oxidation, is used up sufficiently to enable the reaction to proceed. It is not true, as is often erroneously stated, that the chlorine liberated by the aqua regia ($4\,H^+ + NO_3^- + 3\,Cl^- = Cl_2 + NOCl + 2\,H_2O$) is a stronger oxidizing agent than the nitric acid, for if this were the case chloride ion would not be oxidized by nitric acid. Chlorine is, however, a more rapid oxidizing agent, and the effectiveness of the aqua regia is doubtless due to this fact as well as to the formation of the complex chloroplatinic acid. The action of aqua regia on gold is quite analogous to that on platinum. In this case the complex chloroauric acid, $HAuCl_4$, is formed.

32. Cyanide ion, CN^-, forms such a firm complex with both aurous and auric ions that when it is present the oxygen of the air is sufficient to oxidize gold; the reaction is

$$2 Au + \tfrac{1}{2} O_2 + H_2O + 4 CN^- = 2 Au(CN)_2^- + 2 OH^-.$$

This reaction is used in the "cyanide process" for the extraction of gold from its ores.

33. General Table of Oxidizing and Reducing Agents. We may consider the oxidizing and reducing powers involved in changes other than those between the metals and their ions just considered. We find, for example, that chlorine will liberate bromine from bromide ion, and that bromine will liberate iodine from iodide ion. Accordingly, we may conclude that chlorine will liberate iodine from iodine ion. This information may be tabulated in the manner used previously for the metals, as follows:

Weak	Oxidizing Agents	Strong
I_2	Br_2	Cl_2
I^-	Br^-	Cl^-
Strong	Reducing Agents	Weak

By the aid of appropriate experiments we may find the place of other common substances in such a table, and also combine it with the table previously given to compose Table 3.

34. Effect of Concentration. It should be borne in mind that such an arrangement is not altogether rigid, but that it is affected by the concentrations of the reacting substances. According to the table, for example, one might infer that the following reaction would occur:

$$Ag^+ + I^- = Ag + \tfrac{1}{2} I_2.$$

This would undoubtedly take place if Ag^+ and I^- could act upon each other at ordinary concentrations without precipitating insoluble AgI. The same applies to the action of H_2S on Ag^+.

35. The hydrogen ion concentration affects the equilibrium in many cases. For example, the reaction

$$SO_2 + I_2 + 2\,H_2O = SO_4^{--} + 2\,I^- + 4\,H^+.$$

proceeds readily in dilute solution. It will be seen, however, that by diminishing the amount of water present and increasing the relative amount of acid the equilibrium is shifted in favor of those substances on the left, and, as a matter of

TABLE 3

Oxidizing-Reducing Couples[1] Acid Solutions

	Oxidation, electrons lost ⟶	Electrode potential	
Strong	$K = K^+ + e^-$	2.92	**Weak**
	$Ca = Ca^{++} + 2\,e^-$	2.87	
	$Mg = Mg^{++} + 2\,e^-$	2.34	
	$Al = Al^{+++} + 3\,e^-$	1.67	
	$Zn = Zn^{++} + 2\,e^-$	0.76	
	$Fe = Fe^{++} + 2\,e^-$	0.44	
	$Sn = Sn^{++} + 2\,e^-$	0.14	
	$Pb = Pb^{++} + 2\,e^-$	0.13	
	H_2 (on Pt) $= 2\,H^+ + 2\,e^-$	0.00	
Reducing Agents	$H_2S = S + 2\,H^+ + 2\,e^-$	− 0.14	**Oxidizing Agents**
	$Sn^{++} = Sn^{++++} + 2\,e^-$	− 0.15	
	$Cu = Cu^{++} + 2\,e^-$	− 0.34	
	$2\,I^- = I_2 + 2\,e^-$	− 0.53	
	$Fe^{++} = Fe^{+++} + e^-$	− 0.77	
	$Ag = Ag^+ + e^-$	− 0.80	
	$2\,Hg = Hg_2^{++} + 2\,e^-$	− 0.80	
	$2\,Br^- = Br_2$ (aq.) $+ 2\,e^-$	− 1.09	
	$\frac{1}{2}\,I_2 + 3\,H_2O = IO_3^- + 6\,H^+ + 5\,e^-$	− 1.20	
	$2\,H_2O = O_2 + 4\,H^+ + 4\,e^-$	− 1.23	
	$2\,H_2O + Mn^{++} = MnO_2 + 4\,H^+ + 2\,e^-$	− 1.28	
	$2\,Cl^- = Cl_2 + 2\,e^-$	− 1.36	
	$2\,Cr^{+++} + 7\,H_2O = Cr_2O_7^{--} + 14\,H^+ + 6\,e^-$	− 1.36	
Weak	$2\,H_2O + Pb^{++} = PbO_2 + 4\,H^+ + 2\,e^-$	− 1.46	**Strong**
	$4\,H_2O + Mn^{++} = MnO_4^- + 8\,H^+ + 5\,e^-$	− 1.52	

Reduction, electrons gained
⟵

[1] This table has been expanded into an extensive table of Standard Oxidation-Reduction Potentials for half-reactions in the *Reference Book of Inorganic Chemistry* by Latimer and Hildebrand. The Macmillan Company, 1940.

fact, concentrated sulfuric acid readily liberates iodine from solid iodides. Similarly, the following reaction accords with the positions in the table of the substances involved:

$$Cr_2O_7^{--} + 6\ Cl^- + 14\ H^+ = 2\ Cr^{+++} + 3\ Cl_2 + 7\ H_2O,$$

and in concentrated acid the reaction proceeds in this way. The large amount of H^+ used up, however, indicates that the equilibrium would be enormously affected by changing its concentration. In fact the reaction proceeds in the other direction in alkaline solution, the chromium being oxidized and the chlorine reduced, as shown by the equation:

$$2\ CrO_2^- + 3\ ClO^- + 2\ OH^- = 3\ Cl^- + 2\ CrO_4^{--} + H_2O.$$

Although this is apparently very different from the preceding equation, it involves essentially the same oxidation and reduction steps. On account of the great effect on many of these reactions of varying the concentration of the ions of water, a separate table, Table 4, is given for reagents which act in alkaline solution.

TABLE 4

Oxidizing-Reducing Couples Basic Solutions

Oxidation $\longrightarrow$	Electrode potential
$Ca + 2\ OH^- = Ca(OH)_2 + 2\ e^-$	3.02
$Mg + 2\ OH^- = Mg(OH)_2 + 2\ e^-$	2.67
$Al + 4\ OH^- = AlO_2^- + 2\ H_2O + 3\ e^-$	2.35
$Zn + 4\ OH^- = HZnO_2^- + H_2O + 2\ e^-$	1.22
$HSnO_2^- + H_2O + 3\ OH^- = Sn(OH)_6^{--} + 2\ e^-$	0.96
$SO_3^{--} + 2\ OH^- = SO_4^{--} + H_2O + 2\ e^-$	0.90
$Fe + 2\ OH^- = Fe(OH)_2 + 2\ e^-$	0.88
$H_2 + 2\ OH^- = 2\ H_2O + 2\ e^-$	0.83
$AsO_2^- + 4\ OH^- = AsO_4^{---} + 2\ H_2O + 2\ e^-$	0.71
$Fe(OH)_2 + OH^- = Fe(OH)_3 + e^-$	0.56
$S^{--} = S + 2\ e^-$	0.51
$CrO_2^- + 4\ OH^- = CrO_4^{--} + 2\ H_2O + 3\ e^-$	0.12
$Hg + 2\ OH^- = HgO + H_2O + e^-$	− 0.10
$I^- + 6\ OH^- = IO_3^- + 3\ H_2O + 6\ e^-$	− 0.26
$4\ OH^- = O_2 + 2\ H_2O + 4\ e^-$	− 0.40
$Ni(OH)_2 + 2\ OH^- = NiO_2 + 2\ H_2O + 2\ e^-$	− 0.49
$3\ OH^- = HO_2^- + H_2O + 2\ e^-$	− 0.87
$Cl^- + 2\ OH^- = ClO^- + H_2O + 2\ e^-$	− 0.94
$\longleftarrow$ Reduction	

Left margin labels: Strong / Reducing Agents / Weak

Right margin labels: Weak / Oxidizing Agents / Strong

36. Oxidizing Power and Speed of Oxidation. There are some substances, like hydrogen peroxide, H_2O_2, which would have great oxidizing power if they could react rapidly enough. It is important to distinguish between an oxidizing agent that is "strong" because it is rapid, and one which is strong but slow. Thus iodine will often react more rapidly than chlorine, and hence produce more oxidation in a given time. Its true oxidizing power, however, is much less, as shown by the fact that it will not oxidize ferrous ion completely, whereas chlorine will. The oxygen acids, like nitric and sulfuric acids, are not rapid oxidizing agents. This seems to be connected with the fact that they are highly ionized. Nitrous acid, which is not a stronger oxidizing agent in the true sense of the term, is nevertheless a much more rapid oxidizing agent, and is, at the same time, much less dissociated. As we compare the oxygen acids of chlorine, we find that while their reactivity as oxidizing agents decreases in going from HClO to $HClO_3$, their strength as acids increases greatly. In a reaction such as the following:

$$ClO_3^- + S + H_2O = Cl^- + SO_4^{--} + 2\,H^+,$$

although hydrogen ion appears, whence we might expect it to be favored by decreasing the concentration of hydrogen ion, as a matter of fact it will not take place unless the solution is strongly acid. We may infer from this that ClO_3^- is very unreactive, and a large amount of H^+ must be present in order to give a certain amount of the undissociated strong acid, $HClO_3$, which is reactive. With HClO, however, reduction to Cl^- will take place rapidly without adding H^+, because HClO is such a weak acid that most of it is undissociated even in neutral solution. The difference between nitrous and nitric acids may be explained similarly; the latter, being a strong acid, must be rather concentrated in order to give enough undissociated molecules of HNO_3 to react rapidly. In general, when substances react slowly their true place in the table may not be apparent from their ordinary reactions, and the place assigned may not correspond to a reversible reaction.

37. Substances That Can Act Both as Oxidizing and Reducing Agents. Certain substances appear at two places in the table, corresponding to their power to act either as oxidizing or reducing agents. The way in which they will react depends, of course, upon the nature of the substances with which they are mixed. Thus ferrous ion can be reduced to iron by the action of a very powerful reducing agent like calcium, or it can be oxidized to ferric ion by the action of a strong oxidizing agent like chlorine. Iodine may be reduced to iodide or oxidized to iodate according, respectively, as it reacts with a reducing agent stronger than iodine or an oxidizing agent stronger than iodate ion. Hydrogen peroxide, not shown in the table because of the irreversibility and slowness of its reactions, may act as an oxidizing agent with some substances themselves capable of oxidation. In these cases the oyxgen in the hydrogen peroxide is reduced, as illustrated by the reaction,

$$2 H^+ + H_2O_2 + 2 Fe^{++} = 2 Fe^{+++} + 2 H_2O.$$

On the other hand, in the presence of a sufficiently strong oxidizing agent, the oxygen in the peroxide may be oxidized to free oxygen, as illustrated by the reaction,

$$2 MnO_4^- + 5 H_2O_2 + 6 H^+ = 2 Mn^{++} + 5 O_2 + 8 H_2O.$$

38. The Solution of Insoluble Sulfides. In Chapter XIII it was shown how certain metallic sulfides could be separated by controlling the hydrogen ion concentration, and it was pointed out that there is a group of sulfides so insoluble in water that even moderately concentrated hydrochloric or sulfuric acids will not sufficiently remove the sulfide ion, S^{--}, to make the metallic ion concentration large. To dissolve such sulfides it is necessary to remove the sulfide ion more completely. This is possible by the use of a strong oxidizing agent, usually nitric acid, which changes the S^{--} completely into S or even SO_4^{--}. Moderately concentrated hot nitric acid, accordingly, will dissolve CuS, Bi_2S_3, PbS, and Ag_2S.

The solubility of mercuric sulfide is so extremely low, however, that nitric acid is practically without effect. To dissolve it aqua regia is necessary, the effectiveness of which depends upon the greater speed of reaction of chlorine as compared with nitric acid, and also upon the presence of the chloride ion, which unites with the mercuric ion to form undissociated mercuric chloride. The aqua regia thus attacks both constituents of the mercuric sulfide instead of only one.

39. Lead Storage Battery. Other reactions besides the simple change between metals and their ions can be utilized in generating an electric current. A very important one is that occurring in the lead storage battery. The reaction utilized is the following:

$$Pb + PbO_2 + 4\,H^+ + 2\,SO_4^{--} = 2\,PbSO_4 + 2\,H_2O.$$

It is carried out so that the oxidation of the lead to lead sulfate,

$$Pb + SO_4^{--} = PbSO_4 + 2\,e^-,$$

takes place at one electrode and the reduction of lead dioxide to lead sulfate,

$$PbO_2 + 4\,H^+ + SO_4^{--} + 2\,e^- = PbSO_4 + 2\,H_2O,$$

takes place at the other electrode. The electrons travel through the metallic part of the circuit from one electrode to the other. To charge the cell the reaction is reversed by sending a current through the cell in the opposite direction. From the equations it may be seen that the more concentrated is the acid the more is the equilibrium shifted in favor of $PbSO_4$, hence the larger the free energy of the reaction and the electromotive force of the cell. There are other considerations, however, which argue against too concentrated an acid.

40. The nickel-iron storage battery utilizes the following reaction, taking place in alkaline solution:

$$NiO_2 + 2 H_2O + Fe = Ni(OH)_2 + Fe(OH)_2.$$

The electrode reactions are

$$NiO_2 + 2 H_2O + 2 e^- = Ni(OH)_2 + 2 OH^-,$$

and

$$Fe + 2 OH^- = Fe(OH)_2 + 2 e^-.$$

41. Electrode Designations. Confusion often arises in the use of the terms cathode, anode, and positive and negative, as applied to an electrode. Their meaning and proper use may be explained as follows.

Cathode and anode refer to processes which occur as current flows and depend on the direction of the current. The cathode is the electrode through which electrons enter the solution causing reduction. Cations are positive ions which migrate to the cathode and may there be reduced, as illustrated by $2 H^+ + 2 e^- = H_2$, $Cu^{++} + 2 e^- = Cu$, and $Fe^{+++} + e^- = Fe^{++}$. **The anode is, vice versa, the electrode through which electrons are withdrawn, causing oxidation,** as illustrated by $Cu = Cu^{++} + 2 e^-$, $Cl^- = Cl_2 + 2 e^-$, $4 OH^- = 2 H_2O + O_2 + 4 e^-$.

42. These definitions hold regardless of whether the processes are occurring spontaneously, as in a battery, or are being brought about by a stronger external e.m.f. The application of the terms to the copper-zinc cell, described in paragraph 17, on discharging through an external resistance is as follows:

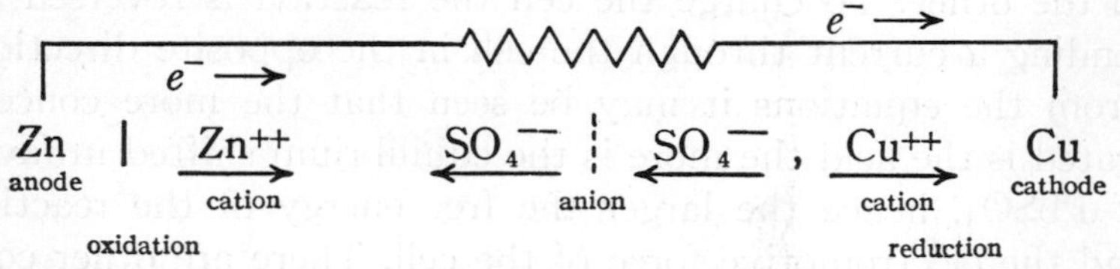

$$
\begin{array}{cccccc}
 & & & e^- \longrightarrow & & \\
\hline
\quad e^- \longrightarrow & & \mathord{\sim\!\!\sim\!\!\sim\!\!\sim} & & & \\
Zn & | & Zn^{++} & SO_4^{--} \;\vdots\; SO_4^{--}, & Cu^{++} & Cu \\
\text{anode} & & \xrightarrow{\text{cation}} & \xleftarrow{\text{anion}} & \xrightarrow{\text{cation}} & \text{cathode} \\
 & & \text{oxidation} & & \text{reduction} &
\end{array}
$$

Suppose, however, that electrons are forced "uphill" in the other direction by a cell such as the lead storage battery with a higher e.m.f. The anode and cathode are then reversed, as follows:

$$\overset{\text{cathode}}{\underset{\text{reducing agent}}{\text{Zn}}} \mid \overset{\text{cation}}{\underset{\longleftarrow}{\text{Zn}^{++}}}, \quad \overset{\text{anion}}{\underset{\longrightarrow}{\text{SO}_4^{--}}} \vdots \overset{\text{anion}}{\underset{\longrightarrow}{\text{SO}_4^{--}}}, \quad \overset{\text{cation}}{\underset{\underset{\text{oxidizing agent}}{\longleftarrow}}{\text{Cu}^{++}}} \mid \overset{\text{anode}}{\text{Cu}}$$

reduction   oxidation

$$\uparrow e^- \qquad\qquad\qquad\qquad\qquad\qquad\qquad\qquad\qquad \downarrow e^-$$

$$\underset{\substack{\text{reducing}\\\text{agent}}}{\text{Pb}} \mid \text{PbSO}_4, \qquad \overset{\text{cation}}{\underset{\longrightarrow}{\text{H}^+}}, \quad \overset{\text{anion}}{\underset{\longleftarrow}{\text{SO}_4^{--}}} \quad \underset{\substack{\text{oxidizing}\\\text{agent}}}{\begin{matrix}\text{PbSO}_4 \mid \\ \text{PbO}_2\end{matrix}} \underset{\text{cathode}}{\text{Pb}}$$

oxidation   reduction

43. The sign of an electrode should always refer to potential difference, not to the direction of the current. The potential of a cell is actually measured by balancing it against a known potential in the reverse direction with no current flowing, as illustrated in Fig. 2. In the case just discussed, electrons are always at a higher negative potential on the zinc than on the copper, regardless of whether they are flowing spontaneously through the wire "downhill" from zinc to copper or forced "uphill" by the greater e.m.f. of the lead storage battery.

The chief cause of difficulty arises from the convention regarding the sign of a single electrode couple. When a piece of zinc is dipped into a solution containing Zn^{++}, a few zinc atoms go into solution as ions, leaving their electrons behind in the metal. When the potential of the electrons becomes sufficient, no more ions can escape and we have a fixed difference of potential between the zinc and the solution, the former negative, the latter positive, as illustrated in Fig. 1. The question then arises, shall we designate this potential difference as positive or negative? The answer has to be quite arbitrary, since all we are observing is a difference. It will depend on whether we are standing in imagination on the zinc electrode or swimming in the solution. In the one case we would call it negative, in the other positive. It is as if John Doe had borrowed a dollar from Richard Roe, is it a credit or a debit? That depends on whether you are Mr. Doe or Mr. Roe.

It is, perhaps, unfortunate that the ordinary convention is to give the sign as that of the solution, for most of us stay outside the cell and have to decide which electrode to connect to the rest of the circuit, but the student who understands the convention and the chemical processes determining where the electrons are going to be liberated from the solution should be able to think out each case correctly.

44. One should not allow himself to be confused further by the engineering practice of referring to electric currents in wires as positive currents. Of course, there can be no positive current flowing in a wire, the real current consists of electrons flowing in the reverse direction. It is otherwise in a conducting solution, for the current there is carried in part by positive ions flowing in one direction and negative ions flowing in the reverse direction, in the ratio of their speeds of migration, as indicated in Fig. 1.

Exercises

1. In the following reactions state which elements are oxidized and which are reduced:

$$2\,Ag^+ + Zn = 2\,Ag + Zn^{++};$$
$$Ag^+ + Cl^- = AgCl;$$
$$Zn + OH^- + H_2O = HZnO_2^- + H_2;$$
$$2\,Hg^+ + H_2S = HgS + Hg + 2\,H^+;$$
$$2\,HgCl_2 + Sn^{++} = Hg_2Cl_2 + Sn^{++++} + 2\,Cl^-.$$

2. Write equations for the following reactions: zinc plus chlorine to give zinc ion plus chloride ion; stannous ion plus bromine to give stannic ion plus bromide ion; ferric ion plus stannous ion to give ferrous ion plus stannic ion; hydrogen sulfide plus iodine to give sulfur plus hydrogen ion plus iodide ion; cupric ion plus iodide ion to give cuprous iodide (ppt.) plus iodine.

3. Write equations for the reactions between: (a) cupric oxide and hydrogen; (b) cupric oxide and hydrogen ion; (c) cuprous oxide and oxygen; (d) magnesium and hydrogen ion; (e) cupric ion and zinc to give copper; (f) copper and cupric ion; (g) silver ion and zinc. State in each case which elements are oxidized and which are reduced.

4. Complete the following incomplete equations:

(a) $H^+ + NO_3^- + Ag = Ag^+ + NO;$

(b) $MnO_4^- + H_2S = Mn^{++} + S$;

(c) $H^+ + NO_3^- + CuS = Cu^{++} + SO_4^{--} + NO$;

(d) $H^+ + NO_3^- + Zn = Zn^{++} + NH_4^+$;

(e) $Bi(OH)_3 + HSnO_2^- = Bi +$;

(f) $HAuCl_4 + Fe^{++} = Au +$;

(g) $S_2O_3^{--} + I_2 = S_4O_6^{--} +$;

(h) $S_2O_3^{--} + Cl_2 = SO_4^{--} +$;

(i) $ClO^- + AsO_2^- = AsO_3^- +$.

5. What is meant by "noble" metals and "base" metals?

6. From the metals given in the table on page 269, construct the battery that would give the greatest electromotive force.

7. Explain how contact with zinc protects iron from corrosion.

8. How can you tell whether a metal will dissolve in any of the following reagents: water, hydrochloric acid, nitric acid, sulfuric acid, sodium hydroxide?

9. How is the oxidizing power of H^+ affected by its concentration?

10. Explain the cleaning of silver by zinc or by aluminum.

11. How would you prepare each of the following:
(a) Br^- from Br_2; (b) HCl gas from Cl_2; (c) I_2 from NaI; (d) $PbCrO_4$ from Pb and $CrCl_3$; (e) Fe from $FeCl_3$; (f) $Fe(OH)_2$ from Fe; (g) Fe_2O_3 from $FeSO_4$; (h) $Mn(OH)_2$ from MnO_4^-; (i) Hg_2Cl_2 from $HgCl_2$; (j) Hg from $HgCl_2$?

12. What new substances, if any, would be found and in what amounts upon bringing together the following substances? All ions are in water solution:

    (a) Ag^+ (1 mole), Cu (1 mole) and Zn (1 mole);

    (b) Ca (1 mole) and Cl^- (1 mole);

    (c) Cl_2 (1 mole), Br^- (2 moles) and I^- (2 moles);

    (d) Fe (3 moles), Fe^{+++} (1 mole) and Zn^{++} (2 moles);

    (e) Zn (1 mole), I_2 (2 moles) and Ag (1 mole).

13. What substance will be present and, if in solution, at what approximate concentrations, in the following cases?

    (a) 1 mole of $FeCl_3$, 4 moles of SO_2 and 10 moles of HCl are mixed in 10 liters of water.

    (b) 1 mole of H_2S is passed into 2 liters of a solution containing 0.5 mole of $CuCl_2$ and 1 mole of HCl.

    (c) 0.2 mole of Cl_2 is passed into 1 liter of a solution containing 0.5 mole of KI and 0.5 mole of KBr.

14. From your knowledge of the oxidation states which the determining elements can assume, state which of the following substances are capable of acting as oxidizing agents, which as reducing agents (or both) and give the substance which each will probably form when so acting: (a) Cl^-, (b) H_2S, (c) SO_2, (d) H_2SO_4, (e) Al^{+++}, (f) H^+, (g) H_2O_2, (h) F_2, (i) F^-, (j) Ag^+, (k) O_2, (l) Hg_2^{++}.

15. Which of the following changes would require (a) an oxidizing agent, (b) a reducing agent, (c) some other type of reagent?

(1) $Sn(OH)_2$ to Sn^{++++}; (4) I_2 to IO_3^-;
(2) $HSnO_3^-$ to Sn^{++++}; (5) H_2S to SO_4^{--}.
(3) ClO^- to Cl^-;

16. A certain metal will dissolve in dilute H_2SO_4. Will it dissolve in a solution of Cu^{++} or not? Explain.

17. Plan an experiment to determine whether Fe^{++} or I^- is the stronger reducing agent. (Fe^{++} on oxidation becomes Fe^{+++} with a change in color.)

18. Plan an experiment to determine whether F^- or Cl^- gives up its electron more readily.

19. State what electron change takes place (a) when metallic calcium dissolves in water, (b) when magnesium burns in air.

20. The following reactions are known to occur as read from left to right:

(a) $2 Fe^{+++} + 2 I^- = 2 Fe^{++} + I_2$;
(b) $2 Br^- + Cl_2 = 2 Cl^- + Br_2$;
(c) $2 Fe^{+++} + Sn^{++} = 2 Fe^{++} + Sn^{++++}$;
(d) $Cl_2 + 2 Fe^{++} = 2 Fe^{+++} + 2 Cl^-$.

What can you conclude *from these data alone* about the occurrence of the following reactions?

(a) $2 I^- + Br_2 = I_2 + 2 Br^-$;
(b) $2 Br^- + 2 Fe^{+++} = 2 Fe^{++} + Br_2$;
(c) $Cl_2 + Sn^{++} = Sn^{++++} + 2 Cl^-$;
(d) $Sn^{++} + I_2 = Sn^{++++} + 2 I^-$. Explain your answer.

21. (a) Sketch the arrangement of a battery in which the reaction between Zn and Cl_2 is used to generate an electric current; (b) From which electrode will the electron stream flow in the wire? (c) How will the e.m.f. of the cell be affected by changing the pressure of Cl_2? (d) How will the e.m.f. be affected by increasing the temperature? Justify your answers.

22. Construct an electric battery to utilize the reaction:

$$14 H^+ + 3 Zn + Cr_2O_7^{--} = 3 Zn^{++} + 2 Cr^{+++} + 7 H_2O,$$

and write the equations for the separate electrode reactions.

23. An electric cell is constructed by placing a zinc electrode in a solution of $ZnSO_4$ and an iron electrode in a solution of $FeSO_4$. The solutions are separated by a porous partition. (a) Write the reaction which takes place when the two electrodes are connected by a copper wire. (b) In which direction will the negative electrons flow through the wire? (c) In which direction will the SO_4^{--} move through the solution?

24. A battery is composed of an electrode of Zn dipping into a solution of $ZnSO_4$ contained in a porous cup. This cup is surrounded by a solution of $Fe_2(SO_4)_3$ and $FeSO_4$, and in the latter is a carbon rod to serve as an electrode. (a) Write the equation for the reaction occurring when the cell discharges; (b) how would the electromotive force change with increasing concentration of (a) $ZnSO_4$, (b) $Fe_2(SO_4)_3$, (c) $FeSO_4$?

25. In the cell $Zn/Zn^{++}/Ag^+/Ag$, what weight of silver will deposit when 0.654 g. Zn dissolves?

26. Which of the following oxidizing agents are stronger in the presence of 0.1 N-H^+ than in the presence of 0.01 N-H^+, which are weaker, and which are unaffected by changing concentration of H^+?

(a) Fe^{+++}, (b) I_2, (c) IO_3^-, (d) MnO_4^-, (e) Ag^+. Justify your answers.

27. An electric current is passed through a solution containing 0.01 M-KBr and 0.01 M-$CuCl_2$, using inert graphite electrodes. Write equations showing what occurs at each electrode.

28. What constituents of an electric cell is it essential to keep out of direct contact with each other?

29. An electric battery is made by immersing an electrode of iron and one of copper oxide in a solution of sodium hydroxide. In the chemical reaction which produces the current, which substance is (a) the oxidizing agent? (b) the reducing agent? (c) Write the equation for the reaction. (d) How would increasing the concentration of the sodium hydroxide affect the electromotive force of the cell? (e) If heat is absorbed by the cell as it generates a current, would a rise in temperature increase or decrease the electromotive force?

30. An electric cell consists of an electrode of silver, coated with Ag_2O, another of metallic aluminum, both dipping into 2 M-NaOH. Write the equations for the separate electrode reactions and for the total cell reaction. How would the e.m.f. be affected by changing to 3 M-NaOH?

31. Explain the changes in the density of the electrolyte and

in the voltage of a lead storage battery that occur as the battery discharges.

32. A cell is constructed with an electrode of zinc dipping into a dilute solution of zinc sulfate at the bottom of which is an electrode of mercury covered with a precipitate of Hg_2SO_4. (*a*) Write the equation for the total reaction occurring as the cell discharges. (*b*) How many grams of zinc ($Zn = 65.4$) would have to dissolve to yield a current of 0.1 ampere for 10 minutes?

33. When an excess of CN^- is added to both sides of the cell

$$Cu \,|\, Cu^{++}, SO_4^{--} \,\vdots\, Zn^{++}, SO_4^{--} \,|\, Zn \,,$$

the direction of the current is reversed. How can you account for this fact?

CHAPTER XVI

THE CONSTITUTION OF THE ATOM

1. The search for the elementary particles constituting matter is as old as science itself. Steadily the size of the supposed ultimate building blocks has decreased until today we speak freely of the structure of the atoms themselves (which were the main elementary units of a generation or two ago). At present only one of the particles in the atom (the nucleus) is supposed to be complex itself and we have reason to believe that we have reliable information even as to its structure. However, it seems certain that the search will continue almost indefinitely even beyond our present advanced stage. It appears probable, though, that as we proceed to more fundamental analyses our present picture of the atoms themselves will be altered little in a practical way, because of our almost complete success in explaining the known chemical properties (i.e., compound formation, etc.). In other words, the one particle in the atom known to be complex, the nucleus, has little effect on the properties of the atom as a whole. This does not detract from the importance of continuing the search, however, for we still have the great cosmological questions to answer: "How was our earth and, in fact, the whole universe made?" "What is the probable future of the universe and in particular the solar system?" "What is the source of the tremendous amount of energy emitted by the sun and other stars?" and numerous other problems. On all of these the properties of the atomic nuclei appear to have immediate bearing, as we shall see briefly later in this chapter. Also, we should remember the well-known fact that very practical results sometimes are obtained from the most fundamental researches in pure science, for example, the uses of X-rays and radium in medicine.

2. The Structure of the Atom. Near the end of the nine-teenth century laboratory electrical technique had developed to a point where it was possible to measure electrical forces easily and to produce rather high energy spark discharges conveniently. Immediately several fundamental discoveries were made. Among these were the following. When an electric discharge is sent through a highly evacuated tube provided with sealed-in electrodes, there is given off from the cathode a characteristic discharge called **cathode rays.** Unlike light, these rays are almost entirely stopped by the glass walls of the tube, producing a fluorescence upon the glass where they strike. A screen of fluorescent material like zinc sulfide, if put into the tube in the path of the rays, shows a brilliant fluorescence, very useful in studying these rays. They are deflected from a straight path by either a magnetic or an electric field, in such a way as to indicate that they consist of streams of negatively charged particles, moving with great velocity, which have been called **electrons.**

3. By measuring the extent of this deflection by both kinds of field, it has been possible to calculate the ratio of the charge on each electron to its mass, and also the speed of the electrons. It is evident that some such calculation should be possible, because any moving body can be deflected from a straight line by a known force to an extent dependent upon its mass and its speed. It obviously takes more force to deflect a swiftly moving bullet than a slowly moving golf ball, and still more force to deflect the heavy shell of a big gun.

The result of these measurements and calculations, carried out by J. J. Thomson, shows that the speed of the electrons ranges from 10,000 to 100,000 miles per second, and it has recently become possible to accelerate electrons nearly to the limiting speed of light, which is 186,000 miles per second. The ratio of the charge to the mass of the electrons is found to be 1850 times the corresponding ratio for a hydrogen ion, which is 96,500 coulombs per gram. Therefore, either the mass of the electrons is less, or the charge is greater than that of a hydrogen ion. Now it has been found that the charge is the same (though opposite in sign), hence we are led to the conclusion that the mass of the electron is $\frac{1}{1850}$ of that of the hydrogen ion, the smallest particle of matter previously known.

The discovery of the electron provided a unit with which atoms may be constructed, and the fact that the nature of the electrons composing the cathode stream is entirely independent of the nature of the cathode used, as well as of the residual gas in the tube, indicates that atoms of all substances contain the same kind of electrons.

4. Isotopes. In addition to the electrons liberated by all substances in a spark discharge, there are produced **positively charged heavy particles** of different masses for each element or compound. For example, if the noble gas, krypton, is placed in the discharge tube, six heavy, singly positively charged particles, six doubly charged, and perhaps even six triply charged will be produced (the relative intensities of the groups with different charges depending on the violence of the discharge and the pressure of the gas). When the masses of the particles are measured in the way described above for the electron they are found to be 78, 80, 82, 83, 84, and 86, the same six appearing in each group and the relative numbers in each of the three groups being exactly the same. The interpretation is that the element, krypton, is a mixture of six different atoms having the different weights given but the same tendency to become positively charged in the discharge (i.e., the same tendency to lose electrons). The relative abundances of the different atoms, called isotopes are determined by direct measurement of the relative numbers in the different charge groups and are found to be:

Kr^{78}, 0.42%; Kr^{80}, 2.45%; Kr^{82}, 11.79%; Kr^{83}, 11.79%; Kr^{84}, 56.85%; Kr^{86}, 16.70%;

giving an average of 83.7 for the weight of the average Kr atom. (This method of determining atomic weights has come to be as accurate as the older method of measuring out a gram-atom of element and weighing it.) Similar experiments on the other elements have shown most of them to be mixtures of two or more isotopes, as shown in Table 1.

We notice that even hydrogen has two isotopes, the ordinary isotope of mass one and a rare one of mass two, called **deuterium** whose symbol is D. In this case the masses differ by two-fold, a larger factor than in any other case, and we are in an excellent position to decide whether the mass of the atom plays a fundamental role in the chemical properties of the atom. Table 3 shows the properties of a series of compounds of the two isotopes of hydrogen. Evidently the mass effect is small even in this case so we conclude that the mass of an atom is not what determines its chemical properties.

5. Ordinary oxygen contains small amounts of the heavier isotopes O^{17} and O^{18}, as shown in Table 2. The mass of the lowest isotope is set as 16.000, as is desirable in the study of the nucleus; the mass of the natural mixture is 16.0044. However, long before isotopes were discovered, chemists adopted 16.000 as the atomic weight of ordinary oxygen. We are thus confronted with two slightly different atomic weight scales, now called the "physical" and the "chemical," related as follows:

	Physical scale	Chemical scale
O^{16} isotope	16.0000	15.9956
Ordinary, mixed oxygen	16.0044	16.0000
Hydrogen, H^1	1.0081	1.0079
Ordinary, mixed hydrogen	1.0083	1.0080

At about the same time that the experiments described above on spark discharges through gases were begun, it was discovered that certain of the elements spontaneously emit radiations, among which are heavy high velocity particles called alpha particles, of double positive charge and atomic weight 4, which we now know to be helium atoms which are lacking two electrons. By virtue of their high energy, it was possible to detect these bodies one at a time and to record their progress through matter until they had lost most of their energy through collision with ordinary atoms. (This

TABLE 1

Stable Isotopes of the Elements

Element	Mass No.	Element	Mass No.	Element	Mass No.	Element	Mass No.	Element	Mass No.	Element	Mass No.
H	1	Sc	45	Br	79	Cd	106	La	139	Hf	176
	2		46		81		108	Ce	136		177
			47	Kr	78		110		138		178
			48		80		111		140		179
He	4		49		82		112		142		180
Li	6		50		83		113	Pr	141	Ta	181
	7	V	51		84		114	Nd	142	W	182
Be	9	Cr	50		86		116		143		183
B	10		52	Rb	85	In	113		144		184
	11		53		87		115		145		186
C	12		54	Sr	84	Sn	112		146	Re	185
	13	Mn	55		86		114		148		187
N	14	Fe	54		87		115	Sm	144	Os	186
	15		56		88		116		147		187
O	16		57	Y	89		117		148		188
	17		58	Zr	90		118		149		189
	18	Co	57		91		119		150		190
F	19		59		92		120		152		192
Ne	20	Ni	58		94		122		154	Ir	191
	21		60		96		124	Eu	151		193
	22		61	Cb	93	Sb	121		153	Pt	192
Na	23		62	Mo	92		123	Gd	155		194
Mg	24		64		94	Te	120		156		195
	25	Cu	63		95		122		157		196
	26		65		96		123		158		198
Al	27	Zn	64		97		124	Tb	159	Au	197
Si	28		66		98		125		160	Hg	196
	29		67		100		126	Dy	161		198
	30		68	Ma	—		128		162		199
P	31		70	Ru	96		130		163		200
S	32	Ga	69		98	I	127		164		201
	33		71		99	Xe	124	Ho	165		202
	34	Ge	70		100		126	Er	166		204
Cl	35		72		101		128		167	Tl	203
	37		73		102		129		168		205
A	36		74		104		130		170	Pb	204
	38		76	Rh	103		131	Tm	169		206
	40	As	75	Pd	102		132	Yb	171	Pb	207
K	39	Se	74		104		134		172		208
	40		76		105		136		173	Bi	209
	41		77		106	Cs	133		174	Th	232
Ca	40		78	Ba	108		130		176	U	235
	42		80		110		132	Lu	175		238
	43		82	Ag	107		134		176		
	44				109		135				
							136				
							137				
							138				

TABLE 2
Relative Abundance of Certain Isotopes

Element	Mass no.	Relative abundance
H	1	99.98
	2	0.02
Li	6	7.9
	7	92.1
B	10	20.6
	11	79.4
O	16	99.76
	17	0.04
	18	0.20
Ne	20	90.00
	21	0.27
	22	9.73
Cl	35	76
	37	24
K	39	93.2
	40	0.012
	41	6.8
Cu	63	68
	65	32
Zn	64	50.9
	66	27.3
	67	3.9
	68	17.4
	70	0.5
Br	79	50.7
	81	49.3

occurs after they have traversed between 2 and 5 cm. of ordinary air, the distance varying, of course, with the energy of the particular alpha particle.) If one fills a glass cylinder

TABLE 3
Comparison of Chemical Properties of the Hydrogen Isotopes

	Hydrogen	Deuterium
Relative ionization potentials of atom (arbitrary unit)	1.000000	1.000270
Heat of dissociation of molecules, H_2, D_2	103,700 calories	105,500 calories

which has a movable bottom with moist air and alternately moves the bottom of the cylinder up and down, one sees lines of water droplets form on the down stroke if there is a small amount of some alpha emitting substance such as the element polonium on the wall of the vessel. This beautiful apparatus, called a "cloud chamber," invented by C. T. R. Wilson, enables one to study the phenomena visually, in an intimate way.

Figure 1 shows two photographs of such tracks, the one on the right containing a track having sharp changes of

Track of a-rays   Track of two
                                   a-rays (enlarged)

Fig. 1

direction such as collisions with heavy bodies in the air would cause. The gas laws have taught us how to calculate the approximate size of the molecules as well as the number in a given volume under any conditions. Consequently, as soon as tracks like the one in Fig. 1 were observed, calculations were made showing that the alpha particles must have hit a heavy body in the air only once in passing through several thousand atoms. This showed immediately that the mass of the air molecules must be concentrated in small regions having only about $\frac{1}{10,000}$, the diameter of the atoms themselves. Also, calculations on the angles through which the alpha particle was deflected showed the mass of the body struck to be the known atomic weight of either oxygen or nitrogen, according to which was involved in the particular collision considered. The startling fact therefore was established that somehow the **mass of the atom was concentrated in a very small part of the total atomic volume. This suggested that the light electrons might be revolving about the heavy, positively charged nucleus in a way similar to that in which the planets revolve around the sun,** which we believe now to be the case.

6. The Quantum Theory. If a beam of high energy electrons is passed through helium gas, the electrons are found to emerge with their energy practically unchanged unless the energy of the electron exceeds a certain minimum value. As the energy of the beam is increased from a value near zero, one finds no slowing of the electrons until a certain value is reached, when many of the electrons lose nearly all of their energy. This experiment shows that the helium atom is incapable of taking energy in amounts smaller than a certain minimum. It is necessary to hit the atom with at least a certain amount of energy before anything happens. Similar experiments with the other atoms have given similar results, the particular minimum energies being different for each element. This concept that atoms can take energy in certain definite amounts only, together with its numerous consequences, is known as the quantum theory.

7. Energy Levels. After the atoms in the above experiment have been struck with high energy electrons, they emit light. (This is the mechanism of the familiar neon sign.) The color of this light is found to be definitely related to the minimum energy required to excite the atom, so we conclude that the atom has emitted this "chunk" of energy as light after having taken it from the electron. By using a gas being bombarded with electrons of a wide range of energies and carefully determining the various wave lengths of the light emitted, it is possible to decide not only what is the smallest amount of energy a given atom will absorb, but what the successively larger amounts are. In this way one is able to say what values the energy of any given atom can have. This set of values, when written in increasing order, is called the **energy level scheme.** Figure 2 represents the scheme for hydrogen, the distance above the bottom line being proportional to the energy values.

8. The problem of correlating the significant facts we have considered above was solved in its first form in 1913, soon after the experiments on alpha particle collisions had shown the mass of the atom to be concentrated in one position. It was postulated that the electrons in the atom move in orbits around the nucleus, held by the positive charge of the nucleus, and that the different energy states correspond to the electrons being moved into orbits farther from the nucleus. The values of the energy states of hydrogen were calculated accurately on this model when the orbits were selected by the rule that only those in which the angular momentum (for circular orbits, the product of the mass of the electron and its velocity and the radius of the orbit) of the system would be an integral multiple of a certain fundamental constant. It was this rule for selecting the orbits which actually occur that was so new and illuminating.

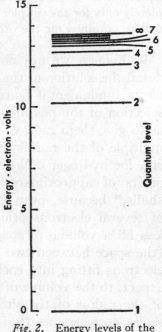

Fig. 2. Energy levels of the hydrogen atom.

The calculation of the energy of an electron rotating in a certain orbit around a nucleus with a given positive charge is quite simple. It is analogous to the calculation of the energy of motion of the earth in its orbit around the sun. Today we have a better idea of the origin of the strange rule which leads to the selection of the particular orbits which occur in atoms but we still find it mysterious and wonderful. The principle involved mainly is that electrons, and in fact all particles, act to varying degrees like light in the way their movements are affected by obstacles in their paths. This point is expressed quantitatively and accurately in a mathematical form which has enabled us to calculate exactly all of the known chemical properties of the hydrogen atom. (The solution of the equations involved is difficult and has been carried through completely only for the simpler atoms, though we are certain the results will be obtained for the others when enough work has been done.)

9. Though we are not in a position here to consider in detail the solution of the problem of atomic structure, certain of its fundamental features will be pointed out. First, the selection of the possible orbits the electrons may fill is such as to give them radii which are approximately some integral multiple of the radius of the innermost orbit (0.506×10^{-8} cm. for hydrogen). We therefore group the electrons filling orbits of approximately the same radius into **"electron shells,"** because, even though plane themselves, the orbits of several electrons oriented in various ways will more or less fill a volume of space of the shape of a spherical shell (the space between two concentric spheres). The number of electrons fitting into each shell is proportional, as we might expect, to the volume of the shell, i.e., it varies as the square of the radius of the shell. Of course the actual size of the shells decreases as the nuclear charge increases and pulls the electrons closer. The number of electrons filling the shell is not decreased, however, because the stronger nuclear attraction enables them to fit more closely, apparently, in just the right way. Since the first shell has two, the next will have 2×2^2 or 8 since its radius is twice that of the first shell, the third has 2×3^2 or 18, the fourth 32, and the fifth 50. These are the only shells involved in the atoms in their ordinary states, though any atom can have one or more of its electrons knocked into higher shells by collision, after which the electrons will fall back into their old position and the energy will be emitted as light. Table 4 gives the electron structures of the atoms.

10. The orbits of the individual electrons in atoms are described by three numbers, called **quantum** numbers. The **principal**

quantum number, n, is the number characteristic of the shell being considered, i.e., $n = 1$ for the first shell, $n = 2$ for the second, etc. The different electron orbits grouped into a single shell are specified in the mathematical treatment by two additional quantum numbers. One of these, designated by l, is concerned with the **shape** of the orbit. The orbits are circles when $l = n - 1$, and have elliptical shapes when l is different from $n - 1$. The other number, designated by m, is associated with the position in space of the plane of the orbit. The mathematical treatment shows that l can have all integral values from 0 to $n - 1$ and m can have all integral values from $- l$ to $+ l$, including zero. These rules, with the additional rule that in a given atom only two electrons can have any one set of values for n, l, and m, allow us to build up the electronic structure of the atoms and account for the maximum number of electrons 2, 8, 18, etc., that can exist in any one principal shell. We can think of the two electrons which are allowed to have the same values for n, l, and m as not being strictly identical but as spinning in opposite directions. Experimentally, we know that all electrons behave as though they were spinning rapidly, the momentum involved being just one half of the fundamental unit mentioned previously in connection with the selection of the allowed orbits in the hydrogen atom. Other particles behaving in a similar way are the proton, neutron, and positive electron.

In the case of $n = 1$, the only value l or m can have is zero, so we are allowed only 2 electrons in the first shell. For $n = 2$, the possible values of l are 0 and 1. With $l = 0$, the only possible value for m is 0 so 2 electrons can have $l = 0$, while $l = 1$ allows three values of m, for each of which 2 electrons are permitted, giving a total of 6 electrons. Adding, we get 8 electrons permitted for the second shell. Similar treatment of the other shells gives 18 for the third, 32 for the fourth, and 50 for the fifth.

The different electrons have been assigned names according to their shell and l quantum number. Electrons with $l = 0$ are called s-electrons; with $l = 1$, p-electrons, and so on, the order being s, p, d, f, and g. The shell is designated by a number in front of the letter name. For instance, $3s$ means one of the two electrons having $l = 0$ in the third shell.

11. The tendency for an atom with several electrons to have them grouped together into shells, each having a definite number of electrons, is fundamental to the study of chemical reactions. The essential cause of chemical bond formation is the tendency of two or more atoms, each of which has a few electrons not in filled shells, called valence electrons, to redistribute their electrons among themselves in a way that as nearly as possible places all electrons in filled shells. For example, two hydrogen atoms combine by sharing their two valence electrons so both electrons can belong to a closed shell of two, at least part of the time. (We may think of the electrons moving around first one proton and then the other, this interchange occurring so rapidly that neither proton has time to get away before the electrons move over to it.) This is one of the two basic kinds of chemical bond and is known as the electron share, or electron-pair or covalent bond, for obvious reasons. It is represented by placing two dots representing the shared valence electrons between the bound atoms, e.g., H:H for H_2 molecule. The other bond results when an atom (nonmetal) whose valence shell lacks just one or two electrons takes the valence electrons from an atom having only one or two (metal). The result of this transfer is a negative charge on the atom gaining electrons and a positive charge on that losing its valence electrons, and the bond consists of the standard electrical attraction between these charges so produced. For example, a sodium atom having 1 valence electron gives it to a fluorine atom having 7 valence electrons to fill up the second shell on the fluorine atom to its proper value of 8 forming the NaF molecule represented by $Na:\ddot{\underset{\cdot\cdot}{F}}:$ or Na^+F^-. This is known as the electrostatic or ionic bond because of its electrical character. It is, of course, not a saturated bond, for the attraction can extend to other neighboring ions.

12. These two bonds differ greatly, in fundamental ways. The electron-pair bond, consisting as it does of a sharing of electrons to close two electron shells, one on each atom, should be broken if the distance between the bound atoms were increased by more than about the thickness of

the average electron shell, a few tenths of an Ångstrom, which is 10^{-8} cm. Furthermore, one would expect the rupture to occur rather suddenly as the distance is increased, much as a cast iron rod breaks if sufficient tension is applied to its ends. On the other hand, since the electrostatic bond is of the nature of an attraction between two charged bodies, increasing the distance of separation by a factor of two (about two Ångstroms) should decrease the bond strength by only a factor of 2^2, or 4, due to the inverse square law of force applying in this case. This makes the electrostatic bond much more elastic in character, and allows molecules with such bonds to be formed and broken more rapidly because the collisions which can lead to formation and destruction do not have to be so exactly right as in the case of the molecules with electron-pair bonds. **In other words, we expect from these considerations to find that molecules with electron-pair bonds can have more definite structures and that, though their formation and destruction may involve no more energy (in fact, generally less) than for those with electrostatic bonds, they will be formed and destroyed less readily due to the exactness with which the atoms have to be placed.** All of these are well-known facts and verify our whole picture. It is interesting that the most essential molecules in living organisms are held together by bonds of the electron-pair type.

13. Certain media, such as water, are able to reduce the force acting between charged bodies by a certain factor called the dielectric constant (cf. Chapter VIII, paragraph 2). The dielectric constant of water is 80, so we expect that molecules held together by electrical bonds will be broken into their charged fragments when they are dissolved in water or any other liquid of high dielectric constant, the mild collisions occurring due to thermal motions of the molecules in the liquid being sufficient to break the weakened bonds. This is the explanation of the phenomena of ionization we have studied in preceding chapters and gives us an immediate and practical test for bond type.

TABLE 4
The Electron Structure of the Elements

Atomic number	Element	Number of electrons in each quantum group																			
		1_s	2_s	2_p	3_s	3_p	3_d	4_s	4_p	4_d	4_f	5_s	5_p	5_d	5_f	5_g	6_s	6_p	6_d	7_s	7_p
1	H	1																			
2	He	2																			
3	Li	2	1																		
4	Be	2	2																		
5	B	2	2	1																	
6	C	2	2	2																	
7	N	2	2	3																	
8	O	2	2	4																	
9	F	2	2	5																	
10	Ne	2	2	6																	
11	Na	2	2	6	1																
12	Mg	2	2	6	2																
13	Al	2	2	6	2	1															
14	Si	2	2	6	2	2															
15	P	2	2	6	2	3															
16	S	2	2	6	2	4															
17	Cl	2	2	6	2	5															
18	A	2	2	6	2	6															
19	K	2	2	6	2	6		1													
20	Ca	2	2	6	2	6		2													
21	Sc	2	2	6	2	6	1	2													
22	Ti	2	2	6	2	6	2	2													
23	V	2	2	6	2	6	3	2													
24	Cr	2	2	6	2	6	5	1													
25	Mn	2	2	6	2	6	5	2													
26	Fe	2	2	6	2	6	6	2													
27	Co	2	2	6	2	6	7	2													
28	Ni	2	2	6	2	6	8	2													
29	Cu	2	2	6	2	6	10	1													
30	Zn	2	2	6	2	6	10	2													
31	Ga	2	2	6	2	6	10	2	1												
32	Ge	2	2	6	2	6	10	2	2												
33	As	2	2	6	2	6	10	2	3												
34	Se	2	2	6	2	6	10	2	4												
35	Br	2	2	6	2	6	10	2	5												
36	Kr	2	2	6	2	6	10	2	6												
37	Rb	2	2	6	2	6	10	2	6			1									
38	Sr	2	2	6	2	6	10	2	6			2									
39	Y	2	2	6	2	6	10	2	6	1		2									
40	Zr	2	2	6	2	6	10	2	6	2		2									
41	Cb	2	2	6	2	6	10	2	6	4		1									
42	Mo	2	2	6	2	6	10	2	6	5		1									
43	Tc	2	2	6	2	6	10	2	6	6		1									
44	Ru	2	2	6	2	6	10	2	6	7		1									
45	Rh	2	2	6	2	6	10	2	6	8		1									
46	Pd	2	2	6	2	6	10	2	6	10											
47	Ag	2	2	6	2	6	10	2	6	10		1									
48	Cd	2	2	6	2	6	10	2	6	10		2									

TABLE 4 (Cont'd)

The Electron Structure of the Elements

Atomic number	Element	Number of electrons in each quantum group																			
		1_s	2_s	2_p	3_s	3_p	3_d	4_s	4_p	4_d	4_f	5_s	5_p	5_d	5_f	5_g	6_s	6_p	6_d	7_s	7_p
49	In	2	2	6	2	6	10	2	6	10		2	1								
50	Sn	2	2	6	2	6	10	2	6	10		2	2								
51	Sb	2	2	6	2	6	10	2	6	10		2	3								
52	Te	2	2	6	2	6	10	2	6	10		2	4								
53	I	2	2	6	2	6	10	2	6	10		2	5								
54	Xe	2	2	6	2	6	10	2	6	10		2	6								
55	Cs	2	2	6	2	6	10	2	6	10		2	6				1				
56	Ba	2	2	6	2	6	10	2	6	10		2	6				2				
57	La	2	2	6	2	6	10	2	6	10		2	6	1			2				
58	Ce	2	2	6	2	6	10	2	6	10	1	2	6	1			2				
59	Pr	2	2	6	2	6	10	2	6	10	2	2	6	1			2				
60	Nd	2	2	6	2	6	10	2	6	10	3	2	6	1			2				
61	—	2	2	6	2	6	10	2	6	10	4	2	6	1			2				
62	Sa	2	2	6	2	6	10	2	6	10	5	2	6	1			2				
63	Eu	2	2	6	2	6	10	2	6	10	6	2	6	1			2				
64	Gd	2	2	6	2	6	10	2	6	10	7	2	6	1			2				
65	Tb	2	2	6	2	6	10	2	6	10	8	2	6	1			2				
66	Dy	2	2	6	2	6	10	2	6	10	9	2	6	1			2				
67	Ho	2	2	6	2	6	10	2	6	10	10	2	6	1			2				
68	Er	2	2	6	2	6	10	2	6	10	11	2	6	1			2				
69	Tu	2	2	6	2	6	10	2	6	10	12	2	6	1			2				
70	Yb	2	2	6	2	6	10	2	6	10	13	2	6	1			2				
71	Lu	2	2	6	2	6	10	2	6	10	14	2	6	1			2				
72	Hf	2	2	6	2	6	10	2	6	10	14	2	6	2			2				
73	Ta	2	2	6	2	6	10	2	6	10	14	2	6	3			2				
74	W	2	2	6	2	6	10	2	6	10	14	2	6	4			2				
75	Re	2	2	6	2	6	10	2	6	10	14	2	6	5			2				
76	Os	2	2	6	2	6	10	2	6	10	14	2	6	6			2				
77	Ir	2	2	6	2	6	10	2	6	10	14	2	6	9							
78	Pt	2	2	6	2	6	10	2	6	10	14	2	6	9			1				
79	Au	2	2	6	2	6	10	2	6	10	14	2	6	10			1				
80	Hg	2	2	6	2	6	10	2	6	10	14	2	6	10			2				
81	Tl	2	2	6	2	6	10	2	6	10	14	2	6	10			2	1			
82	Pb	2	2	6	2	6	10	2	6	10	14	2	6	10			2	2			
83	Bi	2	2	6	2	6	10	2	6	10	14	2	6	10			2	3			
84	Po	2	2	6	2	6	10	2	6	10	14	2	6	10			2	4			
85	At	2	2	6	2	6	10	2	6	10	14	2	6	10			2	5			
86	Rn	2	2	6	2	6	10	2	6	10	14	2	6	10			2	6			
87	Fr	2	2	6	2	6	10	2	6	10	14	2	6	10			2	6		1	
88	Ra	2	2	6	2	6	10	2	6	10	14	2	6	10			2	6		2	
89	Ac	2	2	6	2	6	10	2	6	10	14	2	6	10			2	6	1	2	
90	Th	2	2	6	2	6	10	2	6	10	14	2	6	10	1		2	6	1	2	
91	Pa	2	2	6	2	6	10	2	6	10	14	2	6	10	2		2	6	1	2	
92	U	2	2	6	2	6	10	2	6	10	14	2	6	10	3		2	6	1	2	
93	Np	2	2	6	2	6	10	2	6	10	14	2	6	10	4		2	6	1	2	
94	Pu	2	2	6	2	6	10	2	6	10	14	2	6	10	5		2	6	1	2	
95	Am	2	2	6	2	6	10	2	6	10	14	2	6	10	6		2	6	1	2	
96	Cm	2	2	6	2	6	10	2	6	10	14	2	6	10	7		2	6	1	2	

14. Intermediate between the two types of bond just considered, there is a large and important class of molecules (cf. Chapter V, paragraph 12) in which the electrons are incompletely transferred. For instance, they may spend three fourths of their time on one atom and one fourth on the other, giving us a bond half of the share type and half of the electrostatic type. These bonds of intermediate type, called **polar bonds,** have characteristics intermediate between those discussed above for the pure types. For example, compounds with bonds of this kind may ionize only partially when dissolved in water, constituting the general class of weak electrolytes. Finally, it must be noted that a single molecule may have different types of bonds in its different parts, for instance, in Na_2SO_4 the bonds between the Na and O atoms certainly are electrostatic while those between the S and O atoms are electron-share bonds.

15. Examination of Table 4 reveals that A has only 8 electrons in its third shell, which should have 18 when filled. Argon certainly is an extremely inert element, so we are forced to consider why atoms with three shells of electrons are relatively satisfied when their third shell has 8 instead of 18 electrons. When we consider the courses of action open to the A atom, the impossibility of filling the shell by either kind of chemical bonding becomes clear. By complete transfer of electrons, the A atom has the choice of losing 8 or gaining 10, in either case the charges induced after the removal, or gain, of say 5 electrons, would be so large as to prevent any further transfer. The possibilities through sharing of valence electrons with other atoms appear to be better, but when we realize that about ten other atoms must be grouped around the A atom to fill the 18 shell, we see that this possibility is ruled out because no known ten atoms can be fitted around A closely enough to form electron-share bonds, which are particularly sensitive to structural inconveniences anyway. So it becomes apparent that for the larger shells it is not the shell itself which will be filled by chemical bonding, but rather some smaller group within these larger shells. This group is that of

eight. It is more stable than any other grouping of electrons within the shell, and, for the reasons presented above, assumes the role for bond formation played by the shell as a whole in the lighter atoms. In fact the whole principle of bond formation can be restated in the form that **bonds are formed to complete outer shells or octets.**

16. The Periodic System itself affords abundant justification for this treatment of the octet as a particularly stable subgroup in the larger shells. For example, when one more electron is added to the argon structure to form potassium, instead of going into the third shell, which needs 10 more, it prefers to go into the empty fourth shell. This continues till the fourth shell has three, when the next electron put in (to form Ti) sometimes goes into the third shell. This happens repeatedly until the third shell is finally filled in Cu, which has one electron in the fourth shell. The possibility of having the electrons in either of two shells leads to an atom's having more than one possible set of valence electrons and therefore two or more sets of chemical properties. This, of course, is known to be true of just these elements we have discussed and also of those involved in the same way in the filling of the fourth shell while the fifth has only a few electrons in it.

ATOMIC NUCLEI

17. **Introduction.** In the preceding paragraphs it has been shown that the only property of the nucleus which is of practical importance to the ordinary chemical characteristics of the atom is the positive charge. However, we know much more about the nuclei than the values of their charges and we shall consider their general properties briefly in this section.

At present, approximately 480 nuclei are known. Of these, 261 are stable, or last at least as long as 10^{12} years, and the remainder decompose at various rates to form the stable nuclei. It seems probable that a few more stable nuclei will be found and almost certain that additional unstable ones will appear, so we may expect the total somewhat to exceed 500 in the rather near future.

18. The principal constituents of the nuclei now appear to be the proton and the **neutron.** The proton is the nucleus of the ordinary hydrogen atom, has a mass of 1.0076 and a single positive charge. **The neutron has no charge and weighs 1.0090.** These particles apparently exist together in the nuclei in a way quite analogous to the way the molecules exist in a small drop of liquid, or perhaps a very small crystal. The densities of the nuclei correspond to what would be expected from the masses and sizes of the neutron and proton

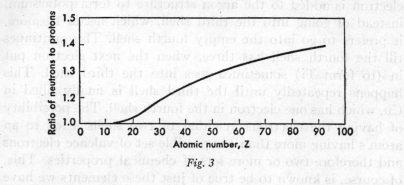

Fig. 3

if they were packed closely together. Also, the observation from collision experiments that only at relatively short distances (of the order of the diameter of the average nucleus, 10^{-12} cm.) do the constituents strongly attract each other leads us to expect that they must be extremely close together in order to account for the great stability of the ordinary nuclei. The nature of the attraction appears to be such that the **most stable structures tend to have about equal numbers of neutrons and protons.** This gives the well-known rule that the atomic weights of the elements are nearly twice the atomic numbers. However, as the nucleus increases in size the strong repulsive forces acting between the protons at these short distances (such electrical forces vary as the square of the reciprocal of the distance of separation) require more neutrons to bind them together. Figure 3 shows this.

19. When the nuclei are heated by bombardment with high energy particles, such as protons, neutrons, alpha particles, the nucleus of the heavy hydrogen isotope (called the **deuteron**), or high energy light (called **gamma rays** or **hard X-rays**) the energy apparently is distributed rather rapidly over the system as a whole and results in an evaporation process causing certain simple particles, such as neutrons, protons, deuterons, or alpha particles, to boil off until the system has cooled. These energies correspond to nuclear temperatures of several hundred million degrees. Loss of the energy by the emission of gamma radiation also occurs. There are differences in mechanism among the various processes which lead to systematic differences in the rates at which these emissions occur.

20. The rate of the evaporation process decreases very sharply with the temperature of the nucleus, so that if the cooling process following bombardment with high energy particles happens to leave the nucleus in a slightly warm condition (as it may if there is only enough energy to evaporate, say, one particle but not two, or two particles but not three, etc.) the rate at which it cools may become very small and may increase the time of cooling from about 10^{-13} seconds (for the rapid evaporation processes following bombardment) to 10^{12} years. These slower processes of course are almost in a different class, experimentally, because they may be detected at convenient times after bombardment rather than requiring investigation during bombardment. The whole set of phenomena associated with these slower transformations is known as **radioactivity.**

21. Types of Radioactivity. When nuclei with the ratio of neutrons to protons somewhat higher than the stable value are formed in a state not too highly excited, the return to the stable state does not occur through the evaporation of a neutron, but through the conversion of a neutron into a proton in the nucleus with the **emission of a negative electron,** and possibly other radiation whose existence we suspect but have not confirmed. This process is known as **beta radioactivity.** For example, the unstable Na^{24} nucleus has 13 neutrons and only 11 protons, while the stable Mg^{24} has 12 neutrons and 12 protons. As a consequence, Na^{24} emits electrons, increasing the nuclear charge from $+11$ to $+12$, changing the chemistry from that of Na to Mg and forming the stable Mg^{24} isotope. Half of any given amount of this Na^{24} changes in this way in 14.8 hours, the **half-life of the radioactivity.**

22. In the other case, for which the neutron to proton ratio is too low, there are three processes which can lead to stability from low states of excitation. One is **alpha particle emission,** which is most effective in readjusting the ratio when the stable ratio is considerably less than unity, i.e., for heavy elements. This is what one expects, because subtracting 2 neutrons and 2 protons helps the ratio most under these conditions. It is a fact that nearly all alpha radioactivities occur in nuclei with masses of 200 or more. The alpha particle is not quite so hard to tear away as the proton because it is itself a very stable nucleus. However, alpha radioactivity in general requires somewhat warmer nuclei than do the other kinds of radioacitivity. Another and more common course taken by these excited nuclei is the emission of a positive electron, called **positron.**

23. The positron has the same characteristics as the electron except that its charge is positive. It does not exist at any appreciable concentration because it reacts immediately (life of about 10^{-4} seconds in ordinary matter) with a negative electron to turn both itself and the ordinary electron into gamma radiation. It is possible to reverse this **annihilation process** by sending gamma radiation through some heavy element like Pb. Sometimes, when the conditions are just right, the high electrical forces near the Pb nuclei help tear the gamma rays apart, the negative electron being attracted to the nucleus and the positron being repelled. Figure 4 is a picture of such an event taken in a Wilson cloud chamber. The whole apparatus was placed in a magnetic field which makes electrons move in circles, the direction depending on the sign of the charge on the electron. Here we see one moving in one direction and the other in the opposite. They originate from the same point and obviously have practically the same energy since the size of the circle measures the energy.

The **positron radioactivity** is in every way analogous to the ordinary negative electron activity except that the positrons are annihilated by surrounding matter to form gamma radiation, so we always have this gamma radiation associated with positron beta activity.

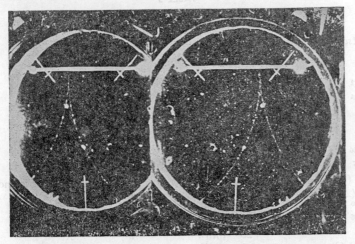

Fig. 4. Stereoscopic cloud chamber photographs of an electron-positron pair ejected from a 1 mm. lead foil by the gamma radiation from boron bombarded by protons. (This photograph was kindly furnished by Dr. Charles C. Lauritzen.)

24. The third way in which a low neutron to proton ratio can be cured is by the nucleus apparently swallowing one of the nearest electrons, from the first shell of two, to convert a proton into a neutron. We do not believe ordinary electrons can exist as such in nuclei, since they are larger than nuclei, hence we think of this as a transformation not only of the proton but of the electron at the same time. This process is known as **K-electron capture** because the first shell of electrons is known as the K shell. The probability of this happening increases as the nuclear charge increases because the electrons are closer. It is difficult to detect, because all we are able to observe is the emission of X-rays, which constitute the high energy light evolved when one of the electrons from the lower shells is removed and an electron from a higher shell falls into the hole left. However, we have reason to believe the process to be quite important.

25. Finally, we must say that the neutron to proton ratio apparently does not completely fix the properties of a nucleus of given mass. In other words, there seem to be several ways

TABLE 5

Sample Radioactivities

Isotope	Half-life	Type of radiation	Product
He^6	0.7 sec.	e^-	Li^6
N^{13}	10.3 mins.	e^+	C^{13}
Na^{22}	3 yrs.	e^+	Ne^{22}
Na^{24}	14.8 hrs.	e^-	Mg^{24}
P^{32}	14.5 days	e^-	S^{32}
S^{35}	80 days	e^-	Cl^{35}
*K^{40}	1.4×10^9 yrs.	e^-	Ca^{40}
Mn^{56}	2.5 hrs.	e^-	Fe^{56}
*Rb^{87}	1×10^{11} yrs.	e^-	Sr^{87}
Br^{80} (1st isomer)	4.5 hrs.	γ	Br^{80} (2d isomer)
Br^{80} (2d isomer)	18 min.	e^-	Kr^{80}
Ag^{106} (isomer)	7.5 days	e^-	Cd^{106}
Ag^{106} (isomer)	25.5 mins.	e^+	Pd^{106}
I^{128}	25 mins.	e^-	Xe^{128}
*Sm^{148} (?)	9×10^{10} yrs.	α	Nd^{144} (?)
Au^{198}	2.7 days	e^-	Hg^{198}
*Ra^{226}	1600 yrs.	α	*Po^{218} (RaA)
*Th^{232}	1.39×10^{10} yrs.	α	*Ra^{228}
*U^{238}	4.56×10^9 yrs.	α	*Th^{234}

of putting a given number of protons and neutrons together to give nuclei of different properties. Such nuclei are called **isomers** and afford us definite evidence of what we may call structural effects in nuclei. The more excited isomer of a pair may change to the other isomer by emission of a gamma ray or both isomers may be beta active, with different half-lives, of course, forming the same final nucleus.

26. Table 5 contains facts about some of the more important radioactive nuclei, those with asterisks being found in nature and the rest having been made since the discovery of artificial radioactivity in 1934.

27. Experimental Technique. The natural radioactive elements, e.g., radium, supply us with a source of high energy alpha particles quite useful in exciting nuclei for certain purposes. For example, neutrons are conveniently produced from beryllium metal by mixing it with radium, according to the reaction,

$$Be^9 + He^4 = C^{12} + n.$$

However, in general both the energies and intensities of these sources of high energy particles are too low to allow us to study the large number of radioactive nuclei successfully, although artificial radioactivity was first produced this way. The great advances made in this field in the last few years have been largely associated with the development of various devices for accelerating the simpler charged particles to high energies. Perhaps the best known of these is the **cyclotron,** which acts by bending the beam into almost a circle in a strong magnetic field and giving the particles a little electrical push every time they pass a certain region in the circular path. They finally become so energetic that they fly out of the circular path. Actually this occurs gradually so their path is like a spiral. They then hit the target being studied. The other devices mainly depend on the development of very high voltages which will accelerate the particles in one push. These methods have not given energies or intensities as high as the cyclotron but they do give beams of somewhat more definite energy, which are useful for certain experiments. The neutron cannot be accelerated electrically, of course, but it is a very useful disintegration tool because it has no charge and is not repelled by the nuclear charges. Most nuclei readily absorb neutrons and after having taken one are left in an excited state because part of the neutron's mass is converted into energy in the absorption process. The equivalence of mass and energy is a well-known law which the work in this field has verified completely (cf. Chapter II, paragraph 3). The absorption of a neutron usually leads to negative electron radioactivity for the reasons given in the preceding section.

28. Applications. Radioactive nuclei are valuable as tracers in the study of chemical reactions. For example, it has been shown by feeding foods containing radiophosphorus that even the bones in the animals become radioactive in a few days, proving that there are constant sloughing away and building up processes occurring in the live animal. There are other important applications in the use of the radiations to destroy unwanted tissue such as cancer.

29. The facts discovered about the nuclei, in particular the tremendous energies involved in the irreactions, seem to supply us with a plausible explanation of the source of **stellar energy.** We can see that the sun, for instance, could shine for a period millions of times longer than the age of the earth, which is approximately 3×10^9 years, if certain simple nuclear reactions were occurring. In fact, physical measurements on the sun almost require us to believe the temperature at the center to be about 10^7 degrees, at which temperatures certain nuclear reactions would undoubtedly occur. The details of stellar constitution and change certainly are not all clear but we feel that we have a good lead.

30. Finally, we must mention the determination by radio activity of the age of rocks. The elements uranium and thorium both are composed entirely of radioactive nuclei, whose rates of decay are known accurately. The products in both cases are lead isotopes, so the amount of lead found in a rock containing a certain amount of uranium or thorium tells us how long it has been since the rock was solidified. This assumes, of course, that no lead was present when the rock formed. Examination of the isotopic constitution of the lead shows whether this is true. The results for the oldest rocks are nearly two billion years.

31. Nuclear Fission. The varieties of nuclear decomposition described in the preceding paragraphs involve only small particles, electrons, positrons, and alpha particles, in most natural radioactive processes, and absorption of protons, deuterons or neutrons in the artificial processes. But in January, 1939, O. Hahn and F. Strassman in Germany published their discovery that an isotope of Ba is produced by bombardment of U with neutrons. It was soon established that such bombardment causes U to split into two approximately equal fragments with release of an enormous amount of energy. This process is now called "fission." Reference to Fig. 3 shows that fewer neutrons are needed in proportion to protons for lighter elements than for heavier elements, so that if one of the three isotopes of uranium, 234, 235, or 238, should split into two atoms of roughly equal weight, they would not need all the neutrons necessary to bind together the U atom. It was soon discovered that U^{235} is the isotope subject to fission and that while one neutron causes the fission, probably 3 neutrons are emitted along with two fission fragments having prodigious kinetic energy. If the U^{235} were pure, and in a large enough mass, these neutrons could explode other atoms, setting up a chain reaction analogous to the explosion of T.N.T. but liberating vastly more energy per pound than T.N.T. The public has now been told that the bomb dropped on Hiroshima, which doubtless contained but a few pounds of U^{235}, was equivalent to 20,000 tons of T.N.T. The nature of this chain reaction is indicated in Fig. 5, taken from *Atomic Energy* by H. D. Smyth, Princeton University Press, 1945.

In order to bring about such an explosion of U^{235}, it is necessary to separate this isotope from U^{238}. The composition of natural uranium is a trace of U^{234}, 0.7% U^{235}, and 99.3% U^{238}. Since all three are identical in chemical behavior, this separation can be accomplished only by taking advantage of their slight difference in mass, in such processes as diffusion of a gaseous or a dissolved compound, or the different bending of charged gaseous ions in a magnetic field (cf. Chapter XII, Paragraph 23).

The discovery that plutonium is, like U^{235}, subject to fission, opened a more feasible source of atomic energy than the difficult physical separation of U^{235} from U^{238}. Plutonium can be produced from the abundant U^{235} by the following series of steps, following bombardment by slow neutrons,

$$U^{238} + n \longrightarrow U^{238} \xrightarrow[23 \text{ min.}]{e^-} Np^{239} \xrightarrow[2.3 \text{ days}]{e^-} Pu^{239}$$

The resulting plutonium, when not bombarded to produce fission, is a radioactive but long-lived element, slowly decay-

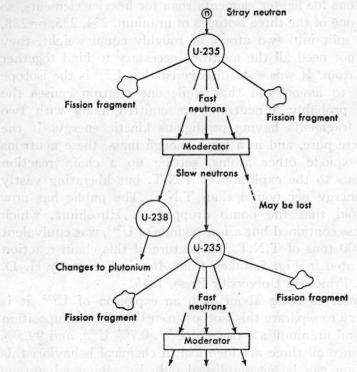

Fig. 5. Fission of U^{235}.

ing to U^{235} with emission of alpha particles, and it differs enough chemically from uranium to permit separation from the latter by chemical processes, as outlined in Chapter XVII, paragraph 25. Its energy release upon fission, instead of being explosive, as in the atomic bomb, can be controlled, and should prove to be a valuable source of energy for peaceful civilization, if mankind can show itself wise enough to use it in such ways. It is thus possible to use all the earth's supply of uranium as a source of energy and not merely the rare U^{235} which is very difficult to extract. It is probable that thorium can also serve as a source of fissionable material.

CHAPTER XVII

THE PERIODIC SYSTEM OF ELEMENTS

1. It became evident to chemists a long time ago that there are certain elements which may be grouped together by reason of their similarity. Among such groups may be mentioned lithium, sodium, and potassium, commonly called the alkali metals; calcium, strontium, and barium, the alkaline earth metals; fluorine, chlorine, bromine, and iodine, called the halogens. In 1866 Newlands read a paper before the London Chemical Society in which he showed that if the then known elements were arranged in the order of increasing atomic weight, as follows:

H	Li	Be	B	C	N	O	F	Na	Mg	Al	Si	P	S	Cl	K	Ca
1	7	9	11	12	14	16	19	23	24	27	28	31	32	35.5	39	40

there is a similarity between every eighth element in the series, so that if it is divided into groups of eight and these placed under each other in successive rows, as follows,

H	Li	Be	B	C	N	O
F	Na	Mg	Al	Si	P	S
Cl	K	Ca	etc.			

then the elements standing in the same vertical column are those which correspond to each other in chemical nature. It is evident from the table that this is the case. Strange as it may seem, this discovery was received with some ridicule, and its value not appreciated till later. In 1869 this same idea was more fully elaborated independently by Mendeléeff and Lothar Meyer. Each of these chemists tabulated the elements substantially by the method shown in Table 1. The fundamental idea expressed by such an arrangement is

TABLE 1

Periodic System.—Mendeléeff (Modified)

0	1	1'	2	2'	3	3'	4	4'	5	5'	6	6'	7	7'	8'	9'	10'
He 2	H 1																
Ne 10	Li 3		Be 4		B 5		C 6		N 7		O 8		F 9				
A 18	Na 11		Mg 12		Al 13		Si 14		P 15		S 16		Cl 17				
Kr 36	K 19	Cu 29	Ca 20	Zn 30	Sc 21	Ga 31	Ti 22	Ge 32	V 23	As 33	Cr 24	Se 34	Br 35	Mn 25	Fe 26	Co 27	Ni 28
Xe 54	Rb 37	Ag 47	Sr 38	Cd 48	Y 39	In 49	Zr 40	Sn 50	Cb 41	Sb 51	Mo 42	Te 52	I 53	Tc 43	Ru 44	Rh 45	Pd 46
Rn 86	Cs 55	Au 79	Ba 56	Hg 80	La 57	Tl 81	Hf 72	Pb 82	Ta 73	Bi 83	W 74	Po 84	At 85	Re 75	Os 76	Ir 77	Pt 78
									(Rare earths, 58–71, unclassified.)								
	Fr 87		Ra 88		Ac 89		Th 90		Pa 91		U (Np, Pu, 92 93 94			Am, Cm 95 96			

that of the periodic recurrence of properties as the atomic weights increase.

2. Various other representations of the Periodic System of elements have been proposed, the most useful of which, given in Table 2, is based upon the facts of atomic structure that have been set forth in the previous chapter, summarized

TABLE 2

Periodic System

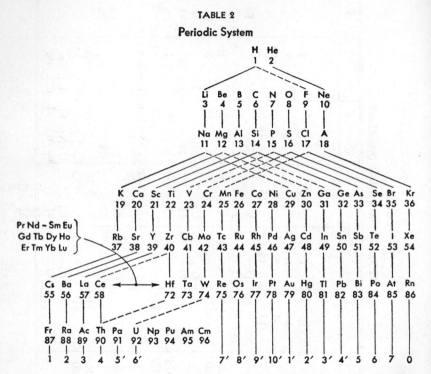

these particularly in Table 4. This arrangement has been made by listing the elements in order of increasing atomic number, separating them into rows, or periods, each beginning at an alkali metal with a new energy level and ending at a noble gas with a completed energy level. The elements in the several rows which are closely related by reason of their equal numbers of valence electrons are connected by lines and constitute a **group** which is designated by the common number of valence electrons. The periods beginning with

K, Rb, and Cs, are longer than the preceding two periods because of the building up of the underlying levels, and there appear two elements in each row with the same number of valence electrons. The one which more closely resembles the corresponding elements in the first two periods is connected with these by a full line and is included with them in a **main**

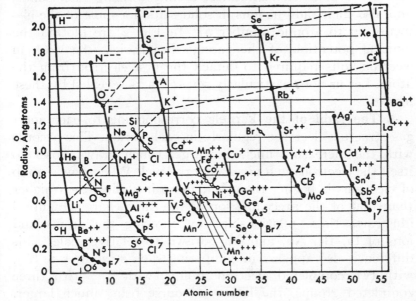

Fig. 1. Ionic radii; ions with identical kernels connected by solid lines; ions with identical charges, +1 and —1, connected by dotted lines; covalent radii indicated by double lines.

group, while the element which less closely resembles the corresponding lighter elements is connected with them by a broken line, indicating the smaller similarity. There elements constitute what is called a **subgroup,** denoted in the table by primed numbers. This arrangement of the Periodic System should be studied, the position of the commoner elements in it learned, and the basis of its construction, as indicated by Tables 4 and 5 in the preceding chapter, thoroughly understood.

3. Almost any property of the elements or any class of

compounds, if plotted against the atomic numbers, would show a periodicity, as does the number of valence electrons; however, the two most fundamental properties for an understanding of chemical and physical behavior are the size of the atom and the ease of removal of electrons. Accordingly, we have plotted, in Fig. 1, the radii of atoms in their covalent bonds, for those elements most readily forming such bonds, and also their radii as ions in solid salts, for most of the elements up to atomic number 57. In Fig. 2 are plotted the ionizing potentials of the gaseous atoms, i.e., the work in electron-volts required to detach the first electron from the atom. Let us note particularly several facts revealed by these figures.

4. The radii of the kernels corresponding to each inert gas structure decrease regularly in each period. This accords with the increasing nuclear charge, which draws closer to itself the electrons in a given energy level. When a new goup of electrons is begun, there is a jump in radius, each higher than that of the preceding ion of the same charge. Figure 3 illustrates these relationships by showing the atoms and ions of Li, Be, Na, and Mg, drawn to relative scale. This difference also appears in comparing such structures as S^{+6}, with two completed electron groups, with S^{--}, with three completed groups, the latter of course being much larger. It is interesting to note that the covalent radius of S is almost exactly midway between the radius of S^{+6} and S^{-2}. The same relation holds for the covalent radii of N, O, F, P, Cl, Br, and I.

5. The ionizing potentials of the gaseous atoms, plotted in Fig. 2, are lowest for the largest atoms, as might be expected, since the farther the negative electron is from the positive nucleus the more easily it can be removed. Except for minor fluctuations, the ionizing potential increases along each period, beginning with an alkali metal and ending with a noble gas. It should be noted that the ionizing potentials here plotted are for the first electron only. In harmony with the increase in size the potentials for each period are lower than the corresponding ones of the previous period.

6. Stability of Compounds. The roles of ionizing potential and atomic size in determining chemical stability are indicated by the scheme in Chapter V, Table 7 and Fig. 8 and we may now correlate the stabilities of compounds with the

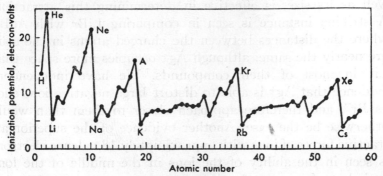

Fig. 2. Ionization potentials of atoms.

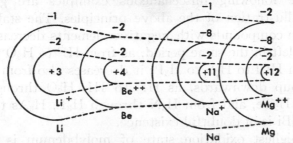

Fig. 3. Relation between size and structure of atoms and ions.

positions of their elements in the Periodic System. Stability is greater the lower the ionizing potential of the metallic atom and the greater the electron affinity of the nonmetallic atom, and both become smaller as we go from the lighter to the heavier members of a main group. On this basis we will expect, for example, KCl to be more stable than NaCl, KCl than KI, CaO than BeO, H_2O than H_2S.

7. Stability is also aided by small size and consequent closeness of approach of the charged atoms, a factor which contributes to the increase in stability in going from iodides to fluorides, but which opposes the effect above noted in going from LiCl to CsCl; indeed it is sufficient to reverse the series in the case of the alkali fluorides, for LiF is the most stable in spite of the larger amount of energy absorbed in changing from Li to Li^+.

8. We should note, however, that the type of kernel, as well as its size, is effective in determining this attraction. A striking instance is seen in comparing LiBr with AgBr, where the distances between the charged atoms in the solid are nearly the same, although Ag^+ occupies more space than Li^+ in most of their compounds. We have independent evidence that Ag^+ is able to distort large negative ions such as Br^-, and therefore approach closer to them than would otherwise be the case. Another evidence of the superior attractive forces of ions with approximately 18 valence electrons is seen in the ability of the ions in the middle of the long periods to form complex ions.

9. The following miscellaneous examples are given as further illustration of the above principles. The stability of hydrogen compounds with negative elements decreases from right to left in the same period, as from HF to H_2O to H_3N, and from HCl to H_2S to H_3P; it decreases also from the top of a group downwards, as HF to HI, H_2O through H_2S, H_2Se to H_2Te, and from H_3N through H_3P, H_3As to H_3Sb, while H_3Bi is of doubtful existence.

The highest oxidation state of molybdenum is seen in MoO_3 and MoF_6 but not in a chloride, the highest being $MoCl_5$. Again, if we compare the compounds of sulfur with bromine, chlorine, oxygen, and fluorine, which is the order corresponding to increasing electronegative character, we find that the highest bromide has the formula S_2Br_2; the highest chloride is SCl_4, the highest oxide is SO_3 but this compound breaks down rather completely above 700° C. into SO_2 and O_2; and finally the fluoride, SF_6, is an exceedingly stable, inert substance.

10. **Strength of Acids and Bases.**[1] If we consider a hydroxide as made up of the charged atoms, $M^+ O^- H^+$, we

---

[1]See also Latimer and Hildebrand, *Reference Book of Inorganic Chemistry,* Chapter III, paragraph 7.

see that there is a possibility of dissociating, either as a base into M^+ and OH^-, or as an acid into MO^- and H^+. Which of these takes place and the extent of each is dependent closely upon the relative sizes of the ions involved, although the type of kernel is also significant. The smaller the M^+ the more closely it is held to the oxygen with a consequent weakening of the attraction between O^{--} and H^+, hence the less basic and the more acidic is the compound. As illustrations we may note that the hydroxides of the large alkali metal ions are all strong bases, the strength increasing with the size. The same increase in basic strength is shown in descending group 2, but these are smaller ions and weaker bases, the weakest, $Be(OH)_2$, being also weakly acidic, belonging to the transition hydroxides that are amphoteric. The influence of kernel type is seen in the fact that Zn^{+2}, with an 18 electron kernel, gives a weaker base, in spite of its larger size, than does the smaller Mg^{+2}.

11. The more completely the electrons on the atom M are removed by surrounding it by oxygen atoms, i.e., the higher its oxidation number, the smaller it is and the more tightly does it hold OH^- and the more readily does it allow H^+ to split off instead. We find, therefore, that sulfuric acid, $SO_2(OH)_2$, is a stronger acid than sulfurous, $SO(OH)_2$; nitric acid is stronger than nitrous, arsenic than arsenous, etc. Again, Mn^{+2} gives a base while Mn^{+7} gives an acid; Cr^{+2} a base, Cr^{+3} an amphoteric hydroxide, and Cr^{+6} an acid.

12. The plot of ionic radii, Fig. 1, serves very well to point out the relation of acid or basic character to the position in the Periodic System. Every positive ion with a radius of less than 0.5×10^{-8} cm. gives an acidic hydroxide, the more so the higher the oxidation number and the higher in the group. Ions slightly exceeding this size may give weak acids in the higher oxidation number, but the ions larger than 0.9×10^{-8} cm. all give bases only. The region of amphoteric behavior, it will be seen, begins with Be in group 2, and runs to Al in group 3, then to group 4 and subgroup 4, with representatives from adjacent groups assisted by variations in

oxidation number. In group 5 we start with HNO_3 and HPO_3 or H_3PO_4, strong acids, then H_3AsO_4, a weak acid, H_3SbO_4, amphoteric, and hence very weak in both roles. In the trivalent state we end with $Bi(OH)_3$, a weak base. In group 3 we find $B(OH)_3$, a very weak acid, $Al(OH)_3$, amphoteric, and $Sc(OH)_3$, basic; in group 4 the weak carbonic and silicic acids, titanic hydroxide, amphoteric, zicronium hydroxide, chiefly basic, and thorium hydroxide, wholly so.

13. Similar trends are evident in the sulfides, where As_2S_3 is acidic, dissolving easily in S^{--}, while Sb_2S_3 dissolves with difficulty and Bi_2S_3 not at all. The increase in oxidation number from Sb_2S_3 to Sb_2S_5 increases the acidic nature sufficiently to allow it to dissolve easily.

14. An apparent exception to this trend exists in the case of the three acids of phosphorus, H_3PO_4, H_3PO_3, and H_3PO_2, which do not decrease in strength with diminishing oxygen content. The discrepancy finds its explanation, however, in the fact that part of the hydrogen in H_3PO_3 and H_3PO_2 is linked, not to oxygen, but to phosphorus. Their structures correspond to

$$
\begin{array}{ccc}
\text{O} & & \text{O} \\
\text{H O P O H} & \text{and} & \text{H P O H} \\
\text{H} & & \text{H}
\end{array}
$$

not $P(OH)_3$ and $HP(OH)_2$,

for the former dissociates but two of its three hydrogen atoms and the latter but one.

15. Oxidation State. The significance of the octet of valence electrons explains the limiting values for the oxidation states found in the various groups:

Group	0	1	2	3	4	5	6	7	8
Oxidation number	0	+1	+2	+3	+4	+5	+6	+7	+8
					−4	−3	−2	−1	

These limiting values do not always appear in all members of a group, thus no other atom is able to strip 7 electrons

from a fluorine atom or 6 from an oxygen atom. The state
+ 8 appears only in RuO_4, OsO_4, RuF_8, and OsF_8.

Oxidation states lying within these extremes also appear,
as illustrated by

	Oxidation no. of P		Oxidation no. of Cl
P_2O_5	+ 5	$KClO_4$	+ 7
P_2O_3	+ 3	$KClO_3$	+ 5
H_3PO_2	+ 1	$KClO_2$	+ 3
H_3P	− 3	$KClO$	+ 1
		KCl	− 1

16. Transition Elements. The horizontal relationships are
rather more significant than the vertical ones among the
subgroup elements. Table 3 gives the ions characteristic of
the various oxidation states of the elements from Ti to Cu.
They all form +2 ions and all but Ni and Cu form +3 ions.
We see, also, a fairly regular trend in the potentials of the
couples, $M = M^{++} + 2 e^-$. The couples $M^{++} = M^{+++} + e^-$
are much less so. The solubility products of the sulfides
show an almost uniform trend, as do the stabilities of the
complex ions, the cyanides showing maximum stability at
Fe and the +2 ammonia complexes at Cu. Similar trends
are discoverable in the other two transition series.

Reference to Table 4, Chapter XVI, will assist in making
clearer the reason for oxidation numbers lower than the
group number in the elements Sc to Cu. We see that in each
series the outermost group, consisting of 4s electrons, remains
at 1 or 2 while the underlying 3d group increases from 1 to
its maximum of 10. The maximum oxidation number is given
by the sum of the 3d and 4s electrons, but smaller oxidation
numbers occur as a result of the possibility of withdrawing
fewer electrons. This transition from a kernel with 8 electrons
to one with 18 gives these elements the name Transition
Elements. The same sort of transition occurs in the succeeding rows from Y to Pd where the 4d group is being filled, and
again from Hf to Au, where the 5d group is being filled.

TABLE 3
Transition Elements

	Ti	V	Cr	Mn	Fe	Co	Ni	Cu
Oxidation States								
1								Cu^+
2	Ti^{++}	V^{++}	Cr^{++}	Mn^{++}	Fe^{++}	Co^{++}	Ni^{++}	Cu^{++}
3	Ti^{+++}	V^{+++}	Cr^{+++}	Mn^{+++}	Fe^{+++}	Co^{+++}		
4	TiO^{++}	VO^{++}		MnO_2		CoO_2	NiO_2	
5		VO_3^-						
6			CrO_4^{--}	MnO_4^{--}	FeO_4^{--}			
7				MnO_4^-				
Electrode Potential								
$M = M^{++} + 2\,e^-$	1.75	1.5	0.86	1.05	0.44	0.28	0.25	
$M^{++} = M^{+++} + e^-$	0.37	0.20	0.41	-1.5	-0.77	-1.84		
Solubility product of sulfide				6×10^{-16}	10^{-19}	7×10^{-23}	3×10^{-21}	4×10^{-38}

17. **The Rare Earths.** Beginning with Ce, atomic number 58, the $4f$ group 14 begins to be filled, giving a group of elements known as the Rare Earths. These elements are very much alike, the most stable ions all being tripositive.

18. **Solubility of Salts.** The solubility of salts changes in regular order according to the Periodic System in nearly all instances. This is illustrated for a single group, the second, by Table 4.

TABLE 4

Solubilities of Salts of Group 2 Ions,
Moles per Liter at 20° C.

$Mg(OH)_2$	0.0003	$MgSO_4 \cdot 7 H_2O$	2.88	$MgCl_2 \cdot 6 H_2O$	5.76
$Ca(OH)_2$	0.022	$CaSO_4 \cdot 2 H_2O$	0.015	$CaCl_2 \cdot 6 H_2O$	6.70
$Sr(OH)_2$	0.066	$SrSO_4$	0.0005	$SrCl_2 \cdot 6 H_2O$	3.33
$Ba(OH)_2$	0.233	$BaSO_4$	0.00001	$BaCl_2$	1.72

19. **Density,** which is mass divided by volume, depends, in the case of solid substances, not only on atomic weight and atomic volume but on the crystal structure and coefficient of expansion as well; hence it is not strange that the density often appears somewhat irregular. Table 5 shows the irregular values for K and Ca which result chiefly from the different rates of increase of atomic weight and atomic volume.

TABLE 5

Densities of Solid Elements

Group 1	Group 2	Group 2'	Group 1'	Group 8'	Group 10'
Li 0.53	Be 1.73	Zn 7.1	Cu 8.9	Fe 7.9	Ni 8.7
Na 0.99	Mg 1.74	Cd 8.6	Ag 10.5	Ru 12.0	Pd 11.5
K 0.86	Ca 1.53	Hg 13.5	Au 19.2	Os 22.5	Pt 21.4
Rb 1.52	Sr 2.55				
Cs 1.90	Ba 3.78				

We see, however, the general increase in density in descending a group due to the fact that atomic weight increases faster than atomic size; further, the high densities of the elements in the subgroups as compared with the main groups resulting from the position of the former in the troughs of the curves of atomic radii.

20. Tensile Strength. The metals with the greatest tensile strength are found among the subgroups, starting with 5 and extending to 10. These groups include iron and the metals alloyed with it to make the modern alloy steels, V, Cr, Mo, W, U, Mn, and Ni. We may connect high tensile strength with small atomic volume, high melting point and many-electron valence shells.

21. Elements Which Form Complex Ions. The elements most prone to form complex ions are in the subgroups and especially in the neighborhood of group 1′ in the second form of the table. Complex ions with ammonia are readily given by the ions of Co, Ni, Cu, Zn, Cd, and Ag. Complex cyanides are given by the same elements, also by the platinum metals and iron. Complex chlorides are given chiefly by the platinum metals and gold, as illustrated by $PtCl_6^{--}$ and $AuCl_4^-$.

22. Resemblance between the First Member of a Group and the Second Member of the Succeeding Group. Some similarity exists between the first element in groups 1, 2, and 3 and the second element in the succeeding group. Thus lithium, though an alkali metal, resembles magnesium in having a hydroxide and carbonate which are not very soluble, a rather insoluble phosphate, and a deliquescent chloride. Beryllium is so much like aluminum that the two elements are difficult to separate. Boron is like silicon in physical properties and gives compounds similar in many respects. The borates of all but the alkali metals, like the corresponding silicates, are insoluble in water, and when fused tend to give glasses on cooling.

23. Radioactive Elements. As might be expected, it is the heaviest and most complex atoms which tend to break down into simpler ones, and all of the elements of higher atomic weight than bismuth are radioactive. These are, accordingly, found at the bottom of the table. The odd-numbered elements are, in general, less stable than the even-numbered ones, as shown by their relative abundance and by their life periods.

24. Prediction of Unknown Elements. The value of the Periodic System was demonstrated in very striking fashion by the prediction of unknown elements by Mendeléeff. At the time he constructed his table it was obvious that several gaps should be left in order to have the succeeding elements fall into their proper groups. Such gaps were to be found at the places now filled by scandium, gallium, and germanium. From the properties of the adjacent elements, Mendeléeff predicted the properties of the unknown elements. The remarkable accuracy of these predictions is illustrated by the following comparison of the unknown element called by Mendeléeff "ekasilicon," with germanium, discovered later by Winkler.

Ekasilicon	*Germanium*
At. wt. 72, density 5.5.	At. wt. 72.5, density 5.46.
Oxide EsO_2, density 4.7.	Oxide GeO_2, density 4.7.
Chloride $EsCl_4$, liquid, boiling slightly below 100° C., density 1.9.	Chloride $GeCl_4$, liquid, boiling at 86° C., density 1.887.
Ethide, $Es(C_2H_5)_4$, liquid boiling at 160° C., density 0.96.	Ethide, $Ge(C_2H_5)_4$, liquid, boiling at 160° C., density slightly less than 1.
Fluoride, EsF_4, not gaseous.	Fluoride, GeF_4, white, solid.

The foregoing comparison should serve as an illustration of the value of the Periodic System to the student of chemistry, for if an undiscovered element can be foretold so brilliantly by its aid, then any knowledge a student may have of some elements may be similarly projected to deduce the properties of adjacent elements. The use of the Periodic System, therefore, enormously increases the effectiveness of a given amount of mental effort, and it is very important to form the habit of using it constantly.

25. The elements with atomic numbers greater than radon, 86, have until recently been assumed to start a row in the Periodic Table similar to the rows containing iron and the "platinum metals." Element 87 is a natural product with a half-life of only 21 minutes, but there is little doubt that chemically it is "eka-cesium," an alkali metal of group I.

Radium, 88, gives Ra^{++}, chemically like Ba^{++}, thorium, 90, gives ThO_2 and other compounds similar to those of the group 4 elements, and uranium, 92, gives UO_4^{--}, analogous to CrO_4^{--}, and has been generally classed as a member of group 6. But the artificial production at the University of California of element number 93, neptunium, designated $_{93}Np$, by McMillan and Abelson, Number 94, plutonium, $_{94}Pu$, by Seaborg, McMillan, Kennedy and Wahl, curium, $_{95}Cu$, by Seaborg, James and Morgan, americium, $_{96}Am$, by Seaborg, James and Ghiorso, has caused a reconsideration of this classification because Np does not belong to sub-group 7, with Mn, but both it and Pu are remarkably similar to U in chemical behavior, all three showing the same oxidation states, 3, 4, 5, 6, and differing only in a shift in stability towards the lower states in going towards Pu. As soon as the study of the chemical separation of these elements became a war problem of the utmost urgency, in order to separate pure Pu from the bulk of U in which it was produced for use in the second "atomic bomb," it became evident that the additional electrons in the elements after Ra might either go into the vacant $6d$ shell (cf. Chapter XVI, Table 4), which would start a series like the three "Transition Series" (cf. paragraph 16), or they might go into the vacant $5f$ shell, giving a series analogous to the Rare Earths (cf. paragraph 17), where the $4f$ shell is being filled. This agrees with the fact that, like the Rare Earths, U, Np and Pu show the same oxidation states and differ only in their oxidation-reduction potentials. To separate U and Pu, the potential must be so adjusted that U is in a higher state, 6, and Pu in a lower one, 4. It seems that the higher states are completely missing in aqueous solutions of Am and Cu.

The production of plutonium, its chemical separation from uranium, its purification and use in the literally and figuratively world-shaking atomic bomb, and the prospect it opens up for the benefit of man, if he is sensible enough to use it beneficently, are such major scientific achievements that it seems appropriate to quote a brief description of the process written by Professor Glenn T. Seaborg.[1]

"The problem of designing a process for separating plutonium was without precedent from almost every standpoint. No one had ever seen any plutonium at the time that plant design was under consideration. The chemical properties attributed to the element at that time had been deduced solely from what might be termed secondary evidence (experiments on the tracer scale).

"The novelty of the problem was enhanced by the fact that not only was Pu^{239} to be the first artificially produced isotope to be seen but as an element it fell beyond the confines of the classical periodic system. These curious conditions, in themselves, would not necessarily produce serious obstacles were they not coupled with other aspects of the problem of an unconventional nature for industrial scale operation. Both the plutonium and the fission products from which it was to be separated would be present in extremely small concentrations in the uranium. These separations would require specialized techniques. The formidable feature of the undertaking was, however, that these minute amounts of the fission product elements would in turn have to be separated from the plutonium to the extent that only of the order of one part per million of each would remain. To add to the complications, the separations process would have to be carried out entirely by remote control because of the staggering levels of gamma-ray activity associated with the fission products. As a result, it was imperative that the process be adaptable to simple equipment that would require a minimum of maintenance and that the limits of control be not too stringent.

"Although four types of method for chemical separation were examined—volatility, adsorption, solvent extraction, and precipitation—the process finally chosen was a precipitation process. S. G. Thompson is largely responsible for the conception and early development of the process actually used. The process depends on the coprecipitation of the plutonium along with a carrier precipitate, a procedure which has been commonly used in radiochemistry. One of the most interesting and awe-inspiring aspects in the development of this process was the necessity for the testing of the process at a time when only microgram amounts of cyclotron-produced plutonium were available. It was necessary to test the process at concentrations corresponding to the full level of Hanford plant operation and therefore the experiments had to be conducted on the ultramicrochemical scale of operation, which employed volumes of only micro-liters. This involved a scale-up between these experiments and the final Hanford plant by a factor of about 10^{10}, surely the greatest scale-up factor ever attempted. In spite of these difficulties, the chemical separation process at Hanford was successful from the beginning and its performance exceeded all expectations. High yields and decontamination factors (separation from fission product activity) were achieved in the very beginning and have continued to improve with time.

"The precipitation process which is being used involves the use of an alternation between the IV and VI oxidation states of plutonium, as pointed out in the Smyth Report. The process involves a precipitation of plutonium (IV), with a chemical compound as a carrier, then dissolution of the precipitate, oxidation of the plutonium to the VI state, and precipitation of the carrier compound while the plutonium (VI) remains in solution. Fission products which are not carried remain in solution when Pu (IV) is precipitated, and fission products which carry are removed from the plutonium when it is in the VI state. Successive oxidation-reduction cycles are carried out until the desired decontamination is achieved.

"These statements on the Hanford Separations Process, to be sure, represent a gross oversimplification of the actual process. There are carried out in all some thirty major chemical reactions involving hundreds of operations before the plutonium emerges from the process. The plants themselves defy description with their massive structures and their intricate maze of equipment, piping, and remotely operated controls. The preliminary design of these plants was underway at a time when the world supply of plutonium was invisible to the naked eye. This remarkable program of investigation with microscopic and sub-microscopic quantities marks only one of a large number of amazing and so far unheralded achievements of the men of chemistry who developed the chemical separation processes which were used on the Atomic Bomb Project."

It is now appropriate to consider the relation of both the rare earths and the trans-uranium elements to the Period

TABLE 6
Lanthanide and Actinide Series

	Cs	Ba	La	Ce	Pr	Nd	—	Sm	Eu	Gd	Tb	Dy	Ho	Er	Tm	Yb	Lu
Atomic No.	55	56	57	58	59	60	61	62	63	64	65	66	67	68	69	70	71
Oxidation States	1	2	3	3	3	3	3 ?	2	2	3	3	3	3	3	3	2	3
					4	4			3	3		4					3	
						5 ?												

	—	Ra	Ac	Th	Pa	U	Np	Pu	Am	Cm	—	—	—	—	—	—	—
Atomic No.	87	88	89	90	91	92	93	94	95	96	97	98	99	100	101	102	103
Oxidation States	1	2	3	—	—	3	3	3	3	3							
					4	5	4	4	4									
							5	5	5									
							6	6	6									

System, as set forth in Tables 1 and 2, where the rare earths were "unclassified." The reason for this was, of course, that the rare earths, like the elements in the neighborhood of iron, have no prototypes among the lighter elements. However, the parallelism between the rare earths and these new elements does lend significance to their proper classification in the Periodic System. Table 6 gives the row containing the trans-uranium elements arranged in parallel with the first part of the row containing the rare earths, together with oxidation states which they exhibit. It is noteworthy that the most stable oxidation state rises uniformly till uranium is reached, then falls stepwise, reaching 3 only with americium and curium. In the rare earth series there is a similar rise and fall but it is less pronounced and has its maximum not in the element above uranium but in praseodymium, consequently there is little chemical resemblance between the several elements 59 to 62 and the ones directly below them, 91 to 94. It is ordinarily more helpful to correlate uranium with tungsten and molybdenum than with neodymium. Nevertheless, the evidence seems unmistakable that, as explained above, the two rows are similar in that f-electrons are being added instead of d-electrons. Seaborg has called the new series the "actinide series," because it starts with actinium, just as the rare earths, starting with lanthanum, may be called the "lanthanide series." It is interesting to note that he chose the name americium as a parallel to europium, and curium, in honor of the Curies, who discovered radium, as a parallel to gadolinium, after Gadolin, who discovered several of the rare earths.

Exercises

1. In what regions of the Periodic System will elements be found which have the following characteristics most strongly marked: tendency to form stable compounds with hydrogen, tendency to form ammonia complex ions, tendency to form strongest oxygen acids, radioactivity, maximum positive oxidation number, lowest melting point, minimum negative oxidation number, the strongest reducing power, amphoteric nature of the hydroxides, the greatest tensile strength?

2. Arrange the following elements in their proper order in groups 1 and 2 of the Periodic System: Li, Mg, Ba, Ca, K, Na, Cs, Be, Rb.

3. $BaCl_2$ is moderately soluble, $CaCl_2$ is deliquescent; what can you conclude regarding $RaCl_2$? How would you expect the solubilities of LiCl and NaCl to compare?

4. How do each of the following properties vary from left to right in the same row of the Periodic System: (a) the basic character of the hydroxide, (b) the melting point, (c) the positive oxidation number, (d) the electrical resistance of the element?

5. Discuss the trend of properties of the elements of group 2 and their compounds as you descend the group.

6. Compare the saltlike characters of binary compounds with the positions of their constituents in the Periodic System.

7. From the place of Cd in the Periodic System, what deduction would you make regarding: (a) the melting point of the metal; (b) the solubility of its sulfate; (c) the ionization of its chloride?

8. Compare the strength as acids of (a) H_3AsO_3 and H_3SbO_3, (b) H_3AsO_3 and H_3AsO_4. Justify your answers by either experimental facts known to you, or by theoretical considerations, or by valid analogies.

9. How do the differences between H_3AlO_3 and H_3BO_3 agree with the places of Al and B in the Periodic System?

10. Explain on theoretical grounds which you would expect to be more hydrolyzed, (a) $NaNO_2$ or $NaAsO_2$; (b) Na_2SO_3 or Na_2TeO_3?

11. (a) Name the halogens in their order. (b) Which one has the greatest tendency to take on electrons? (c) Which has the highest melting point? (d) Which is the weakest oxidizing agent?

12. From the position of beryllium in the Periodic System, deduce (a) whether $Be(OH)_2$ or $Mg(OH)_2$ is the stronger base; (b) whether BeS could be precipitated with H_2S; (c) whether $BeSO_4$, or $MgSO_4$ is more soluble; (d) whether Be or Mg evolves more heat upon reaction with chlorine.

13. Explain on a theoretical basis which of the 2 elements, Ti or Th, would (a) more likely form a compound with hydrogen; (b) be the better conductor of electricity; (c) be more easily reduced from its dioxide; (d) give the more basic hydroxide; (e) give a more completely hydrolyzable chloride.

14. Classify the following compounds according to the oxidation number of the phosphorus they contain: (a) P_2O_5; (b) PCl_3; (c) PH_3; (d) H_3PO_2; (e) $H_4P_2O_7$; (f) HPO_3; (g) $NaPO_2$; (h) $PbHPO_4$; (i) PCl_5; (j) $Ca(H_2PO_4)_2$.

15. Deduce from their positions in the Periodic System whether (a) Os or Ir should show the higher oxidation number, (b) Rh^{++} or Pd^{++} should give the more stable complex with NH_3; (c) $Ni(OH)_2$ or $Co(OH)_2$ should be the stronger base.

16. Compare the stabilities of the trichlorides of the elements in group 5 and justify your comparison upon theoretical grounds.

17. State 5 chemical or physical characteristics of the element below iodine in group 7.

18. Which would you expect to be the stronger reducing agent, (a) Fe^{++} or Co^{++}; (b) H_2S or H_2Te? Explain your answer very briefly.

19. Which would you expect to be the stronger oxidizing agent, $Ni(OH)_2$ or $Fe(OH)_2$? Give the basis for your answer.

20. Deduce from the positions in the Periodic System of Ni and Co (a) whether Ni^{++} or Co^{++} is the stronger reducing agent; (b) whether $Ni(OH)_2$ or $Co(OH)_2$ is more easily soluble in NH_4OH; (c) which element is harder; (d) which has the higher melting point; (e) whether CoS or NiS is more soluble in water.

21. From your knowledge of the properties of Fe^{++} and Cu^{++}, compare (a) the solubility of NiS and CuS, (b) the stability of the ammonia complexes of Ni^{++} and Cu^{++}, (c) the oxidizing power of $Fe(OH)_3$ and $Ni(OH)_3$.

*22. On the basis of your knowledge of atomic structure, offer an explanation for the fact that the formula for mercurous ion is Hg_2^{++} rather than Hg^+.

23. The atoms X, Y, and Z have atomic weights increasing in that order. Y has 2, 8, 8, 1 electrons outside its nucleus. The atomic number of X is 15 less than that of Y, while Z's atomic number is greater (than X) by 26. From your knowledge of the Periodic Table identify X, Y, and Z. Which is the strongest reducing agent? Which has the greatest tendency to form complex ions?

24. Compare the basic properties of the hydroxides of sodium, magnesium, and aluminum, and explain very briefly in terms of the atomic structure of these elements.

25. The elements A, B, C, D, E have atomic numbers 11, 1, 18, 20, and 17 respectively. (a) Which are metals? (b) What compounds

*Question of greater difficulty.

does E form with the others. (Use the symbols above in writing formulas of compounds.) (c) If the atomic weight of D is 41, how many neutrons are in its nucleus?

26. Compare Cu and K as to (a) atomic radius, (b) ionizing potential, (c) structure of outer electrons of the +1 ion, (d) electric conductivity, (e) heat conductivity, (f) melting point, (g) density, (h) atomic number, (i) strength as reducing agents, (j) tendency to form complex ions.

CHAPTER XVIII

ORGANIC CHEMISTRY

1. An understanding of molecular structure was first obtained in connection with the compounds of carbon. Both plants and animals are made up chiefly of carbon compounds, from which it is evident that nature has prepared an enormous variety of them. It used to be thought that such compounds could be synthesized only through the aid of living matter, whence they were called **organic** compounds. Although we have since learned that no such limitation exists, we still designate the chemistry of the carbon compounds as **organic chemistry,** and find it advantageous, on account of its peculiarities, to treat it as a very distinct branch of chemistry. The labors of chemists have added greatly to the number of carbon compounds until today there are known over 200,000 of them. The majority contain only carbon, hydrogen, oxygen, and nitrogen. Now the simple determination of the number of atoms of each kind in the molecule does not suffice to identify the substance, or to suggest methods for its preparation, any more than given amounts of lumber, nails, bricks, mortar, etc., would serve to identify a house. Indeed there are many instances where several substances contain atoms of the same kind and number. For example, there are two substances having the formula C_2H_6O: one is ordinary alcohol, a liquid with a boiling point of 78° C. and a density of 0.789 at 20° C.; the other is dimethyl ether, a gas which becomes liquid at − 23.6° C. under 1 atmosphere pressure, and which has a different odor and generally different properties. Taking a more complex formula such as $C_6H_{12}O_6$, we find a much larger number of corresponding substances, in this case not less than 64. Such substances are called **isomers.** The differences in their properties can, of course, be due only to differences in arrangement of the atoms within the several molecules. The determination of this arrangement has therefore been a fundamental task in the study of carbon compounds.

2. The nature of the evidence used in the determination of the structure of these molecules is not difficult to comprehend. **The first principle used is that the covalence of carbon is four.** It is rarely if ever necessary to assume that any carbon atom is surrounded by more than four other atoms. Thus we may start with CH_4, which is known as methane or marsh gas, and is a prominent constituent of natural gas, and in which we might be inclined to say that the carbon is negative, and we can change progressively, by the successive substitution of chlorine for hydrogen, to CH_3Cl, CH_2Cl_2, $CHCl_3$, which is chloroform, and finally CCl_4 (used in fire extinguishers and in cleaning). In this last we would doubtless conclude that the carbon is positive, but in the intermediate compounds we see that the question of sign becomes rather confusing. Since we usually consider hydrogen positive and chlorine negative, we might assume the charges on the carbon to be -2 in CH_3Cl, 0 in CH_2Cl_2, and $+2$ in $CHCl_3$, that is, different in all five cases. However, we note that in all of them the carbon remains attached to four other atoms, without regard to sign.

The organic chemist takes as fundamental the existence of four "bonds" for every carbon atom. Each bond is usually indicated by a simple dash, thus the four compounds given above are usually written as follows:

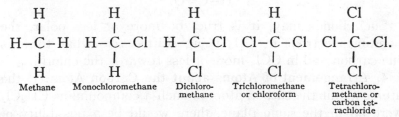

If a "bivalent" element is combined with carbon it is assumed that two of the bonds of carbon are required, thus forming a "double bond," in harmony with the fact that a carbon atom can hold but two atoms of oxygen, as shown by the following formulas:

$$\begin{array}{c} \text{H} \\ | \\ \text{H}-\text{C}=\text{O} \\ \text{\footnotesize Formaldehyde} \end{array} \qquad\qquad \begin{array}{c} \text{O}=\text{C}=\text{O.} \\ \text{\footnotesize Carbon dioxide} \end{array}$$

Other examples of formulas written upon this basis will be found later in this chapter.

3. The Electron-Pair or Covalent Bond. The reason for the four bonds per carbon atom is seen in the four valence electrons, each forming a pair with an unpaired electron from another atom. The hydrogen atom, .H, and the chlorine atom, $\overset{..}{.\,\text{Cl}}\overset{}{:}$, alike have one such electron and can form not only

$$\begin{array}{c} \text{H} \\ \overset{..}{\text{H}:\text{C}:\text{H}} \\ \text{H} \end{array} \qquad \text{and} \qquad \begin{array}{c} :\overset{..}{\text{Cl}}: \\ :\overset{..}{\text{Cl}}:\overset{..}{\text{C}}:\overset{..}{\text{Cl}}: \\ :\overset{..}{\text{Cl}}: \end{array}$$

but the intermediate compounds as well. An oxygen atom, O, can take up 2 of the electrons of a carbon atom, leaving the other two free to unite, say, with hydrogen, giving

$$\begin{array}{c} \text{H} \\ \overset{..}{\text{H}:\text{C}::\overset{..}{\text{O}}:} \end{array}$$

which would be written ordinarily with a "double bond" between C and O, thus,

$$\begin{array}{c} \text{H} \\ | \\ \text{H}-\text{C}=\text{O.} \end{array}$$

Such bonds may, it is true, be more or less polar, the bonding electrons in CH_4 being shifted somewhat towards the carbon and in CCl_4 more or less towards the chlorine.

4. Arrangement of Atoms about the Carbon Atom. If the atoms about the carbon atom in such a compound as CH_2Cl_2 were all in the same plane, there would be a possibility of two arrangements which might give rise to isomers having somewhat different properties, as follows:

$$
\begin{array}{ccccc}
& H & & & Cl \\
& | & & & | \\
H- & C & -Cl & H- & C & -H. \\
& | & & & | \\
& Cl & & & Cl
\end{array}
$$

In one case the like atoms are adjacent, in the other they are opposite. The fact is, however, that neither in this case, nor yet when any other atoms or groups have been substituted for the hydrogen and chlorine respectively, has it been possible to prepare different isomers. However, if the surrounding atoms or radicals are arranged in tetrahedral form about the central atom, as shown in Fig. 1, there can be only one arrangement, for each corner of a tetrahedron is adjacent to every other.

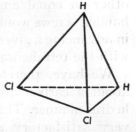

Fig. 1. Tetrahedral arrangement about a carbon atom.

The non-existence of such isomers, therefore, is evidence for the tetrahedral arrangement.

This tetrahedral arrangement again corresponds to the nature of the isomers found in cases where the central carbon

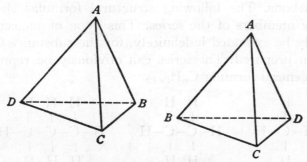

Fig. 2. Optical isomerism.

atom is surrounded by four different atoms or groups. Figure 2 shows two arrangements which are different in the sense that the right and left hands are different, or right- and left-handed screws are different. In each case, one is the mirror image of the other. These are called **asymmetric** forms. There exist great numbers of such isomers, alike in all ordinary properties, just as right- and left-handed screws may be identical in weight, form, etc., but which show a remarkable difference in optical behavior. Light which is made to vibrate all in one plane, or polarized, when passing through one of these isomers will be rotated to the right, and through the other an equal amount to the left, just as right- and left-handed screws would be rotated equally in opposite directions in advancing a given distance. This behavior is thus consistent with the tetrahedral structure.

We have, therefore, very good evidence that the atoms about a carbon atom are arranged approximately in tetrahedral manner. The representation of this upon paper is not very satisfactory since it requires the use of perspective, but since optical isomers are possible only when the four surrounding atoms or groups are different, it suffices for most compounds to use the plane arrangement.

5. Paraffin Series. The immense number of carbon compounds is chiefly due to the ability of carbon atoms to link to each other indefinitely. The simple linear arrangement of the carbon atoms gives rise to the **paraffin series** of hydrocarbons. The following structural formulas show the first few members of the series. This type of molecule can evidently be extended indefinitely, for the substance $C_{60}H_{122}$ has been prepared. The series can obviously be represented by the general formula C_nH_{2n+2}.

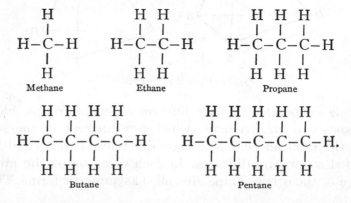

The characteristics of the series are indicated in Table 1, containing selected members. Its members are constituents of paraffin petroleums and the neighboring members come over together as the petroleum is distilled. The gaseous members are contained in natural gas, the low boiling liquids are in gasoline, and as the boiling points rise we find the substances successively in "distillate," kerosene, "light" and "heavy" lubricating oils. When the melting points enter the range of ordinary temperatures we get vaseline, then soft paraffin, and then hard paraffin.

Beginning with butane, isomers are possible. Thus we may have, in addition to the straight chain, an arrangement with a side chain, as follows, called isobutane.

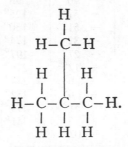

This has somewhat different properties, e.g., a boiling point of − 17° C., whereas normal butane boils at + 1° C. With pentane there are two additional isomers, and the number rapidly increases with increasing molecular complexity.

6. To justify these structures we must introduce a **second principle** used in determining molecular constitution of carbon compounds. This asserts that **in organic reactions ordinarily the smallest possible number of bonds are broken.** Organic reactions are characterized by a much greater slowness than most inorganic reactions. It is often necessary to heat the reacting substances together for hours. This inertness makes it possible to disturb only a part of the molecule, so that a certain group, or "radical," known to be present in the molecule before the reaction, is likely to remain intact in some product of the reaction.

7. Let us illustrate this principle. Ethane can have only the structure already assigned, in view of the covalences. By allowing bromine to act upon ethane in the presence of

TABLE 1

Paraffin Series of Hydrocarbons

Formula	Name	Melting point °C.	Boiling point °C.	Density	
CH_4	Methane	− 184°	− 161°		
C_2H_6	Ethane	− 172°	− 88°		
C_3H_8	Propane	− 190°	− 45°		
C_4H_{10}	Butane	− 135°	+ 1°		
C_5H_{12}	Pentane	− 131°	+ 36°		
C_6H_{14}	Hexane	− 94°	69°		
C_7H_{16}	Heptane	− 90°	98°	.700	At 0°
C_8H_{18}	Octane	− 57°	125°	.718	
C_9H_{20}	Nonane	− 51°	150°	.733	
$C_{10}H_{22}$	Decane	− 32°	174°	.745	
$C_{11}H_{24}$	Undecane	− 27°	197°	.774	
$C_{12}H_{26}$	Dodecane	− 12°	216°	.773	
$C_{13}H_{28}$	Tridecane	− 6°	234°	.775	
$C_{14}H_{30}$	Tetradecane	+ 6°	252°	.775	At the melting point
$C_{24}H_{50}$	Tetracosane	+ 51°	243° ⎫	.779	
$C_{35}H_{72}$	Pentatriacontane	+ 75°	331° ⎰ At 15 mm. pressure	.782	
$C_{60}H_{122}$	Dimyricyl	+ 102°	——	——	

light it is possible to replace hydrogen by bromine and to prepare monobromoethane, $C_2H_6 + Br_2 = C_2H_5Br + HBr$. This can hardly have any other than the ethane structure,

$$
\begin{array}{ccc}
\text{H} & \text{H} & \\
| & | & \\
\text{H}-\text{C}-\text{C}-\text{Br.} \\
| & | & \\
\text{H} & \text{H} &
\end{array}
$$

(Remember that all of the carbon bonds are alike, in view of their tetrahedral arrangement, so that the formula just written is identical with the following, which only appears to be different because they are written in one plane.)

$$\begin{array}{cc} H & H \\ | & | \\ H-C-C-H. \\ | & | \\ H & Br \end{array}$$

Now if this bromide is treated with zinc, we get zinc bromide and butane, the isomer boiling at $+ 1°$ C. It seems that the bromine has been removed and the remainders of the two molecules have joined together without further alteration. (This remainder, C_2H_5, is called the **ethyl radical**.) To consider this isomer as isobutane would obviously require us to assume that the reaction involved a much more complicated and hence far more improbable breaking and rejoining of bonds. Isobutane must be prepared in a very different way.

8. As a further example of the application of this principle to the determination of structure, let us consider the isomers first mentioned, ethyl alcohol and dimethyl ether, both C_2H_6O. Starting with the methane structure, we will consider CH_3- to be the **methyl radical**, which would be left by the removal of one atom of hydrogen. Methyl iodide (or monoiodomethane) when treated with a solution of KOH gives methyl hydroxide (methyl alcohol, "wood alcohol"),

$$\begin{array}{c} H \\ | \\ H-C-O-H. \\ | \\ H \end{array}$$

(Additional evidence for this structure will be given later.) Treatment with sodium replaces *one* hydrogen atom, giving

$$\begin{array}{c} H \\ | \\ H-C-O-Na. \\ | \\ H \end{array}$$

If this is allowed to react with methyl iodide, sodium iodide is produced, and the simplest possible way for the remainders

of the 2 molecules to react is simply to join together, with
an oxygen atom linking 2 methyl groups.

$$
\begin{array}{ccccc}
\text{H} & & \text{H} & \text{H} & \text{H} \\
| & & | & | & | \\
\text{H}-\text{C}-\text{O}-\boxed{\text{Na}+\text{I}}-\text{C}-\text{H} &=& \text{NaI}+\text{H}-\text{C}-\text{O}-\text{C}-\text{H}. \\
| & & | & | & | \\
\text{H} & & \text{H} & \text{H} & \text{H}
\end{array}
$$

This is the gaseous isomer, and is called dimethyl oxide, or
dimethyl ether.

The structure of the other isomer is indicated by the fact
that it is easily derived from ethyl bromide by the action
of a solution of KOH.

$$
\begin{array}{ccc}
\text{H}\ \text{H} & & \text{H}\ \text{H} \\
|\ \ | & & |\ \ | \\
\text{H}-\text{C}-\text{C}-\text{Br}+\text{KOH} &=& \text{H}-\text{C}-\text{C}-\text{OH}+\text{KBr}. \\
|\ \ | & & |\ \ | \\
\text{H}\ \text{H} & & \text{H}\ \text{H}
\end{array}
$$

This isomer, therefore, appears to be ethyl hydroxide in
structure. To assume that this reaction involves breaking
the bond between the carbon atoms to give dimethyl ether
would appear highly improbable, just as it would be to assume
that the previous reaction would directly link the carbon
atoms.

It is usually possible to prepare a given compound from
more than one source, or to decompose it in more than one
way. Where the same structural formula can account for
all known reactions it naturally inspires a high degree of
confidence. There are, however, cases where extensive re-
arrangements evidently take place during certain reactions.
The determination of structure in such cases has often proven
very difficult, and the history of organic chemistry is not
without its sharp controversies.

9. **Unsaturated Hydrocarbons.** There are a number of
hydrocarbons which contain less than the maximum amount
of hydrogen. Thus ethane is C_2H_6, while **ethylene** is C_2H_4.
The unused carbon bonds are commonly supposed to be

joined together, thus

$$\begin{array}{ccc} H & & H \\ \diagdown & & \diagup \\ & C=C & \\ \diagup & & \diagdown \\ H & & H \end{array}$$

giving a double bond. This corresponds to a bond of 4 electrons instead of 2, and may be represented

$$H : \overset{\cdot\cdot}{C} :: \overset{\cdot\cdot}{C} : H$$

The four electrons of the double bond are, of course, not stationary, and their motion, through different positions, called resonance, may lead to a variety of instantaneous configurations, including not only the above but also

$$H : \overset{\cdot\cdot}{\underset{\cdot\cdot}{C}} : \overset{}{C} : H \qquad \text{and} \qquad H : \overset{\cdot\cdot}{\underset{\cdot}{C}} : \overset{}{\underset{\cdot}{C}} : H$$

Such resonance may allow a compound to react in a way favored by one of these configurations even though the molecule spends but a small portion of the time therein.

The double bond is more or less readily "broken" by the addition of other atoms giving "saturated" compounds. Ethylene may be made to add more hydrogen, becoming ethane.

10. Still more hydrogen may be lacking, giving acetylene, C_2H_2, usually prepared by the action of water on calcium carbide,

$$CaC_2 + 2 H_2O = C_2H_2 + Ca(OH)_2.$$

The acetylene molecule requires the asumption of a **triple bond,** if the quadrivalence of carbon is to be maintained, and is written

$$H-C\equiv C-H.$$

Hydrocarbons with longer chains may have double or

triple bonds occurring anywhere in the chain, such as

$$H_3C-CH=CH_2, \text{ and } HC\equiv C-CH_2-CH_2-C\equiv CH.$$

11. Derivatives of the Paraffin Series. A hydrogen atom in a paraffin hydrocarbon may be replaced by another atom or radical giving different series of derived substances. The nomenclature of most of these is based upon the name of the univalent radical that would be left upon the hypothetical removal of an atom of hydrogen. The first eight of these radicals are as follows: CH_3- **methyl**; C_2H_5- **ethyl**; C_3H_7- **propyl**; C_4H_9- **butyl**; $C_5H_{11}-$ **amyl**; $C_6H_{13}-$ **hexyl**; $C_7H_{15}-$ **heptyl**; $C_8H_{17}-$ **octyl**. It will be seen that the names of all but the fifth are derived from those of the corresponding hydrocarbons. The radical $C_5H_{11}-$ might be called pentyl, but is called amyl instead.

The name of the derivative is thus simply derived in most cases from that of the radical: for example, C_2H_5Cl is ethyl chloride; C_4H_9I is butyl iodide; CH_3-O-CH_3 is dimethyl oxide, or, since such oxides are called ethers, dimethyl ether; $C_2H_5-O-C_3H_7$ is ethyl-propyl ether; $C_2H_5NO_3$ is ethyl nitrate. Other examples will appear in the following paragraphs.

12. Halogen Derivatives. Chlorine and bromine react directly with the hydrocarbons, replacing one or more hydrogen atoms. Iodine is substituted by way of other derivatives, for example, $CH_3OH + HI = CH_3I + H_2O$. A few examples of such derivatives have already been given. Other structures can be written *ad libitum* from the principles already given. Isomerism is encountered even in such a simple derivative as $C_2H_4Br_2$, which can be either

$$
\begin{array}{ccc}
\begin{array}{cc} H & H \\ | & | \\ H-C-C-H \\ | & | \\ Br & Br \end{array}
& \text{or} &
\begin{array}{cc} H & H \\ | & | \\ H-C-C-Br. \\ | & | \\ H & Br \end{array}
\end{array}
$$

The first is got by adding bromine to ethylene, and is therefore called ethylene bromide, while the second is called ethylidene bromide. (Both are dibromoethanes.)

13. Alcohols. The hydroxides of the paraffin radicals are the alcohols. In fact, the name alcohol has caused the radicals of the paraffin series to be called the **alkyl** radicals. If we represent such a radical by the symbol, Alk, we can express the general formula of an alcohol by the formula, AlkOH. The first member of the series is CH_3OH, called methyl alcohol or methanol. (This latter name is preferable, because it avoids the suggestion of beverage use, which is very dangerous.) It is one product of the destructive distillation of wood, hence the name "wood alcohol."

The second member is C_2H_5OH, ethyl alcohol or ethanol. This is the alcohol chiefly produced in fermentation. The layman usually thinks of it as the important constituent of various beverages, which he regards as a blessing or a curse, according to his point of view, but he rarely realizes that it plays an exceedingly important part in chemical industry.

14. We may introduce in this connection a **third principle** which aids in determining molecular constitution, which is that **substances which have similar constitution show similar behavior.**

Water may be regarded as hydrogen hydroxide, and methyl alcohol as methyl hydroxide, and this corresponds to the similarity of certain of their reactions, for example,

$$\begin{cases} HOH + Na = HONa + \tfrac{1}{2}H_2, \\ CH_3OH + Na = CH_3ONa + \tfrac{1}{2}H_2, \end{cases}$$

$$\begin{cases} 3\,HOH + PBr_3 = 3\,HBr + H_3PO_3, \\ 3\,CH_3OH + PBr_3 = 3\,CH_3Br + H_3PO_3. \end{cases}$$

Again, the alcohols act similarly to bases in some of their reactions, as shown by the equations

$$\begin{cases} NaOH + HCl = H_2O + NaCl, \\ CH_3OH + HCl = H_2O + CH_3Cl, \end{cases}$$

$$\begin{cases} NaOH + H_2SO_4 = H_2O + NaHSO_4, \\ CH_3OH + H_2SO_4 = H_2O + CH_3HSO_4, \end{cases}$$

$$\begin{cases} 2\,CuOH = Cu_2O + H_2O, \\ 2\,CH_3OH = (CH_3)_2O + H_2O. \end{cases}$$

The graphic formulas of the alcohols should, therefore, be related to those of water and bases in being hydroxides.

$$H-O-H \qquad Na-O-H \qquad \underset{\displaystyle H}{\overset{\displaystyle H}{H-\underset{|}{\overset{|}{C}}-O-H.}}$$

Alcohols are divided into three classes, according to the number of carbon atoms linked to the one bearing the hydroxyl. The three structures are:

Primary   Secondary   Tertiary

The vacant bonds may be occupied by either hydrogen or further carbon atoms. There are also alcohols containing more than one hydroxyl. We will mention only two, glycol, and glycerol or glycerin.

Glycol   Glycerol

15. Ethers. When alcohols are distilled with sulfuric acid water is removed and alkyl oxides, called ethers, are produced, as illustrated by the preceding reaction. The most important is diethyl ether, used extensively as an anaesthetic. The general formula of an ether is Alk—O—Alk. The two alkyl groups need not be the same.

16. Ketones. The primary, secondary, and tertiary alcohols behave differently upon oxidation. The tertiary are split up into simpler products. The secondary are changed to ketones, whose general formula is

$$\text{Alk} - \underset{\underset{\displaystyle O}{\|}}{C} - \text{Alk}.$$

Thus secondary propyl alcohol,

$$\begin{array}{c} CH_3 \\ | \\ H-C-OH \\ | \\ CH_3 \end{array}$$

would give dimethyl ketone,

$$\begin{array}{c} CH_3 \\ | \\ C=O \\ | \\ CH_3 \end{array}$$

commonly called acetone, a liquid much used as a solvent for varnishes, etc.

17. Aldehydes. The primary alcohols upon mild oxidation give first aldehydes, characterized by the group

$$-\underset{\underset{\displaystyle O}{\|}}{C} - H.$$

The simplest aldehyde is H_2CO, formaldehyde, made by passing air and vapors of methyl alcohol over a glowing platinum catalyst. It is a gas, soluble in water or alcohol, and is much used as a disinfectant. The second is acetaldehyde,

$$
\begin{array}{c}
\text{H} \\
| \\
\text{H}-\text{C}-\text{C}-\text{H.} \\
| \quad || \\
\text{H} \quad \text{O}
\end{array}
$$

The next would have ethyl in place of methyl, and so on.

18. Acids. The further oxidation of the aldehyde group gives the **carboxyl** group,

$$
\begin{array}{c}
-\text{C}-\text{O}-\text{H}, \\
|| \\
\text{O}
\end{array}
\qquad \text{often written} \qquad -\text{COOH},
$$

characteristic of organic acids. Ethyl alcohol thus finally becomes acetic acid,

$$
\begin{array}{c}
\text{H} \\
| \\
\text{H}-\text{C}-\text{C}-\text{O}-\text{H}, \\
| \quad || \\
\text{H} \quad \text{O}
\end{array}
$$

in the process of forming vinegar. The acids of the paraffin series include many important substances. The following are the names corresponding to the number of carbon atoms present: 1, formic; 2, acetic; 3, propionic; 4, butyric (the acid responsible for the odor of rancid butter); 4, valeric; 16, palmitic; 18, stearic. We may mention also oleic acid, which differs from stearic in having a double bond between two of its carbon atoms. The sodium salts of these last three acids are present in ordinary soaps.

There are other acids containing more than one carboxyl group, such as

$$
\begin{array}{ccc}
& & \text{O}=\text{C}-\text{O}-\text{H} \\
& & | \\
& \text{O}=\text{C}-\text{O}-\text{H} & \text{H}-\text{C}-\text{H} \\
& | & | \\
\text{O}=\text{C}-\text{OH} & \text{H}-\text{C}-\text{H} & \text{H}-\text{C}-\text{H} \\
| & | & | \\
\text{O}=\text{C}-\text{OH} & \text{O}=\text{C}-\text{O}-\text{H} & \text{O}=\text{C}-\text{O}-\text{H.} \\
\text{Oxalic acid} & \text{Malonic acid} & \text{Succinic acid}
\end{array}
$$

There are others containing both carboxyl and hydroxyl groups, such as tartaric acid, one of the acids of grapes, and citric acid, the acid of lemons and oranges.

$$
\begin{array}{cc}
O=C-O-H & \\
| & \\
H-C-O-H & H_2C-COOH \\
| & | \\
H-C-O-H & H-O-C-COOH \\
| & | \\
O=C-O-H & H_2C-COOH. \\
\text{Tartaric acid} & \text{Citric acid}
\end{array}
$$

The two middle carbon atoms of tartaric acid are joined each to four different atoms or groups, so that optical isomers are possible. The construction of tetrahedral models is necessary to make this altogether clear. Citric acid has no asymmetric carbon atom.

19. Esters. We have seen that the alcohols are hydroxides, analogous to bases, and that they react with acids (slowly) with elimination of water (which is usually removed by mixing with sulfuric acid) to form substances analogous to salts; these are called esters. We may have esters of either inorganic or organic acids. We have already given examples of the former. The latter may be illustrated as follows:

$$
C_2H_5OH + H-O-C-CH_3 \rightarrow C_2H_5-O-C-CH_3 + H_2O.
$$
$$
\underset{\text{Ethyl alcohol}}{} \qquad \underset{\text{Acetic acid}}{\overset{\displaystyle O}{\|}} \qquad \qquad \underset{\text{Ethyl acetate}}{\overset{\displaystyle O}{\|}}
$$

The esters of the organic acids are pleasant smelling liquids, many of which are used in artificial flavorings.

Glycerol forms important esters. Its trinitrate is commonly called nitroglycerin, which is a constituent of dynamite and of smokeless powders. Its esters with the higher paraffin acids are the fats. Glyceryl tripalmitate is palmitin, the chief constituent of palm oil; glyceryl tristearate is stearin, the chief constituent of beef tallow; glyceryl trioleate is olein, found in olive oil, lard, etc. Most fats and oils of animal or vegetable origin contain varying amounts of these esters.

20. Amines. The substitution of the hydrogen atoms of ammonia by alkyl radicals gives amines.

$$
\begin{array}{cccc}
\text{H} & \text{H} & \text{H} & \text{CH}_3 \\
| & | & | & | \\
\text{N--H} & \text{N--CH}_3 & \text{N--CH}_3 & \text{N--CH}_3. \\
| & | & | & | \\
\text{H} & \text{H} & \text{CH}_3 & \text{CH}_3
\end{array}
$$

| Ammonia | Methylamine A primary amine | Dimethylamine A secondary amine | Trimethylamine A tertiary amine |

The amines obey the rule regarding the parallelism of properties and structure in that they are chemically like ammonia.

21. The combination of $-NH_2$ and $-COOH$ in the same molecule gives an **amino acid.** These are peculiar in having both a basic and an acidic group; hence both are weak, and there is the possibility of self-neutralization. These acids can combine with each other indefinitely to form the proteins, essential constituents of our food, and the basic material of living organisms.

22. Cyclic Compounds. In all of the preceding compounds we have straight or branching chains of carbon atoms. There is another important class of organic compounds in which the carbon atoms are joined to form closed rings. They are called cyclic or **aromatic** compounds, to distinguish them from the straight chain or **aliphatic** compounds.

The most important aromatic compound is **benzene,** C_6H_6, in which the carbon atoms form a ring with a hydrogen atom on each,

$$
\begin{array}{ccc}
\text{H} & & \text{H} \\
\text{C} & & \text{C} \\
\text{HC}\diagup\ \ \diagdown\text{CH} & \text{or} & \text{HC}\diagup\ \ \diagdown\text{CH} \\
\text{HC}\diagdown\ \ \diagup\text{CH} & & \text{HC}\diagdown\ \ \diagup\text{CH} \\
\text{C} & & \text{C} \\
\text{H} & & \text{H}
\end{array}
$$

(a) Armstrong and Beyer   (b) Kekulé

23. Resonance in the Benzene Molecule. What to do about the fourth carbon bond has always been something of a problem, for the organic chemist does not like to abandon the quadrivalence of carbon, in spite of the extraordinary stability of benzene. Indeed, the extra bond can be called into play, strong reduction adding six more hydrogen atoms. Kekulé drew alternating double and single bonds, as shown at (b), but benzene does not show the ordinary reactions of the double bond, such as the addition of bromine. If the carbon bonds are represented in tetrahedral form, it is possible to construct a very compact structure corresponding to the first formula.

It seems probable that the extra electrons or bonds in the benzene molecule are not permanently in any one position, such as those represented by the above two formulas, but are moving about with great rapidity from one extreme Kekulé formula to the other, with the double bonds in the alternate positions, with the Armstrong and Beyer position traversed on the way. There is reason to believe that still another position is involved, represented by

$$
\begin{array}{ccc}
 & \overset{\displaystyle H}{\underset{\displaystyle C}{}} & \\
 & / \; | \; \backslash & \\
HC & & CH \\
\| & & \| \\
HC & & CH. \\
 & \backslash \; | \; / & \\
 & \underset{\displaystyle H}{C} & \\
\end{array}
$$

In representing the benzene ring for ordinary purposes we usually ignore the above complexities and write a simple hexagon, with hydrogen understood at the corners unless occupied by some other element or radical.

Evidence for the ring structure is found, first, in the fact that when one hydrogen atom is substituted by something else, say bromine, giving monobromobenzene, there are no isomers. On the other hand, if bromine is substituted in the corresponding open chain, such as hexane, three isomers are possible, depending upon whether the bromine is on the end carbon, next to the end, or the third from the end.

Additional evidence is furnished by the number of disubstitution products. There are three dibromobenzenes, corresponding to the three following arrangements:

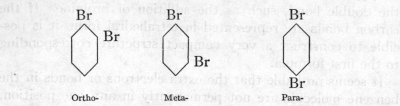

Ortho-   Meta-   Para-

Which of the three substances actually corresponds to each arrangement is readily determined by substituting a third hydrogen atom, when the orthodibromobenzene can give two isomeric tribromobenzenes, the meta three and the para only one.

24. Benzene Derivatives. If we designate the benzene ring minus one of its hydrogen atoms as the **phenyl** radical by the symbol ϕ, then we can represent very simply a few of the important derivatives as follows:

ϕ OH	Phenol (carbolic acid)
ϕ COOH	Benzoic acid
ϕ CH$_3$	Toluene
ϕ NH$_2$	Aniline
ϕ NO$_2$	Nitrobenzene
ϕ CH$_2$OH	Benzyl alcohol
ϕ CHO	Benzaldehyde
ϕ CO $\cdot$ CH$_3$	Phenyl methyl ketone
$\phi-N=N-\phi$	Azobenzene
$\phi-\phi$	Diphenyl

Further substitutions may be made, as in

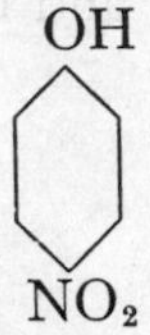

OH	NH$_2$	CH$_3$	COOH

Br $\bigcirc$ Br

$\bigcirc$ COOH

$\bigcirc$ OH

NO$_2$ Br

Paranitrophenol	Tribromaniline	Metatoluic acid	Orthohydroxybenzoic acid (Salicylic acid)

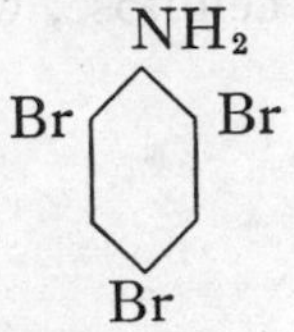

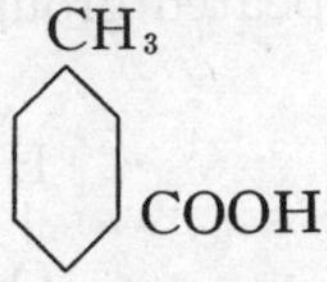

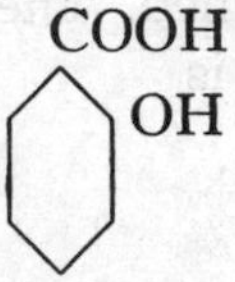

The artificial dyestuffs are rather complicated molecules, most of which contain one or more benzene rings. One of the simplest is indigo,

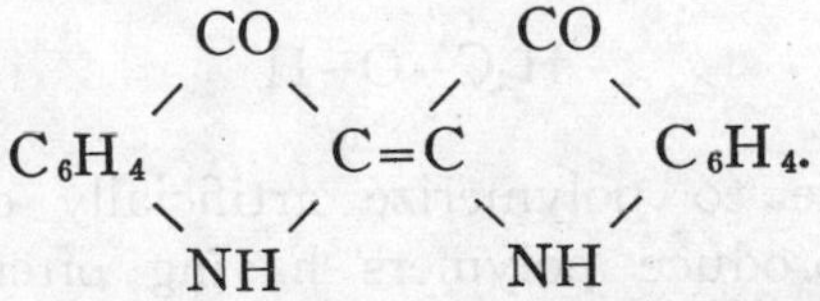

$$
\begin{array}{ccc}
\text{CO} & & \text{CO} \\
\diagup \quad \diagdown & \diagup & \diagdown \\
\text{C}_6\text{H}_4 \quad\quad \text{C}=\text{C} & & \text{C}_6\text{H}_4. \\
\diagdown \quad \diagup & \diagdown \quad \diagup \\
\text{NH} & & \text{NH}
\end{array}
$$

There are other substances containing several benzene rings linked together, illustrated by the following:

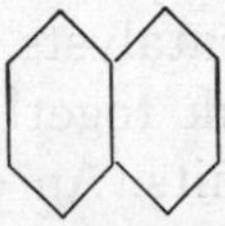

Naphthalene	Anthracene

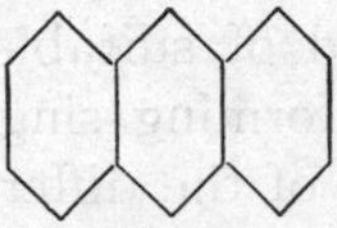

25. Polymers. Many natural organic materials owe their usefulness to their mechanical strength or their elasticity, and to the fact that they do not dissolve easily in the ordinary liquids which are likely to come in contact. Wood, cotton, wool, silk, and rubber are familiar examples. These properties arise from continuous linking of atoms, usually in chains in which certain groups are repeated over and over again, whence they are called polymers. Natural rubber consists of indefinitely long chains in which the repeated group is

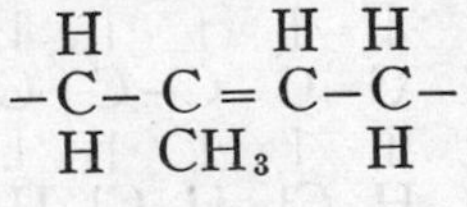

$$
\begin{array}{ccc}
\text{H} & \text{H} & \text{H} \\
-\text{C}- & \text{C} = \text{C} - & \text{C}- \\
\text{H} & \text{CH}_3 & \text{H}
\end{array}
$$

The single carbon-carbon bonds are tetrahedrally arranged,

so that the atoms form a zigzag chain which can be bent or stretched. The repeated group in cellulose, wood and cotton fiber, is

$$
\begin{array}{cc}
\text{H} & \text{H} \\
| & | \\
\text{O} & \text{O} \\
| & | \\
\text{H–C–C–H} \\
\diagup \quad \diagdown \\
\text{–C} \qquad \text{C–} \\
\diagup \quad | \\
\text{H} \quad \text{H–C–O} \quad \text{H} \\
| \\
\text{H}_2\text{C–O–H}
\end{array}
$$

It is possible to polymerize artificially certain simple molecules to produce polymers having often very useful properties. Probably the simplest type of polymerization occurs with molecules having double bonds on the carbon atoms at each end of the chain. These bonds can be opened up by the aid of suitable reagents or catalysts, furnishing electrons for forming single bonds to link together the end carbon atoms of the different building units. An exceedingly simple case is presented by the formation of "koroseal," a rubberlike polymer. The following are the steps in the formation:

$$
\begin{array}{ccccc}
\text{H H} & & \text{H H} & & \text{H H} \\
| \ | & & | \ | & & | \ | \\
\text{C=C} & \xrightarrow{\text{Cl}_2} & \text{Cl–C–C–Cl} & \xrightarrow{\text{NaOH}} & \text{C=C} \\
| \ | & & | \ | & & | \ | \\
\text{H H} & & \text{H H} & & \text{H Cl} \\
\text{Ethylene} & & \text{Ethylene chloride} & & \text{Vinyl chloride}
\end{array}
$$

$$
\begin{array}{c}
\text{H H H H H H H H} \\
| \ | \ | \ | \ | \ | \ | \ | \\
\text{etc.–C–C–C–C–C–C–C–C–etc.} \\
| \ | \ | \ | \ | \ | \ | \ | \\
\text{H Cl H Cl H Cl H Cl} \\
\text{"Koroseal"}
\end{array}
$$

The result is an artificial rubber, inert to oxidizing agents and oils, for which there are many uses.

A similar process yields "neoprene."

$$
H-C\equiv C-H \longrightarrow \underset{\text{Acetylene}}{\overset{\displaystyle H \quad\quad H\ \ H}{\underset{\displaystyle H}{C\equiv C-C=C}}} \xrightarrow{\text{HCl}} \underset{\text{Chloroprene}}{\overset{\displaystyle H \quad\quad\quad H}{\underset{\displaystyle H\ \ Cl\ \ H\ \ H}{C=C-C=C}}} \longrightarrow
$$

$$
\underset{\text{Neoprene}}{\text{etc.}-\overset{\displaystyle H}{\underset{\displaystyle H}{C}}-\overset{\displaystyle\ }{\underset{\displaystyle Cl}{C}}=\overset{\displaystyle\ }{\underset{\displaystyle H}{C}}-\overset{\displaystyle H}{\underset{\displaystyle H}{C}}-\text{etc.}}
$$

The repeated unit in "plexiglass," or "lucite," used for windows of airplanes is

$$
\begin{array}{cc}
H & CH_3 \\
| & | \\
-C & -C- \\
| & | \\
H & C=O \\
 & | \\
 & O-CH_3
\end{array}
$$

The unit of "nylon," a now well-known, valuable substitute for silk is

$$
\underset{\underset{\displaystyle H\ \ H\ \ H\ \ H}{|\ \ |\ \ |\ \ |}}{\overset{\overset{\displaystyle O\ \ H\ \ H\ \ H\ \ H\ \ O\quad\quad H\ \ H\ \ H\ \ H\ \ H\ \ H}{\|\ \ |\ \ |\ \ |\ \ |\ \ \|\quad\quad\ |\ \ |\ \ |\ \ |\ \ |\ \ |}}{-C-C-C-C-C-C-N-C-C-C-C-C-C-N-}}
$$

Two different molecules are linked together to form the repeating unit in both "butyl rubber" and "buna-S" or "styrene" rubber, as follows:

$$
\begin{array}{cccc}
\overset{\displaystyle H}{\underset{\displaystyle H}{|}} & & \overset{\displaystyle H}{\underset{\displaystyle H}{|}} & \overset{\displaystyle H}{\underset{\displaystyle H}{|}}\ \overset{\displaystyle CH_3}{\underset{\displaystyle CH_3}{|}}
\end{array}
$$

C=C–C=C + C=C → –C–C=C–C–C–C–

Butadiene   Isobutylene   Butyl rubber

Butadiene + C=CH₂ → –C–C=C–C–C–C–

Stryene   Styrene rubber

The above are only illustrations selected from a long list of polymers that have achieved great commercial prominence during recent years.[1]

26. Silicones.[2] An interesting and useful series of compounds has recently come into prominence in which silicon atoms are involved in place of carbon. Metallic magnesium reacts with a mixture of an organic chloride, RCl and $SiCl_4$ to yield compounds of the type R_mSiCl_n, where $m + n = 4$, which can undergo further changes, as follows:

$$
RSiCl_3 \xrightarrow{H_2O} RSi(OH)_3 \longrightarrow
\begin{matrix}
R & & R \\
| & & | \\
-Si-O-Si-O- \\
| & & | \\
O & & O \\
| & & | \\
 & R & \\
 & | & \\
\end{matrix}
$$

$$
R_2SiCl_2 \xrightarrow{H_2O} R_2Si(OH)_2 \longrightarrow
\begin{matrix}
R \\
| \\
-Si-O- \\
| \\
R
\end{matrix}
$$

$$
R_3SiCl \xrightarrow{H_2O} R_3SiOH \longrightarrow R_3Si-O-SiR_3
$$

---

[1]References: P. O. Powers, "Synthetic Resins and Synthetic Rubbers," *Chemical and Engineering News*, Vol. 20, p. 536 (1942). H. L. Fisher, "Synthetic Rubbers," *Ibid.*, Vol. 21, p. 781 (1943).

[2]Reference, Shailer L. Bass *et al.*, "Silicones—High Polymeric Substances,"

The first two types are repeating units in polymers, the third type gives liquids with low freezing points, low vapor pressures, low rates of change of viscosity with temperature, remarkable chemical stability. Greases have been prepared which do not melt between − 40° C. and 200° C. A plastic material has been produced which can be moulded with the fingers, like putty, but will bounce like rubber when thrown onto the floor.

Exercises

1. Write formulas of the following so as to show the constituent radicals.

(*a*) Propyl alcohol, (*b*) Methyl-ethyl ether, (*c*) Dibutyl ketone, (*d*) Amyl acetate, (*e*) An aldehyde containing two carbon atoms, (*f*) An acid containing six carbon atoms, (*g*) Hexyl chloride, (*h*) Ethyl nitrate, (*i*) Diphenyl ketone, (*j*) Pentadecane, (*k*) Dimethyl sulfate, (*l*) Ethyl sulfide, (*m*) Dipropyl oxalate, (*n*) Methyl amine, (*o*) Propyl cyanide, (*p*) Dichloromethane, (*q*) Trichloromethane, (*r*) Glyceryl triacetate, (*s*) Phenyl amine, (*t*) Acetic anhydride.

2. Name the following compounds:

(*a*) C_3H_7Br, (*b*) $CH_3-CO-CH_3$, (*c*) $C_8H_{17}NH_2$, (*d*) C_6H_6 (cyclic), (*e*) $CH_3COOC_5H_{11}$, (*f*) $C_4H_9-O-C_2H_5$, (*g*) $C_2H_4(OH)_2$, (*h*) a hydrocarbon with ten carbon atoms and twenty-two hydrogens, (*i*) CH_3COOH, (*j*) C_2H_5OH, (*k*) C_6H_5COOH (cyclic), (*l*) $HCHO$, (*m*) C_2H_4.

3. Give the principles used in determining the structure of organic compounds.

4. What evidence is there that the benzene molecule has a ring structure?

5. Define: isomer, organic chemistry, aromatic compound, aliphatic compound, unsaturated compound.

6. Show the structural formulas for all the isomers of monobromobutane (C_4H_9Br).

7. Certain organic compounds have the property of rotating the plane of polarization of polarized light which passes through them.

(*a*) What property of the molecule is responsible for this effect?

Modern Plastics, Vol. 22, pp. 124–126, 212, 214 (November, 1944). E. G. Rochow, "The Organosilicon Polymers," *Chemical and Engineering News*, Vol. 23, p. 612 (1945).

(b) Give the structural formula of a molecule which has this property.

8. Three isomeric dichlorobenzenes, $C_6H_4Cl_2$, have the following different melting points, (a) $-24.8°$, (b) $-17.6°$, (c) $+52.9°$. When an additional Cl is substituted for H in the benzene ring, the first gives 3 different trichlorobenzenes, the second gives two, and the third gives one. Identify the dichlorobenzenes as ortha, meta, and para respectively.

9. How many dichloro-propanes are there?

10. How many isomeric monochloro-monobromo-propanes are there?

*****11.** How many optical isomers are possible with monochloro, monobromo ethane?

*****12.** "Mustard gas" vapor is toxic in a concentration of about 0.02 milligram per cubic meter. What is its partial pressure at that concentration in millimeters of mercury? Its formula is $C_4H_8Cl_2S$.

*Questions of greater difficulty.

CHAPTER XIX

DISPERSED SYSTEMS

1. In Chapter I a distinction was made between heterogeneous and homogeneous material, between mechanical mixtures and solutions. It was there pointed out, however, that, while such distinctions as this are often useful, there may be no sharp line of demarcation. We here deliberately examine the intermediate zone. If we have a bottle containing water in the lower portion and moist air in the upper, we would not hesitate to call the system heterogeneous. Even if the water were blown into the air from an atomizer, we would doubtless still consider the system heterogeneous. Suppose, however, that we could break up the droplets into successively smaller and smaller ones, ending finally with molecules of water vapor in air. The system finally resulting we would have to consider as homogeneous. At what stage in the disintegration process, we may well ask, did the system cease to be heterogeneous and become homogeneous? We might imagine a similar gradation starting with sand and water, which would be heterogeneous, through successively finer and finer suspensions of silica powder in water until we would have a solution of silica molecules in water. There is, evidently, no sharp boundary between systems certainly heterogeneous, on the one hand, and solutions, on the other hand, and between these two extremes there are systems which should have some of the characteristics of both. These we will call **dispersed** systems, one phase being highly dispersed in another. The following scheme gives a survey of the types of dispersed systems, classified according to the nature of the phases. We distinguish, on the one hand, between the dispersed phase, .which is discontinuous, minute isolated

particles, drops or bubbles, and the dispersing medium, on the other hand, which is continuous.

Dispersed phase	Inclosing phase	Type
Liquid	Gas	Fog
Gas	Liquid	Foam
Solid	Gas	Smoke
Gas	Solid	Solid foam (e.g., pumice)
Liquid	Liquid	Emulsion
Solid	Liquid	Suspension
Liquid	Solid	
Solid	Solid	Many alloys

In addition there are systems, such as sponge, charcoal, and gelatin jelly where both phases are continuous, with a network structure.

The most important of these from a chemical stand point are emulsions and suspensions, and our attention will be largely confined to them.

2. Brownian Movement. As the dispersed phase in suspensions and emulsions becomes more and more finely divided it is possible to get systems in which the two phases do not separate on standing under the influence of gravity. A relatively large body like a grain of sand, dropped into water, will fall through the water at a rate of speed dependent on its size, the difference in density between it and water, and the viscosity of the water. A very small sand particle will fall more slowly through the water, because as the size diminishes, the surface, upon which the resistance depends, does not decrease as fast as the weight. Fine suspensions, therefore, settle out more slowly than coarse ones. When a sufficiently minute particle is observed with a microscope it may be seen that it no longer falls in a straight line, but follows an irregular zigzag path. The reason for this is as follows: the molecules of water, according to the kinetic theory, are in rapid motion, with a mean kinetic energy proportional to the absolute temperature. In disordered motion of this sort some molecules, at a given instant, will be moving more rapidly and some more slowly than the average. When the particle of sand is so large compared with the water molecules that it is being bombarded by a very large number of the latter, the effect of differences in their kinetic energy will be neutralized; but when the particle is sufficiently minute, an especially hard impact on one side of it may not be neutralized by the impacts of other molecules on the other side, hence the particle will be slightly displaced. Since these abnormally hard impacts are constantly

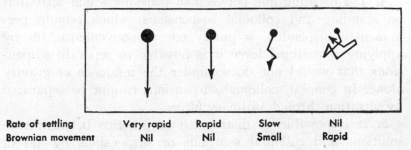

Rate of settling	Very rapid	Rapid	Slow	Nil
Brownian movement	Nil	Nil	Small	Rapid

Fig. 1.   Effect of size on particle sedimentation.

occurring irregularly from different directions the result is the irregular zigzag movement of the particle above referred to. As smaller and smaller particles are taken, the chances for inequality in the momentum of the impacts upon them increase, and their resulting displacement also increases, for a molecule of water striking a small body will have more effect on it than upon a larger one. In fact it can be seen by the aid of the microscope that the particles of fine suspension are in much more violent motion than those of a coarse suspension. This progression is illustrated in Fig. 1. This movement is known from its discoverer as the **Brownian movement,** and gives us very direct evidence of the truth of the kinetic theory.

3. When sufficiently fine particles are taken, the Brownian movement overcomes the effect of gravity so that the particles remain in permanent suspension. The system is then known as a **colloidal suspension,** or **colloidal solution.** There will be,

in such a suspension, if time is allowed, an increasing concentration of particles from the upper to the lower portions
of the vessel, analogous to the increasing concentration of
the atmosphere from high altitudes to lower. In fact, a French
physical chemist, Perrin, showed that the rate of increase
in the concentration of the particles in suspensions obeys
the same laws that govern the change in barometric pressure
with altitude, a most striking proof of the truth of the kinetic
theory and of the real existence of molecules.

4. The dividing line between suspensions which settle out
on standing and colloidal suspensions, which remain permanently suspended, is purely one of convenience, for by
applying centrifugal force it is possible to separate suspensions that would not do so under the influence of gravity
alone. In general, colloidal suspensions cannot be separated
by filtration through ordinary filters.

5. It is possible to distinguish in practice between true
solutions and colloidal solutions or suspensions by aid of
the great differences in their rates of diffusion. The Brownian
movement of colloidal particles is so much less than the
movement of the much smaller molecules of substances in
true solution that the former diffuse from regions of greater
to regions of smaller concentration with much less rapidity.
The first distinction between the two types of solutions
was made upon this basis by Graham, in 1862. He obtained
the following figures for the time required for the equal
diffusion of various substances:

HCl	1	MgSO$_4$	7
NaCl	2.3	Albumin	49
Sugar	7	Caramel	98

To the class of substances which diffuse slowly he gave
the name **colloids**, from the Greek name for glue, a member
of this class.

6. The molecular weight can be calculated from the rate
of diffusion and also from the lowering in vapor pressure or
in freezing point, as explained in Chapter IV. These methods

all agree in ascribing very high moelcular weights to substances in colloidal solution, as is to be expected. The following figures illustrate the values found:

Substance	Molecular weight
Egg albumen	20,000
Gelatin	40,000
Pepsin	12,000

7. Optical Properties of Colloidal Suspensions. When a colloidal suspension is viewed by transmitted light it usually appears homogeneous, like a true solution, its color depending on the size of the particles and on the nature of the material. By reflected light we usually notice a somewhat different color and an opaque, muddy appearance similar to that of ordinary suspensions. The microscope will detect particles as small as 0.000,25 millimeter in diameter. Smaller particles than this cannot be viewed directly as they are smaller than the wave length of light, so that the latter cannot be regularly reflected from them. It is possible, however, to detect the presence of particles as small as 0.000,006 millimeter by looking at them in a strong transverse beam of light against a dark background. (The diameters of the molecules of most ordinary substances are less than 0.000,001 millimeter.) Although no real image of the particle may be seen, there is a scattering of the light by it so that a bright speck of light can be seen in the microscope. The same effect is responsible for the visibility of a beam of light in a dark room through illumination of dust particles, invisible, perhaps, even in a microscope. A microscope arranged for use with a powerful transverse illumination against a dark background is called an **ultramicroscope.** By knowing the concentration of the material in a colloidal suspension, and counting the number of particles in a tiny beam of known dimensions it is possible to determine the average size of the particles.

8. Adsorption. Solid surfaces have the power of condensing gases upon them. The amount of gas so adsorbed depends upon the nature and area of the surface, the temperature and the nature of the gas. The lower the temperature the more slowly do the gaseous molecules move, and the more easily are they held by the attraction exerted by the solid surface. Hence the gases which are most easily condensed to the liquid state are also more highly adsorbed by solid surfaces. Of all gases helium, which boils at 4.5° K, is least adsorbed, followed by hydrogen, whose boiling point is 20.5° K, then by gases like nitrogen, oxygen, etc., then by ammonia, water vapor, etc. It is a fact familiar to chemical analysts that considerable amounts of water may be condensed upon the surfaces of pieces of apparatus like crucibles and glass beakers, so that it is necessary to have them in a dry atmosphere in order to get exact and reproducible weights. If the solid is porous, like charcoal, or finely powdered, its surface is vastly increased, allowing the same amount to adsorb very much more of the gas. The use of charcoal to adsorb odorous gases in this way is very familiar.

9. A similar adsorption of dissolved substances can take place from solutions upon solid surfaces immersed in them. "Boneblack," formed by the strong heating of ground bone, turning its animal matter into charcoal, is used in the refining of sugar to remove the yellow coloring matter present. The colored bodies are mainly substances with large molecules, which are readily adsorbed on the large surface of the boneblack, from which the solution of sugar can be filtered clear and colorless. Cottonseed oil is decolorized by fuller's earth in the same way. On account of the large surface exposed by even a small amount of solid in colloidal suspension (a cube having a diameter of 1 cm. and a surface of 6 cm.², if divided into cubes with a diameter of 0.0001 cm., would have a surface of 60,000 cm.²) the adsorption of dissolved substances upon the colloidal particles exerts an important effect upon their properties.

10. Electrical Migration of Colloidal Particles. An especially important effect upon the properties of fine suspensions is exerted by adsorbed ions. It is seldom that electrolytes are absent from aqueous suspensions, and even where such is the case, the ions of water may be differentially adsorbed. Certain kinds of suspensions are prone to adsorb positive ions in excess, whereby the particles acquire a positive charge, while others, in a similar way, become negative. As a result they are able to migrate with an electric current flowing through the solution, the direction depending upon the sign of the adsorbed ions. This phenomenon is known as cataphoresis. The speed with which they move is comparable

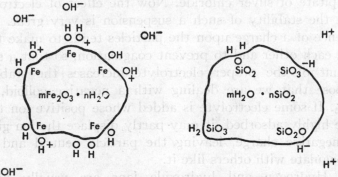

Fig. 2. Relation between chemical nature and particle charge.

to that of the slower ions, about 7 mm. per hour under a drop of potential through the solution of 1 volt per centimeter. It is thus possible to classify suspensions as positive or negative, just as the ions themselves were classified in Chapter VIII. Among the positive suspensions are those of the metallic hydroxides and sulfides; the negative suspensions include arsenous sulfide, silicic acid, graphite, and the noble metals.

Figure 2 illustrates how the positive charge on ferric hydroxide results from its basic nature, while the negative charge on silicic acid corresponds to its acid character. There is no essential difference between adsorption of OH^- and adsorption of water followed by ionization of H^+.

11. Relation between Charge and Stability. Coagulation. Even though a suspended particle may be so small that its Brownian movement prevents its settling out under the influence of gravity, a suspension of such particles may not be stable, because of the tendency of the particles to adhere to one another on impact, forming successively larger aggregates until settling out can occur. This process may be seen when silver chloride is formed by mixing its ions. At first a very fine suspension is formed, which, if not too concentrated, appears quite stable, and may run through an ordinary filter. On standing, however, and more rapidly if the solution is heated and stirred, these extremely fine particles adhere to each other, forming eventually the familiar curdy precipitate of silver chloride. Now the effect of electrolytes upon the stability of such a suspension is very great. The presence of a charge upon the particles tends to make them repel each other and to prevent coagulation, so that a small amount of the proper electrolyte increases the stability. Suppose that we are dealing with a negative colloid, like As_2S_3. If some electrolyte is added whose positive ion tends to be highly adsorbed, it may partly displace the ion giving the negative charge, leaving the particle neutral and free to coagulate with others like it.

12. Hydrogen and hydroxide ions are usually highly adsorbed, so that the addition of a small amount of acid to a suspension of arsenous sulfide suffices to coagulate it, while the addition of a small amount of alkali to a positive suspension like that of ferric hydroxide coagulates it completely. In general, then, negative suspensions are coagulated by acids and positive suspensions by alkalis. There appear to be no striking differences in the extent to which most other ions are adsorbed, but the effect of the charge of the adsorbed ion upon its ability to coagulate a suspension is very great. Let us suppose that Na^+, Ca^{++}, and Al^{+++} are adsorbed by suspended As_2S_3 to the same degree. It is evidently not the amount of substance adsorbed but the amount of positive charge that it carries with it that determines its ability to neutralize the charge on a negative suspension. To have the same amount of electricity adsorbed, we will need but half as much of the doubly charged Ca^{++}, and but one third as much of the triply charged Al^{+++}, as we will of the singly charged Na^+. Hence it will take very much less Ca^{++} and still less Al^{+++} to have the same effect as a given amount of Na^+. Moreover, it is the amount adsorbed, and not the amount in solution, that determines the coagulating effect, and since the concentration of a substance in solution increases more rapidly than the amount adsorbed, the concentration of Na^+ in the solution must be considerably more than three times that of the Al^{+++} in order that the amount of the former adsorbed be three times the latter.

13. Aluminum sulfate is extensively used in connection with filtration plants to increase the efficiency of the filtration on account of the great coagulating power of aluminum ion upon the negative suspension of mud in water. The aluminum hydroxide formed by the hydrolysis of the aluminum sulfate is itself a positive colloid, and also aids considerably in the coagulation, since a positive colloid acts like a positive ion in neutralizing the charge on a negative suspension.

14. The ions in sea water have a similar coagulating effect upon muddy river water discharged into it, a factor which aids in the formation of bars at river mouths.

15. Most dyes are very fine suspensions, which are themselves adsorbed or absorbed in animal or vegetable fibers. When the fiber is unable to hold the dye permanently, the color may frequently be made "fast" by using a coagulant, called a "mordant." The mordant is the salt of an ion with a multiple charge like Al^{+++} or Sn^{++++}, which can diffuse into the fiber and hydrolyze, giving a positive hydroxide, which can hold the dye firmly. A "lake" is a pigment made of such a coagulum of a hydroxide, like $Al(OH)_3$, with a suitable dye. The "purple of Cassius" is a similar coagulum of gold and stannic hydroxide, formed simultaneously in the reaction of stannous ion with chloroaurate ion, as follows:

$$2\ AuCl_4^- + 3\ Sn^{++} + 12\ H_2O$$
$$= 2\ Au + 3\ Sn(OH)_4 + 12\ H^+ + 8\ Cl^-.$$

16. In washing precipitates it is often found that the precipitate tends to become suspended and run through the

filter. It is possible to prevent this resuspension by washing
with water containing a little acid, or ammonium salt, or
ammonia, etc., as the case requires.

17. The effect of the charge of negative ions in coagulating
positive suspensions follows the principles laid down for
the corresponding effect upon negative colloids. Ferric
hydroxide suspension, for example, is more easily coagulated
by sodium sulfate than by sodium chloride.

18. Emulsions. We have thus far been considering dispersed
systems in which a solid is suspended in a liquid. We will
now consider those systems, called emulsions, in which the
suspended phase is a liquid. Much of what has been said in
regard to solid suspensions applies here. When the suspended
droplets are small enough, as in cream, they are subject to
Brownian movement, though in this case not sufficient to
prevent their slow rise to the top by reason of gravity. The
optical properties of emulsions are similar to those of suspensions. It is possible, however, to have stable emulsions
with the suspended material less highly dispersed and in
larger amounts than is the case ordinarily with solid suspensions, as illustrated by cream and mayonnaise dressing.
In order to do this, however, an emulsifying agent must be
used, for two pure liquids will not form a stable emulsion.
The reason for this is as follows:

When two suspended droplets come together they will
tend to coalesce into one, for the surface tension operates
to make the surface as small as possible, and one spherical
drop will have less surface than two of the same total volume.
In order to prevent their coalescing it is desirable to have
the liquid in which they are suspended viscous, but especially
is it necessary that the film of liquid which separates them
when they are close together should be difficult to rupture,
like the soap film which prevents two adjacent air bubbles
from coalescing. Now a stable liquid film can be produced
by some substance which greatly lowers the surface tension
of the liquid. An exact proof of this could be given, but the
following simpler explanation may suffice. The diminution

in the surface tension is an evidence that the substance added diminishes the attractive forces of the molecules within the liquid; consequently there will be a tendency for molecules of the solvent to restore the condition of the pure solvent, where the molecules are probably closer together, by squeezing out, as it were, the molecules of the solute, which will therefore tend to be concentrated at the surface, still further lowering the surface tension. In fact we find that the surface tension of soap solutions is much less than that of water, and also that the tension at a surface that has stood for a short time is less than it is at a fresh surface, as illustrated by the following figures:

Surface Tension

	Fresh surface	Old surface
Water	79	79
1.25 per cent soap solution	62	26

19. Suppose, now, that we consider a film of such a solution, representing in Fig. 3, at *a*, the greater concentration of the soap at the surface by the shading. If a strain is put upon the film so that it starts to rupture at a certain place, repre-

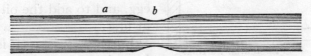

Fig. 3. Automatic strengthening of a film of soap solution on stretching.

sented at *b*, the effect is to bring from the interior to the surface at this point solution in which the soap is at first less concentrated, and whose surface tension is, therefore, *greater* than that of the old surface. Consequently, whenever rupture threatens, the film becomes automatically stronger, and hence is stable. Sufficient soap dissolved in water will therefore give either a stable foam, if shaken with air, or a stable emulsion if shaken with oil. Other substances, like saponin, gelatin, albumen, the casein of milk, etc., may have the same effect in greater or less degree. The substances in the egg act in this way in making mayonnaise. Milk, when concentrated in the form of evaporated milk, can serve also for making mayonnaise.

It is possible to have either phase the inclosed phase, the oil being the inclosing phase in mayonnaise that has "separated," and in the water-petroleum emulsions that often give trouble in oil refining.

20. It follows from the foregoing theory that the type of emulsion favored will be the one in which the emulsifying agent is soluble in the outer phase, the one in which stable films are desired. Thus, sodium soaps favor oil-in-water emulsions, while aluminum soaps favor water-in-oil.

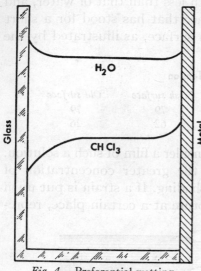

There is a tendency, also, for the phase present in smallest amount to be the inclosed phase, and one of the secrets of success in making mayonnaise is accordingly to wet the sides of the vessel with egg, and to add the oil slowly at first.

Further assistance is given by using a vessel whose material is better wet by the outer phase, e.g., glass or china rather than metal.

Fig. 4. Preferential wetting.

21. Differential Wetting. The different degrees of wetting between liquids and solids is often quite evident. Everyone is familiar with the fact that tiny globules of mercury roll about on a wood surface; that water globules are only partly flattened out on a paraffin surface while they spread completely on clean glass. The difference between a clean and a greasy windshield is well known to all automobile drivers. The simple experiment illustrated in Fig. 4 shows the tendency of water to displace chloroform on a glass surface while chloroform displaces water on a bright metal surface. Accordingly, if metallic powder were dropped onto the interface between these liquids, it would descend into the chloroform while glass powder would be floated on the interface, supported by the surface tension. If one liquid does not completely displace the other, but the interface forms some finite angle of contact, the particles may remain in the interfacial surface, but protruding more into one liquid than into the other. If the less-wetting liquid is in drops, the adhering

Fig. 5.   Toluene emulsified in water by powdered pyrite.

particles will then be mostly on the outside of the drop, and can serve as a sort of armor to hold drops apart and prevent coalescence. Solid powders may thus serve as emulsifying agents, the type of emulsion being determined by relative wetting as just explained. Figure 5 illustrates an emulsion of toluene in water by the aid of powdered pyrite, FeS_2, which is wet somewhat better by water than by toluene. The particles of pyrite can be seen coating the droplets, sticking to them but mainly in the water. Figure 6 shows the water as the inside phase in kerosene, brought about by using powdered charcoal, wet better by kerosene than by water.

Particles of metallic sulfide ores can be effectively purified from accompanying earthy material by grinding the crude ore with a suitable oil and water, suspending the mass in water to which a foaming agent has been added and blowing air bubbles up through the suspension. The oil-coated metallic particles trying to escape from the water, attach themselves to the bubbles and are carried out over the rim of the tank where the froth is broken down and the pure ore recovered; the water-wet earthy impurities remain in the tank. This process is known as **ore-flotation** and has greatly increased the efficiency of ore-recovery.

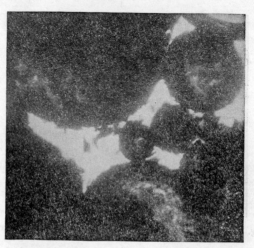

Fig. 6. Water emulsified in kerosene by powdered charcoal.

22. Lyophilic Colloids. There are a number of colloids, most of which are obtained directly or indirectly from plant or animal organisms, which readily remain in combination with water or some other appropriate solvent. These include albumens, soaps, gums, tannins, starch, gelatin, glue, caramel, rubber, and nitro-cotton (nitro-cotton is extensively used in making collodion, celluloid, smokeless powders, varnishes, and artificial leather). These substances instead of being difficult to bring into solution and easy to coagulate, like most colloidal suspensions, give solutions or jellies very rapidly. Where water is the dispersing liquid, as with albumin or gelatin, the colloid may be called **hydrophilic**, signifying that it is a "lover of water," and in distinction to the **hydro-**

phobic colloids such as arsenous sulfide. Where some other dispersing medium than water is used the more general terms **lyophilic** and **lyophobic** may be used, signifying respectively "lover" and "hater" of the solvent. Thus nitro-cotton is lyophilic to a mixture of ether and alcohol but lyophobic towards water.

These colloids have also been called "reversible colloids," because, like gelatin, they can usually be easily redissolved after drying out. Again they have been called "emulsion colloids" since they behave in many respects like emulsions. It seems rather certain, however, that in many cases the dispersed phase is not in the form of droplets, but consists rather of threads which stretch through the solution forming a network. Such solutions, even when very dilute, often have a very high viscosity, and when more concentrated yield a jelly. Ions may migrate through a gelatin jelly almost as rapidly as through water.

23. Some of these substances, such as gelatin and albumins, are made up of amphoteric molecules containing both carboxyl and amino groups. These can unite with each other indefinitely to give the large colloidal aggregates or the solid jelly structure. The addition of either acid or alkali tends to break up the aggregates, decreasing viscosity and making the solution more difficult to gelatinize. If the jelly does not melt upon treatment with acid or alkali it at least swells by taking up more water.

Since most of the material of which living organisms are made is colloidal in nature, it will be perceived that the subject of colloids becomes one of great importance to the biologist.

24. Protective Colloids. If an oil emulsion were mixed with a metallic suspension, the oil drops would tend to inclose the metal particles, and the resulting system would behave essentially like a pure emulsion. Similarly, when a "reversible" colloid, or hydrophilic colloid, is mixed with a hydrophobic colloid, the mixture behaves like a colloid of the former class. Since the hydrophilic colloids are relatively stable, a hydrophobic colloid may be made stable in this way. For example, if gelatin is present in a solution in which silver chloride is formed from its ions, each particle of the silver chloride is coated with gelatin so as to prevent the coagulation that would otherwise ensue. The retention of this highly dispersed state in the solidified gelatin makes possible the photographic dry plate. Again, when gelatin is added to a suspension of arsenous sulfide it requires much more concentrated acid to coagulate it.

25. Preparation of Colloidal Solutions. In addition to the colloids obtained from biological sources, such as gelatin, albumins, starches, etc., it is possible to prepare highly dispersed systems of other materials by various methods, which may be classified as dispersion or condensation methods, according, respectively, as we start with undispersed material or with molecularly dispersed material, molecules and ions.

(*a*) **Dispersion Methods.** Colloidal solutions of the nobler metals may be prepared by passing an arc between electrodes of that metal under water. The metal is vaporized in the arc and the vapor is condensed to solid particles in a highly dispersed state.

Previously coagulated material may often be redispersed by washing out the coagulant, as occurs in washing certain precipitates. Basic ferric acetate, precipitated by boiling a solution containing ferric acetate, may be redispersed by washing with water containing a trace of acid.

Some substances can be dispersed by the aid of a **"pep- tizer,"** usually a protective colloid, taking its name from the action of pepsin in dispersing albuminous material in the process of digestion. Thus graphite can be peptized, or suspended, by grinding it with tannin. The resulting solution is known commercially as "aquadag," and can be used as a lubricant. The cleansing action of soap, which is in the colloidal state when dissolved in water (not when in alcohol), is of this nature.

(*b*) **Condensation Methods.** By starting with ordinary solution it is possible to get suspensions by suitable means.

Thus a solution of a ferric chloride always contains free H^+, Cl^-, and $Fe(OH)_3$ (or basic chloride), the last of which is partly agglomerated, so that it will not pass through a very fine membrane like parchment. Accordingly, if such a solution is separated by parchment from pure water, the H^+ and Cl^- can diffuse out. The $Fe(OH)_3$ accumulates as the hydrolysis proceeds, as represented by the equation,

$$Fe^{+++} + 3\,Cl^- + 3\,H_2O = Fe(OH)_3 + 3\,H^+ + 3\,Cl^-.$$

By continually renewing the water into which the hydrochloric acid diffuses, the hydrolysis may be made complete, leaving a colloidal solution of ferric hydroxide. Such a process of separation by differential diffusion is called **dialysis.** Other hydroxides can be obtained in colloidal solution by the same method. That a colloidal solution is obtained by dialysis but not by the addition of alkali, is due to the coagulating effect of the hydroxide ion which would be present under the latter circumstances.

Whenever a relatively insoluble substance can be produced in the absence of any considerable amount of electrolytes, it is possible to prepare it as a colloid. Thus the action of H_2S on a solution of As_2O_3 will give a suspension of As_2S_3, since the substances involved are all practically un-ionized. A suspension of HgS can be obtained by the action of H_2S on $Hg(CN)_2$ for the same reason. Colloidal gold can be prepared by the reduction of a very dilute solution of $HAuCl_4$ by some nonionized reducing agent, such as formaldehyde, CH_2O, or a solution of phosphorus in ether. The addition of some protective colloid, like gelatin, allows the solution of the metal to be prepared in much more stable form, and also more concentrated. The "argyrol," used in treating cold in the head, is a concentrated protected solution of colloidal silver.

Exercises

1. Discuss the conditions necessary for the existence of stable foams and emulsions.

2. Summarize the characteristics of hydrophilic and hydrophobic colloids, respectively.

3. Assuming that you have discovered that a certain colloid migrates with the positive current, decide whether it would be coagulated more easily by HCl or NaOH.

4. When a substance is dispersed in a liquid the behavior of the system will depend mainly upon the following factors: (*a*) the size of the dispersed particles, (*b*) the magnitude of the surface tension between the phases, (*c*) whether the dispersed phase is solid or liquid, (*d*) whether the dispersed particles absorb positive or negative ions more readily. Decide what effect, if any, each of the above factors would have upon each of the following phenomena: (1) the Brownian movement, (2) the electric migration, (3) the rate of diffusion, (4) coagulation, (5) separation on standing, (6) absorbing power, (7) protective action on other dispersed substances.

5. What conditions should be observed in the formation of colloidal solutions?

6. Outline experiments to enable you to determine the most effective means for coagulating a colloidal suspension of an unfamiliar substance.

7. Make a classification of dispersed systems that will, in your opinion, best express their various behaviors.

8. How would you expect the Brownian movement to be affected by (*a*) the size of the dispersed particles; (*b*) the viscosity of the dispersing liquid; (*c*) the temperature; (*d*) the concentration of suspended particles?

9. State essential differences between (*a*) emulsions and suspensions; (*b*) suspensions and colloidal suspensions; (*c*) hydrophilic and hydrophobic colloids.

10. Classify the following into two groups, hydrophilic and hydrophobic, respectively: (*a*) gelatin; (*b*) albumen; (*c*) cooked albumen; (*d*) As_2S_3; (*e*) gold; (*f*) soap; (*g*) cooked starch; (*h*) graphite; (*i*) rubber; (*j*) argyrol.

11. Briefly explain the mutual coagulation of colloidal As_2S_3 and $Fe(OH)_3$.

12. Explain the coagulation of colloidal $Fe(OH)_3$ by NaOH.

13. How may emulsions be stabilized?

14. Define or explain the terms (*a*) Brownian movement, (*b*) osmotic pressure, (*c*) hydrophobic colloid, (*d*) ultra miscroscope, (*e*) peptizer.

15. List and illustrate five different types of dispersed systems.

16. How would the rate of diffusion of a hydrophobic colloid probably be affected by (*a*) temperature, (*b*) size of particles, (*c*) concentration of particles, (*d*) viscosity changes in the water produced by adding a neutral substance like glycerine. Explain each case very briefly.

17. How do you think the following electrolytes would compare in their effectiveness in coagulating a negative sol of As_2S_3, (*a*) NaCl, (*b*) $CaCl_2$, (*c*) Na_2SO_4, (*d*) $AgNO_3$?

CHAPTER XX

SOLUBILITY

1. The property of solubility is one of the most interesting and important of physicochemical phenomena. Some phase of it is encountered frequently, not only in everyday life, but in industry and scientific investigations. To remove from clothing a grease spot, a grass stain, or a smear made by sitting on a chocolate cream requires a different solvent in each case. Most chemical reactions occur in solution and appropriate solvents must be selected. Separations, both analytical and industrial, are effected chiefly by the aid of differences in solubility. Molecular weights often cannot be determined by vapor density since the temperature necessary for vaporization may be so high as to be inconvenient or cause decomposition; we may then determine it in solution and must know, of course, how to choose an appropriate solvent. Again, materials for vessels should be made of substances as insoluble as possible in the liquids likely to be put therein. In order to understand such phenomena, it does not suffice to commit to memory a few simple rules, for the factors involved are numerous and often complicated. It is likely to be profitable, nevertheless, to consider some of the more important factors and to gain some notion of the general methods of attacking these problems.

2. As a first step, we may recall the classification of molecular types previously given (Chapter V, paragraph 13) into nonpolar, polar, and ionic molecules. Each molecular type crystallizes in a corresponding solid lattice, also set forth in an earlier chapter (Chapter V, paragraph 15). We may recall, furthermore, the general nature of the process of solution for each of these lattice types (Chapter VIII, paragraph 2)

374

and proceed now to a more detailed discussion of each. We shall find that not only is solubility determined by the type of molecule and intermolecular force, but also by its strength. By way of illustration of the variety possible when we are able to vary both the strength and the type of intermolecular field, we may consider the system illustrated in Fig. 1, showing six substances sufficiently insoluble in each other to exist in six distinct liquid layers. This is a truly stable system and does not depend for the existence of layers upon mere slowness of diffusion, but would be reformed even though the system were shaken.

3. Nonpolar Molecules. Molecules which are uncharged and nonpolar are able to attract each other only because of disturbances produced by mutual interaction of their rapidly moving electrons. This disturbance has no exact counterpart in ordinary mechanical systems, but is remotely analogous to the interaction that would exist between two vibrating tuning forks. The magnitude of the force between a pair of such molecules depends on the total number of electrons in the molecule and the looseness with which they are held; also upon the closeness of approach possible before repulsion between them sets in. The force falls off

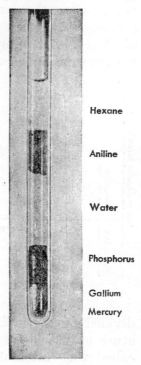

Hexane

Aniline

Water

Phosphorus

Gallium

Mercury

Fig. 1. Six stable liquid layers.

approximately with the seventh power of the distance between the molecular centers, and therefore practically disappears when a pair of molecules are only two or three molecular diameters apart. When two molecules come sufficiently close to each other, "repulsion" sets in, with something like a tenth or twelfth power of the distance. Molecules are, of course, not absolutely rigid, hard spheres. Figure 2 illustrates how the attraction between a pair of molecules grows rapidly at first as the distance between them diminishes and then turns very abruptly into repulsive force. A comparison of curves A and B shows how the substance represented by A may have a higher intermolecular attractive force at the same distance than the substance represented by curve B; nevertheless the force between the molecules for B may actually be greater at equilibrium than for A, on account of their closer approach to each other. It is not easy to measure the force existing between single pairs of molecules,

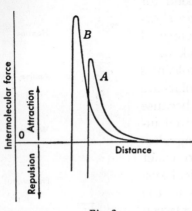

Fig. 2

and it is actually more important, of course, to consider the total resultant forces existing within a mass of liquid. This bears a relation, too complex to be explained here, to the forces between pairs of molecules which shows that it is possible to measure the total attractive energy existing within a mass of liquid by the energy of vaporization per cubic centimeter of liquid or the energy of vaporization per mole divided by the molal volume of the liquid at the temperature at which the vaporization takes place. This is often called the **"internal pressure"** of the liquid. Table 1 gives the values of this quantity for a number of more or less familiar substances. A few of them are substances which ordinarily exist as solids at 25° C., and the values given are for the supercooled liquid, which is unstable with respect to the solid at this temperature. The substances have been arranged in order of increase from the top to the bottom of the table.

4. The significance of this order of arrangement is as follows: Liquids which are close together in internal pressure are able to mix with each other with very little difference between the attractive forces of the like and the unlike

molecules. A given molecule, therefore, has about the same tendency to escape into the vapor phase from a solution as it would have from its own pure liquid; hence the number of molecules in the vapor phase is proportional to the mole fraction of them in the liquid. This law, known as **Raoult's Law,** may be written

$$p = p^\circ \text{N}$$

where p equals the partial vapor pressure of the substance from the solution, p° is its vapor pressure in the pure state and N is the mole fraction of that species in the solution. In cases where this law holds, it is possible to calculate solubility from the above equation, not only of vapors, but also for gases and solids. (Cf. Chap. IV, par. 14.)

5. The solubility of a gas is usually expressed in terms of the amount which dissolves when the gas is at 1 atmosphere partial pressure over the solution. In such a case

$$p = 1 \qquad \text{and} \qquad \text{N} = 1/p^\circ.$$

p° is in this case the vapor pressure of the pure gas over its own liquid and is higher the lower the boiling point of the gas. If the temperature in question lies above the critical pressure of the gas, of course p° has no obvious physical meaning. A fictitious value for it, however, can be derived by extrapolating the vapor pressure above the critical temperature. For making such an extrapolation, a plot of the logarithm of the vapor pressure of the gas against the reciprocal of the absolute temperature can be used; this gives a straight line from which the extrapolation can easily be made to some higher temperature. Table 1 contains, for illustration, the solubilities of three gases, hydrogen, nitrogen, and chlorine. Their boiling points increase in that order, and their solubilities, as will be seen from the table, increase in the same order. To put it in another way, chlorine is the gas most easily condensed to a pure liquid and hydrogen is the one most difficult to condense. Correspondingly, chlorine is most readily condensed into a solution and hydrogen least readily.

TABLE 1

Internal Pressure and Solubility

Liquid	Volume per mole, cc.	Energy of vaporiz., cals. per cc.	Solubility, moles per 100 moles of solution					
			H_2 (20°)	N_2 (20°)	Cl_2 (0°)	I_2 (25°)	S_8 (25°)	P_4 (25°)
n-Heptane	147.6	54.0	—	—	0.270	0.68	0.14	—
Ethyl ether	104.5	55.5	0.061	0.124	—	—	.30	0.82
Silicon tetrachloride	115.3	57.3	—	—	.288	.50	—	—
Carbon tetrachloride	97.1	72.9	.032	.063	.298	1.15	.50	—
Chloroform	80.7	79.7	—	.043	—	2.28	.57	—
Benzene	89.3	83.6	.025	.043	—	4.82	.63	2.28
Chlorine	50.9	87.7	—	—	—	—	—	—
Carbon disulfide	60.7	99.6	.008	.013	—	5.76	13.8	93.
Bromine	51.2	135.	—	—	—	—	—	—
Sulfur, S_8	136.	136.	—	—	—	(21)	—	—
Iodine, I_2	59.2	190.	—	—	—	—	(28)	—
Phosphorus (active), P_4	70.4	194.	—	—	—	—	—	—

6. We see from the values in the table for the solubilities of hydrogen and nitrogen, that these values decrease as we go from liquids of lower to liquids of higher internal pressure. The explanation of this trend lies in the fact that the molecules of hydrogen and of nitrogen have very low fields of force, and hence they are able to penetrate most readily into liquids in which the forces of attraction between the molecules are low. As we descend the table to liquids of higher internal pressure, such as carbon disulfide, it is difficult for hydrogen and nitrogen molecules to get in between the molecules of solvent, hence their solubility is low. Chlorine, on the other hand, although a gas at ordinary temperatures, has small molecules and we see from the value of the energy of vaporization per cubic centimeters that the attractive forces between chlorine molecules are rather high; consequently, this substance dissolves most readily in the liquid nearest to it in the table, and its solubility falls off in both directions.

7. Solids. Iodine, sulfur, and phosphorus have very high attractive fields; hence they mix most readily with liquids near them toward the bottom of the table, and their solubilities decrease as we ascend the table, the opposite order to that found for hydrogen and nitrogen. Accordingly, we could fill in missing values in this, or even in a more extended table, with a considerable degree of confidence. For example, the solubility of sulfur in silicon tetrachloride should doubtless be a little more than 0.3 mole per cent. The solubility of phosphorus in carbon tetrachloride may be expected to lie between 1 and 2 mole per cent.

8. The solubility of a solid, in the absence of chemical reactions, will normally be a maximum in a solvent which is close to it in internal pressure. This is true, for example, with sulfur and iodine, which do not react chemically. In such a case, the solubility in terms of mole fraction, N, can be calculated at a given absolute temperature, T, from the heat of fusion per mole of the solid solute, ΔH, at its melting point, T_m, by the following equation:

$$\log N = \frac{-\Delta H(T_m - T)}{4.58 \, T_m T}.$$

The equation corresponds to the fact, which should be more or less obvious, that the higher the melting point of the substance and hence the harder it is to melt it to its own pure liquid, the harder it is, likewise, to get it to enter into a liquid state in some other solvent; hence the solubility of a substance normally increases with temperature, and a substance with a lower melting point is more soluble. A large value for the heat of fusion of the solute likewise tends to diminish solubility. If we are considering a solvent and a solute which have rather different internal pressures, then the solubility will be normally less than that calculated by the above equation. This is illustrated by the decrease in the values for the solubility of iodine, sulfur, and phosphorus in the liquids higher up in the table.

9. The effect of melting point on solubility is beautifully illustrated by the comparison, shown in Table 2, between phenanthrene and anthracene, two substances which have

TABLE 2

	Molal vol. cc.	Melt. pt.	Solubility mole per cent at 25° C. in benzene	Boil. pt.
Phenanthrene	174	99.6	18.6	340
Anthracene	142	218.	0.63	342

the same composition, $C_{14}H_{10}$, but differ only in the arrangement of the carbon atoms as shown in the table. The hexagons of carbon atoms are in a straight line in the latter but not in the former. The result is that the anthracene molecules pack much more closely in the solid crystal, as shown by the volume. They therefore attract each other more strongly, so that this substance both melts at a higher temperature and dissolves in all solvents to a far smaller extent. To appreciate this, you have only to recall how much better your trout fit your frying pan before they are cooked than they do later, when they curl up. It is interesting to note that the two substances here considered, although they have very different melting points, have practically the same boiling point. This we may attribute to the fact that at high temperatures there is sufficient thermal motion so that the liquid in either case consists of molecules jumbled up in all positions.

10. An interesting contrast in solubility is presented by two forms of sulfur. The molecules of ordinary sulfur consist of octagonal rings of atoms, represented in Fig. 3. These molecules retain their identity when dissolved. When these crystals are melted at 115° C., the same octagonal molecules persist for a while. As the temperature is raised, however, the more violent agitation gradually knocks the rings apart, with the formation of chains of varying lengths. These chains become entangled with each other, so that the liquid becomes very viscous, quite contrary to the usual behavior of liquids on heating. If we heat the sulfur still further,

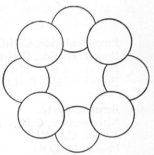

Fig. 3. Molecule of rhombic sulfur.

it gradually becomes more fluid as the chains become shorter, but if suddenly cooled by pouring into water, the rings do not have time to reform and the chains are "frozen." The chains are zigzag and can be extended by pulling, and the mass consequently behaves like rubber. The sulfur in this form is not soluble, since the chains are all tangled up like a mass of tangled string and small soluble units are not detachable.

11. Polar Molecules. Polar molecules cannot be expected to fit rigidly into the relation between internal pressure and solubility shown in Table 1, and discussed in preceding paragraphs. In many cases, however, departures from the preceding regularities are absent or small. This is particularly the case for substances whose electric dipoles are fairly well buried within the molecule, as is the case with ether and with chloroform, both of which possess considerable dipole moment but fit, nevertheless, very well into the series of internal pressures and solubilities. In other cases the polarity may have considerable significance. Table 3 gives the comparison between the dipole moments of propyl chloride, propyl bromide, and propyl iodide and their solubility in water. Water, as explained elsewhere in this book, is a highly polar substance, and it is not surprising, therefore, that the solubility of the propyl chloride in water is the greatest, due to its possessing the highest dipole moment.

TABLE 3

	Dipole moment $\times 10^{18}$ e.s.u.	Solubility in water. Per cent at 20°
Propyl chloride, C_3H_7Cl	2.0	0.27
Propyl bromide, C_3H_7Br	1.8	0.24
Propyl iodide, C_3H_7I	1.6	0.11
Propyl alcohol, C_3H_7OH	1.7	Unlimited
Benzene, C_6H_6	0	0.057
Nitrobenzene, $C_6H_5NO_2$	4.19	0.19
Aniline, $C_6H_5NH_2$	1.51	3.49
Phenol, C_6H_5OH	1.70	8.2

12. There is, however, one group of dipoles for which dipole moment alone is quite insufficient to yield a guide to solubility relationships. The dipoles present in water, the alcohols, ammonia, organic amines, and hydrogen fluoride are attracted to each other by exceptionally strong forces called "hydrogen bonds." This is illustrated particularly in Fig. 4, where boiling points of certain series of compounds are plotted against molecular weights. For most of the compounds shown, the boiling point increases with increasing molecular weight, but water, hydrogen fluoride, and ammonia have much higher boiling points than would be expected on this basis. These liquids also freeze at abnormally high temperatures, forming solids having a peculiar type of structure. The structure of ice is indicated in Fig. 5. This is a comparatively open structure, with a density less than that of water. Each atom of oxygen is surrounded by four others, and atoms of hydrogen are on a line between the atoms of oxygen, although nearer one atom of oxygen than the other.

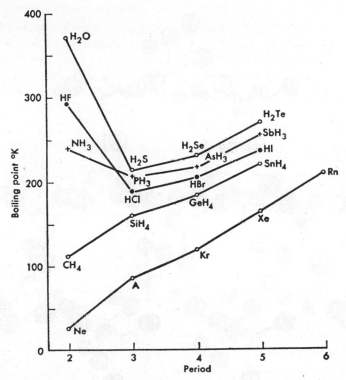

Fig. 4. Effect of hydrogen bonds on boiling point.

It follows that a substance, in order to be soluble in water, must be capable of tearing apart the hydrogen bonds and the substances here under discussion all readily mix with each other. Nonpolar molecules, however, or even those containing ordinary dipoles, often fail to penetrate the structure of water. Referring again to Table 3, we see that propyl alcohol has about the same dipole moment as propyl iodide and propyl bromide, but that whereas the latter two have very limited solubility in water, the first is completely miscible with water, due to the fact that its hydroxyl groups are able to take part in the structures appropriate to water. Again, in Table 3 we see the dipole moment and solubility in water of benzene and three other substituted products,

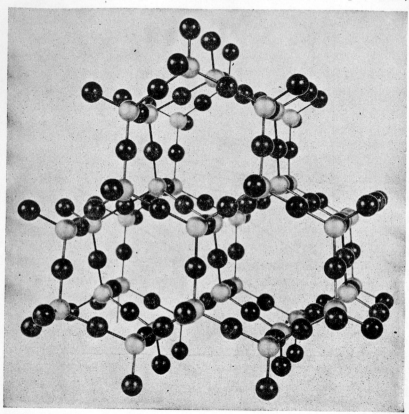

Fig. 5.   Structure of ice. The light spheres represent oxygen atoms, the dark ones hydrogen. It is evident that melting, which partly breaks up this structure, permits a closer packing and therefore higher density.

nitrobenzene, aniline, and phenol. The relative solubilities in water evidently have no relation to the dipole moment, but they do accord well with the ability to form hydrogen bonds with water, the − OH of phenol entering most readily into the structure and the − NH₂ of aniline less readily.

The nitro group of nitrobenzene, although it is the most polar of all, does not help a great deal in bringing nitrobenzene into solution in water.

13. Electrolytes. The nature of the process of solution of a salt was illustrated in Chapter VIII, Fig. 1. It is evident from this that the solubility of a salt is favored by high dielectric constant on the part of the solvent, and therefore water and ammonia are particularly effective. In order to compare the solubilities of different salts, let us break up the process of the solution of the solid in water into two steps: first, the separation of the ions of the solid crystal into gaseous ions, and then the hydration of these ions by bringing them separately into water.

$$\text{MX (s)} \rightarrow \text{M}^+ \text{(g)} + \text{X}^- \text{(g)} \rightarrow \text{M}^+ \text{(aq.)} + \text{X}^- \text{(aq.)}.$$

Such a process is, of course, not easy to realize practically, but it is quite legitimate to consider it theoretically. The energy required for the first part of this process, that is, the separation of the solid ions into gaseous ions, is called the lattice energy of the substance. This process was one of the steps considered in Chapter V, Table 7 and Fig. 8. The amount of energy that must be put in for this step in the process evidently depends, first, upon how close the solid ions are in the lattice; second, upon their charge; third, upon the nature of the ions themselves—for example, whether their kernels have 8 or some other number of outer electrons. Kernels with 18 electrons are, as it were, softer, more deformable, and can get closer to ions of the opposite charge than kernels containing fewer electrons. The energy recovered in the second stage of the process, the hydration of the gaseous ions, depends on the size and charge of the ions and the nature of the electron kernel. The same factors, therefore, tend both to assist the solubility insofar as the second step in the process is concerned, and to oppose it in the first. However, the different steps do not operate in quite the same way in the two cases, and the net result differs for different substances. It is obvious here, as in so many other cases of physicochemical phenomena, that no extremely simple rules can be formulated. A few illustrations will show, however, the usefulness of the above scheme of analysis.

TABLE 4

Hydration, Solubility, and Ionic Size for Sulfates of the Type, MSO_4

Ion	Radius $\times 10^8$ cm.	H_2O in solid	Solubility g. per 100 g. H_2O
SO_4^{--}	3.0	—	—
Ba^{++}	1.4	0	0.0002
Pb^{++}	1.3	0	0.004
Sr^{++}	1.15	0	0.01
Ca^{++}	1.0	2	0.2
Fe^{++}	0.8	7	21.
Mg^{++}	0.75	7	27.

14. In Table 4 are given the solubilities of a series of sulfates of doubly charged positive ions, together with the water of hydration of the solid crystal and the radii of the ions. The sulfate ion is of course larger than any of the positive ions with which it is combined. The smallest positive ion of the series, Mg^{++}, does not by itself fill up very well the space between the sulfate ions, and there is room for 7 molecules of water around each magnesium ion. Even in the solid state, the magnesium sulfate is already largely hydrated and it is an easy process for the ions to be further separated on going into solution; that is, the substance is very soluble in water. As the size of the positive ion increases, however, in going finally to barium ion, Ba^{++}, we arrive at a substance whose two ions have more nearly equal size and which can pack firmly into a solid crystal, with no need for water to fill it out. The result is an extremely insoluble substance.

TABLE 5

Substance	Ions	Radii $\times 10^8$ cm.	Solubility g. per 100 g. H_2O
NaCl	Na^+, Cl^-	1.0, 1.8	24
CuS	Cu^{++}, S^{--}	1.0, 1.8	0.00003

15. The combined effect of ionic charge and a many-electron kernel is illustrated in Table 5, comparing NaCl and CuS, both of which have the same crystal structure and practically the same ionic radii. The greater attraction of the ions of CuS for each other is attributable, first, to their double charge, which, according to Coulomb's Law, means 4 times the interionic attraction at equal distances; second, to the greater interaction of the larger number of electrons. The greater strength of hydration, due to these same causes, evidently is not sufficient to offset the large lattice energy.

CHAPTER XXI

CARBONIC ACID AND ITS IONS

1. Frequent reference has been made elsewhere in this book to carbon dioxide, carbonic acid, carbonate ion, bicarbonate ion, and insoluble carbonates. The purpose of this chapter is to amplify this material into a coordinated whole; first, because it can afford excellent practice in applying the principles of chemical equilibrium; second, because these substances are involved in an extraordinary number of interesting industrial, geological, and biological processes. These include industrial preparation of sodium carbonate and bicarbonate in huge tonnages, the solution of limestone rock by ground water, forming limestone caves, and the redeposition of crystalline calcium carbonate as stalagmites; the formation of marine shells, pearls, and coral rock from sea water by marine organisms; the formation of egg-shells; the "softening" of "hard water" for industrial or laundry use; and the buffer mechanism which maintains the blood at constant alkalinity.

2. **Carbon dioxide molecules** have a linear structure, OCO. The most probable electron structure is indicated by the formula $: \overset{..}{O} : : \overset{..}{C} : : \overset{..}{O} :$, that is, the carbon and oxygen are joined by double bonds (cf. Chapter XVIII). If the bonds consisted of ordinary electron pairs, the tetrahedral bond angles characteristic of carbon would be found and the molecule would be unsymmetrical and show a dipole moment (cf. Chapter V, paragraph 14; Chapter XXIII, paragraphs 12, 13).

3. **Physical Characteristics.** Liquid CO_2 is available commercially in steel cylinders. It has a vapor pressure of 59 atmospheres at 20° C. If the cylinder is tilted so that liquid

instead of gas escapes through the valve, part of this liquid vaporizes, cooling the rest sufficiently to form solid, which can be caught in a cloth bag. This solid has a vapor pressure of 1 atmosphere at $-78.5°$ C., therefore it sublimes without melting. Solid CO_2 is known as "dry ice," and is much used for refrigeration. It melts at $-56°$ C. under a pressure of 5.3 atmospheres. When liquid and gas sealed in a stout glass tube are heated, the liquid phase expands and the gas phase becomes more concentrated till finally their densities are identical and the meniscus of separation disappears at 31.35° C., the critical temperature. The pressure at this point is 73 atmospheres.

4. Carbonic Acid. The solubility of CO_2 in water at a partial pressure of one atmosphere at temperatures of 0° C. to 30° C. is shown in Table 1.

TABLE 1

Solubility of CO_2 at 1 Atmosphere in Water

$t°$ C.	0	10	15	20	25	30
g. per liter	3.32	2.35	2.00	1.72	1.49	1.31
moles per liter	0.076	0.053	0.045	0.039	0.034	0.030

the solubility at other pressures can be calculated approximately by Henry's Law (cf. Chapter III, paragraph 19). It is convenient to remember that about 1 liter of CO_2 dissolves in 1 liter of water at 20° C., regardless of the pressure, since the volume of gas and the weight of it which dissolve in 1 liter are both proportional to the pressure.

Equilibrium is attained rather slowly, since part of the CO_2 reacts somewhat slowly with water to form about 1 per cent of H_2CO_3 as follows:

$$CO_2 + H_2O = H_2CO_3 = H^+ + HCO_3^-$$

The fact that plain soda water has only a very mild acid taste is evidence that the above ions are formed only in very low concentration. The concentration of H^+ can be determined, among other ways, by the aid of indicators sensitive within the proper range. Methyl orange, for example, shows an orange color in solutions of CO_2 at 1 atmosphere pressure indicating $(H^+) \approx 10^{-4}$. To perform an accurate experiment, one should make up a series of buffer solutions (cf. Chapter XIII, paragraph 51) in steps covering the desired range, add uniform amounts of indicator to the buffer solutions and to the carbonic acid solution, and determine the best color match under conditions of equal solution depth and illumination. Another method is to measure the e.m.f. of a hydrogen electrode in a solution of CO_2 (cf. Chapter XV, paragraph 22).

Now the other ion must be mainly HCO_3^-, not CO_3^{--}, for the second H^+ of a weak dibasic acid always ionizes much less easily than the first. We may connect this with the much greater attraction of the doubly charged CO_3^{--}. This conclusion is easily confirmed by experiment. The solubility of $CaCO_3$ is very small, and its product is $(Ca^{++})(CO_3^{--}) = 4.8 \times 10^{-9}$, therefore 0.1 M-Ca^{++} can detect CO_3^{--} in any concentration greater than 4.8×10^{-8}. The fact that $CaCl_2$ (aq.) forms no precipitate when added to 0.034 M-CO_2 indicates that the concentration of CO_3^{--} in this solution is far less than the concentration of the H^+, which is approximately 10^{-4} at $25°$ C., more precisely, 1.2×10^{-4}. The state of affairs in the solution can therefore be summarized as follows:

$$\underbrace{CO_2(1 \text{ atm.}) + H_2O = H_2CO_3}_{0.034 \ M} =$$

$$\begin{array}{cc} H^+ & + \quad HCO_3^- \\ 1.2 \times 10^{-4} \ M & 1.2 \times 10^{-4} \ M \end{array}$$

The (CO_3^{--}) in this solution is much less than 10^{-4} M and the (OH^-) is, of course, $10^{-14}/10^{-4}$ or 10^{-10} M.

5. The first ionization constant of carbonic acid is

$$\frac{(H^+)(HCO_3^-)}{(H_2CO_3)} = K_1$$

where we understand that (H_2CO_3) represents both the H_2CO_3

and the dissolved CO_2. The above figures yield $1.2 \times 10^{-4} \times 1.2 \times 10^{-4}/0.034 = 4.3 \times 10^{-7}$.

6. Sodium Carbonate Solutions. Let us consider next solutions of Na_2CO_3, leaving till later the more complicated intermediate case of solutions of $NaHCO_3$. Since there is not enough CO_3^{--} in solutions of CO_2 to precipitate Ca^{++}, the second ionization of carbonic acid, $HCO_3^- = H^+ + CO_3^{--}$, must be extremely weak. Solutions of CO_3^{--} must, therefore, be strongly hydrolyzed (cf. Chapter XIII, paragraph 25) and this is indeed the case, the reaction being

$$CO_3^{--} + H_2O = HCO_3^- + OH^-.$$

If we use $0.5\ M\text{-}Na_2CO_3$, which, as a strong salt, contains $1\ M\text{-}Na^+$ and $0.5\ M\text{-}CO_3^{--}$, we find, on careful investigation with a suitable indicator, such as alizarin yellow R, that $(OH^-) \approx 0.01\ M$. This alkaline reaction is responsible for many important uses of Na_2CO_3.

7. The second ionization constant of carbonic acid can be calculated by the aid of the above figures. We took 0.5 mole of Na_2CO_3 and found 0.01 mole of OH^-. For every molecule of OH^- thus liberated, one molecule of HCO_3^- was formed, hence $(HCO_3^-) = 0.01\ M$. This leaves $(CO_3^{--}) = 0.49$. Now

$$K_2 = \frac{(H^+)(CO_3^{--})}{(HCO_3^-)}$$

and $(H^+) = 10^{-14}/(OH^-) = 10^{-12}$, hence,

$$K_2 = \frac{10^{-12} \times 0.49}{10^{-2}} = 4.9 \times 10^{-11}$$

This agrees closely with the accepted value, 4.7×10^{-11}. In reality, small differences in temperature cause greater variations than this.

8. Sodium Bicarbonate Solutions. If we use $1\ M\text{-}NaHCO_3$, we have in solution primarily $1\ M\text{-}Na^+$ and $1\ M\text{-}HCO_3^-$, but the latter can undergo two further reactions. It is a weak acid, therefore it can ionize according to reaction (a) below. But it is also the ion of a weak acid, and can therefore hydrolyze as shown in (b).

$$(a) \qquad HCO_3^- \qquad\qquad = H^+ + CO_3^{--}$$

$$(b) \qquad HCO_3^- + H_2O = OH^- + H_2CO_3$$

If (a) alone occurred the solution would be weakly acid ($\sqrt{K_2}$) and if (b) alone occurred the solution would be considerably more alkaline than a solution of sodium acetate, because H_2CO_3 is a much weaker acid than acetic acid, as anyone can see by comparing the tastes of soda water and vinegar; just how much, an understanding student would see from their ionization constants, 4.3×10^{-7} for H_2CO_3 and 1.8×10^{-5} for acetic acid. But since reaction (a) liberates H^+ and reaction (b) liberates OH^-, these neutralize each other, causing both more CO_3^{--} and more H_2CO_3 to be formed than would be formed by either reaction alone, while preventing either H^+ or OH^- from increasing very much. Indicator tests on a solution of $1\ M\text{-}HCO_3^-$ show that $(OH^-) = 2 \times 10^{-6}$, therefore reaction (b) evidently gains a little over (a). The net result of both (a) and (b) is mainly

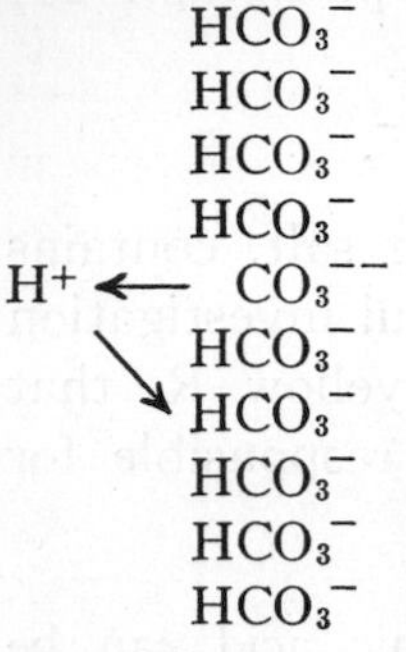

HCO_3^-
HCO_3^-
HCO_3^-
HCO_3^-
$H^+ \longleftarrow CO_3^{--}$
$\diagdown\ HCO_3^-$
$\diagup\ HCO_3^-$
HCO_3^-
HCO_3^-
HCO_3^-
Fig. 1

$$2\,HCO_3^- = CO_3^{--} + H_2CO_3$$

Equilibrium
concs.   0.98   .01   .01

There is a somewhat different way of understanding this result without invoking the role of water. In a solution containing many HCO_3^- ions, an occasional H^+ splitting off might find its way back later to its CO_3^{--} partner, but although the attraction of CO_3^{--} for H^+ is much stronger than that of HCO_3^-, there are so many more HCO_3^- ions that the H^+ has a good chance of uniting for a while with one of them, forming H_2CO_3, as illustrated by Fig. 1. It is obvious that, one H_2CO_3 is formed for every CO_3^{--} left behind, except as altered by the water, which is very little.

9. The equilibrium constant of the bicarbonate equilibrium can be calculated from $K_1 = \dfrac{(H^+)(HCO_3^-)}{(H_2CO_3)}$ and $K_2 = \dfrac{(H^+)(CO_3^{--})}{(HCO_3^-)}$ by eliminating (H^+), which gives

$$\frac{(H_2CO_3)(CO_3^{--})}{(HCO_3^-)^2} = \frac{K_2}{K_1} = \frac{4.7 \times 10^{-11}}{4.3 \times 10^{-7}} \approx 10^{-4}$$

If (HCO_3^-) is chosen as 1, then $(H_2CO_3) = (CO_3^{--}) = 10^{-2}$, as given above.

10. Displacing the Bicarbonate Equilibrium. Removal of CO_3^{--}, as by adding Ca^{++}, of course increases (H_2CO_3) till it becomes sufficiently large to stop the reaction at a new set of equilibrium concentrations. Adding the reactions gives

$$2\,HCO_3^- = CO_3^{--} + H_2CO_3$$
$$\underline{Ca^{++} + CO_3^{--} = CaCO_3}$$
$$Ca^{++} + 2\,HCO_3^- = CaCO_3 + H_2CO_3$$

This is the important equilibrium involved in the solution of limestone by natural water, the equation as read from right to left, and its reprecipitation by loss of CO_2, such as occurs in the formation of stalagmites in limestone caves, or on boiling this variety of "hard water," forming scale in steam boilers and kitchen kettles.

11. The equilibrium constant for this reaction can be obtained by combining the constant for the pure bicarbonate equilibrium with the solubility product of $CaCO_3$. We write

$$\frac{(H_2CO_3)(CO_3^{--})}{(HCO_3^-)^2} = 10^{-4}$$

and $(Ca^{++})(CO_3^{--}) = 4.8 \times 10^{-9}$.

Dividing the former by the latter gives

$$\frac{(H_2CO_3)}{(Ca^{++})(HCO_3^-)^2} = \frac{10 \times 10^{-5}}{4.8 \times 10^{-9}} \approx 2 \times 10^4.$$

As an example of the use of this constant, we may calculate (Ca^{++}) in a solution of limestone in water charged with carbonic acid from pure air, in which the partial pressure of CO_2 is 3×10^{-4} atm.

Taking the concentration of H_2CO_3 when the pressure of CO_2 is 1 atm. as roughly 0.04 (cf. Table 1) then, when the partial pressure of CO_2 is reduced to 3×10^{-4} atm., the value of (H_2CO_3) is reduced to $0.04 \times 3 \times 10^{-4} = 1.2 \times 10^{-5}$, which we may introduce into the above equilibrium constant. We see from the equation that $2 HCO_3^-$ are formed along with each Ca^{++}, therefore $(HCO_3^-) = 2 (Ca^{++})$. Substituting these values in the above equation gives

$$\frac{1.2 \times 10^{-5}}{4 (Ca^{++})^3} = 2 \times 10^4,$$

which yields $(Ca^{++}) = 2.5 \times 10^{-4}$. A cubic meter of surface water, 1000 liters, flowing over limestone, could dissolve 0.25 moles or 25 grams of $CaCO_3$, and this amount of hard water, evaporated in a steam boiler, would deposit 25 g. of boiler scale. If used in a laundry, it would destroy the equivalent weight of soap. If the soap were pure sodium oleate, $C_{18}H_{33}O_2Na$, this would weigh 152 g. It is evidently important to "soften" hard water by removing this Ca^{++}.

12. Water Softening. Hard water formed by the solution of limestone as above can be softened by (1) boiling, a prohibitively expensive method, (2) neutralizing the H_2CO_3, using any alkali or salt reacting alkaline by hydrolysis, including ammonia, borax, monosodium phosphate, sodium silicate. $Ca(OH)_2$ can be used under analytical control so as to get the exactly equivalent amount. Hardness due to dissolving $CaSO_4$ must be removed by adding a precipitant, such as Na_2CO_3. An artificial or natural zeolite, which is insoluble in water, can exchange its Na^+ for Ca^{++} by the reaction:

$$Ca^{++} + 2 NaH_6AlSiO_7 = 2 Na^+ + Ca(H_6AlSiO_7)_2.$$

When the material is exhausted, it can be regenerated by washing with concentrated brine.

Magnesium ion may also contribute to the hardness of water and its chemistry is similar to that of calcium ion.

13. The principal equilibrium in a solution of $NaHCO_3$, $2 HCO_3^- = CO_3^{--} + H_2CO_3$, **is shifted** by boiling or even on standing exposed to the air, since the equilibrium concentration of H_2CO_3 in pure 1 M-$NaHCO_3$ is 0.01, while the CO_2 in pure air can maintain only $(H_2CO_3) = 1.2 \times 10^{-5}$. Consequently, although the (OH^-) in a pure solution is 2×10^{-6} (cf. paragraph 8) it rises on standing exposed to air, or rapidly on boiling the solution, increasing the (CO_3^{--}) which, as we have seen (paragraph 6) gives a strongly alkaline reaction. If solid $NaHCO_3$ is heated, H_2O and CO_2 are evolved, and Na_2CO_3 is left by a reaction similar to the above: $2\ NaHCO_3 = Na_2CO_3 + H_2O + CO_2$

14. Summary. Let us now collect, in Table 2, the knowledge we have gained concerning the concentrations of the various substances present in solutions of CO_2, $NaHCO_3$, and Na_2CO_3.

TABLE 2

Solution	Principal substances present	Present in smaller concentrations
CO_2 at 1 atm.	$.03\ M$-$H_2CO_3 + CO_2$	$10^{-4}\ M\ H^+$ $10^{-4}\ M\ HCO_3^-$
1 M-$NaHCO_3$	1 M-Na^+ $\sim 1\ M$-HCO_3^- $(0.98\ M)$	$0.1\ M$-H_2CO_3 $.01\ M$-CO_3^{--} $(OH^-) = 2 \times 10^{-6}$
0.5 M-Na_2CO_3	1 M-Na^+ $\sim 0.5\ M$-CO_3^{--} $(0.49\ M)$	$.01\ M$-HCO_3^- $.01\ M$-OH^-

The numerical values in this table are worth remembering. This is made easier by the fact that $.01\ M$ occurs in several places.

15. Plot of pH. Fig. 2 gives a further graphical insight into the nature of these solutions. It represents the values of $-\log (H^+)$ or pH for solutions made by starting with 1 liter of 1 M-$NaHCO_3^-$ and adding, on the one hand, fractions of a liter of 1 M-$NaOH$, giving eventually 0.5 M-CO_3^{--}, and, on the other hand, fractions of a liter of 1 M-HCl, to give H_2CO_3 and then an excess of H^+. This plot reveals in graphic form a number of the points brought out in previous discussion. The points of inflection represent the values of pH for pure CO_3^{--}, HCO_3^-, and H_2CO_3, respectively, although in the case of the last we have assumed that the CO_2 formed is kept in the solution under pressure, giving $(H_2CO_3) = 0.5\ M$, not $0.04\ M$, as when the CO_2 is at 1 atmosphere. We see, also, that the curve is very flat in the intermediate ranges so that these solutions could serve as buffers (cf. Chapter XIII, paragraph 51). The buffer containing HCO_3^- and H_2CO_3 is extremely important to man for it is partly responsible for keeping the pH of the blood at its normal

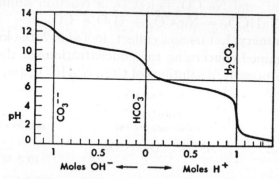

Fig. 2. Change in pH on adding to 1 liter of 1 M-NaHCO₃, fractions of a liter of (*a*) 1 M-NaOH (to the left of 0), and (*b*) 1 M-HCl (to the right).

value of about 7.4. This buffer action is so reliable as to make unnecessary the anxiety of many people over "acidosis" and the "acid ash" of foods, stimulated by skillful commercial advertising designed to sell at a high price sodium bicarbonate disguised under various brand names.

The curve shows, also, that CO_3^{--} could be determined by titration with acid using an indicator changing at between pH 8 and 9, indicating one equivalent of acid, or by one changing at about pH $= 3$, for two equivalents of acid. The curve is much steeper for the latter change, so that the end point would be sharper. Combinations of NaOH and Na₂CO₃ or of Na₂CO₃ and NaHCO₃ can be analyzed by getting both end points.

16. Disposition of CaCO₃ by Marine Organisms. The value of (Ca^{++}) in sea water is given as $10^{-2}\ M$. Since $(Ca^{++})\ (CO_3^{--}) = 4.8 \times 10^{-9}$, which we will round off to 5×10^{-9}, it is necessary, in order to precipitate CaCO₂ from sea water, to have (CO_3^{--})

= 5 × 10⁻⁷, at least. If this must be obtained from the dissolved
CO_2, it will, of course, be necessary for (H^+) to be less than a certain
value. Let us calculate this value. The (H_2CO_3) in sea water we can
calculate from the partial pressure of CO_2 in pure air, 3×10^{-4}
atmosphere, and its solubility in water at 1 atmosphere and 25° C.,
which is $3.4 \times 10^{-2} M$, according to Table 1. We will assume tropic
water. In sea water, accordingly, we should find that (H_2CO_3)
$= 10^{-5}$ approximately. In order to calculate what value of (H^+) is
necessary to give $(CO_3^{--}) = 5 \times 10^{-7}$ in the presence of (H_2CO_3)
$= 10^{-5}$, we may substitute these values in the expressions for K_1
and K_2, paragraphs 5 and 7, getting $(H^+) (HCO_3^-) = 4.3 \times 10^{-12}$
and $(H^+) = 10^{-4} (HCO_3^-)$. Eliminating (HCO_3^-) gives $(H^+)^2$
$= 4 \times 10^{-16}$ and $(H^+) = 2 \times 10^{-8}$. Evidently the organism must be
able to establish a slight alkalinity in order to deposit $CaCO_3$ if it
has to depend solely upon the dissolved CO_2. Since, however, it
produces CO_2 by its own metabolism, the (H^+) may be somewhat
higher and still give a sufficient (CO_3^{--}).

Conversely, it follows that coral rock should dissolve in sea
water, in which $(H^+) > 2 \times 10^{-8}$.

It should be recognized, of course, that such a calculation as the
above is only approximate and exploratory. The equilibria involved
should all be affected not only by temperature, but also by the
other constituents present in sea water and by the biochemical
composition of the secreting organs of the animal. Nevertheless, no
one could properly investigate the physiologic process who does not
understand the basic inorganic chemistry involved.

17. The Solvay Process for the manufacture of sodium
carbonate and bicarbonate is an interesting example of one
which is successful by reason of using cheap raw materials,
low energy costs, and little waste by-product. The central
reaction is the precipitation of solid $NaHCO_3$ from its ions
at low temperature. Its solubility is $0.82 M$ at 0° C. The
Na^+ comes from $NaCl$ and the HCO_3^- from the reaction:
$NH_3 + H_2O + CO_2 = NH_4^+ + HCO_3^-$. The CO_2 comes from
"burning" $CaCO_3$ and the NH_3 is recovered from the NH_4^+
by the action of $Ca(OH)_2$ obtained from the limestone. The
demand for Na_2CO_3 is satisfied by heating $NaHCO_3$, return-
ing the liberated CO_2 to the process. The only waste product

is $CaCl_2$, for which there is some market. The steps in the process and the coordination between them are represented in a flow diagram, Fig. 3.

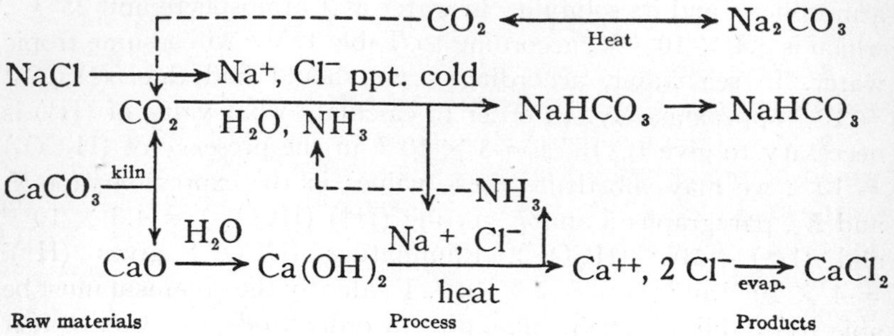

Fig. 3. Diagram of Solvay Process.

Exercises

See Appendix II for answers

1. Write equations for the principal equilibrium in solutions of (*a*) 0.034 M-H_2CO_3 (or CO_2 aq.); (*b*) 1 M-$NaHCO_3$; (*c*) 0.5 M-Na_2CO_3.

2. Give the approximate concentration of each substance present in the above solutions.

3. Can the following substances be present at moderate concentrations, say 0.1 molal, in the same solution? If not, what is formed?

(*a*) H_2CO_3 and H^+, (*b*) H_2CO_3 and Ca^{++}, (*c*) H_2CO_3 and HCO_3^-, (*d*) HCO_3^- and H^+, (*e*) HAc and CO_2, (*f*) Ca^{++} and NO_3^-, (*g*) OH^- and HAc, (*h*) H_2CO_3 and CO_3^{--}, (*i*) Ca^{++} and SO_4^{--}, (*j*) NH_3 and OH^-.

4. Give equations for five positive cases in question 3.

5. How will the concentrations of H_2CO_3 and CO_3^{--} in a solution of $NaHCO_3$ be altered by (*a*) adding $CaCl_2$, (*b*) adding NaOH, (*c*) adding CO_2, (*d*) adding more $NaHCO_3$, (*e*) boiling?

6. Write equations showing what happens in each of the following cases:

(*a*) Solid $NaHCO_3$ is heated, (*b*) A solution of $NaHCO_3$ is mixed with one of NaOH, (*c*) Solid $CaSO_4$ is treated with a solution of Na_2CO (*d*) CO_2 gas is passed into a suspension of $CaCO_3$.

7. Certain of the following pairs react to a considerable extent when mixed in 0.1 molal solutions; write the formulas of the substances formed in such cases.

(a) H^+ and H_2CO_3, (b) HCO_3^- and CO_3^{--}, (c) Ca^{++} and H_2CO_3, (d) Ca^{++} and $C_2O_4^{--}$, (e) OH^- and CO_3^{--}, (f) H^+ and CO_3^{--}, (g) Ca^{++} and Cl^-, (h) HAc and HCO_3^-, (i) Ba^{++} and NH_4OH.

8. How can you prove that the main reaction of CO_2 with water produces HCO_3^- rather than CO_3^{--}?

9. What volume of CO_2 gas, measured at standard conditions, would be produced by heating 21.0 grams of $NaHCO_3$?

10. One mole of CO_2 gas is passed into 1 liter of each of the following: (a) water, (b) 0.01 M-HCl, (c) 0.001 M-KOH, (d) 0.1 M-NaHCO$_3$, (e) 0.1 M-KCl. Arrange in order of the extent to which CO_2 is used up according to the reaction: $CO_2 + H_2O = H^+ + HCO_3^-$.

11. The concentration of OH^- in 1 M-NaHCO$_3$ is less than 1 M-NaAc. Does this agree with the relative strengths of the acids H_2CO_3 and HAc? Explain.

12. Why is $NaHCO_3$ "baking soda" and Na_2CO_3 "washing soda"?

*13. What is the relation between the equilibrium constant, K, for the reaction, $2 HCO_3^- = H_2CO_3 + CO_3^{--}$, and the two ionization constants, K_1 and K_2 for carbonic acid?

*14. If 1 M-NaHCO$_3$ is shaken with CO_2 at 1 atmosphere, what will (CO_3^{--}) become?

*15. Using the values $K_1 = 7.5 \times 10^{-3}$ and $K_2 = 6.2 \times 10^{-8}$ for the first and second dissociation constants of H_3PO_4, calculate (a) the equilibrium constant for the reaction $2 H_2PO_4 = H_3PO_4 + HPO_4^{--}$, and (b) the concentration of HPO_4^{--} in 0.3 M-NaH$_2$PO$_4$.

*16. What will (H^+) be in soda water charged with CO_2 at 4.0 atm. at 25° C.?

*17. What will (OH^-) be when (CO_3^{--})/(HCO_3)$^-$ = 0.4?

*18. What will (H^+) be in a solution made by passing CO_2 at 1 atm. into 0.1 M-NaHCO$_3$?

*19. If the pH of blood is 7.4, i.e., log (H^+) $= -7.4 = 0.6 + 8$ and (H^+) $= 4 \times 10^{-8}$, what is the ratio, (H_2CO_3)/(HCO_3^-)?

*20. What is the effect on the pH of blood of forced, rapid breathing?

21. Why can concentrated $NaHCO_3$ be used in the eye to neutralize accidental contamination by either acid or alkali?

*Questions of greater difficulty .

*22. Calculate (OH^-) in 1 M-$NaHCO_3$ at 25° C. from the values of K_1, K_2, and K_w, and instead of setting $(H_2CO_3) = (CO_3)^{--}$, note that in reality $(H^+) + (CO_3^{--}) = (OH^-) + (H_2CO_3)$. Do you see why?

CHAPTER XXII

ACID-BASE SYSTEMS

1. Resume of the Water System of Acids and Bases. Acids and bases have till recent years usually been defined as explained in Chapter V, by their properties in aqueous solutions. In general, acids taste sour, they react with base metals to liberate H_2 and with carbonates to liberate CO_2, and they give characteristic colors to a class of highly colored organic substances called "indicators," and they neutralize bases, their "opposite numbers." They are compounds of hydrogen which ionize in water to give hydrogen ion, usually written H^+, or, more explicitly, $H^+(aq.)$, but also H_3O^+, called "hydronium ion," with its assumed single molecule of water of hydration, in analogy with NH_4^+, ammonium ion.

2. Most bases are rather insoluble in water, so that they are experimentally marked chiefly by their ability to neutralize acids, as shown by the disappearance of the sour taste, the characteristically acid colors of indicators, etc. A few soluble bases exist, including the hydroxides of the "alkali" elements of group 1, the "alkaline earth" elements of group 2, ammonium hydroxide and organic amines (cf. Chapter XVIII, paragraph 20). These not only destroy acids but, in higher concentrations, give their own characteristic colors to appropriate indicators, and they precipitate the insoluble bases. They are hydroxides, and insofar as they go into solution yield hydroxide ion, OH^-.

3. Since the H^+ of acids and the OH^- of bases neutralize each other instantaneously when mixed to form water, the solvent used in excess of all others, the historical system of acids, bases, and neutralization is this "water system." Degrees of acidity and alkalinity of solutions are expressed

401

in terms of the concentrations of H^+ and OH^-, related, of course, by the dissociation constant of water, $(H^+)(OH^-) = K_w = 1.0 \times 10^{-14}$ at 25° C. (cf. Chapter XIII, paragraphs 11–13). We have seen, further, how certain substances, although containing no ionizable hydrogen or hydroxyl, can produce acid or alkaline reactions by hydrolysis, uniting with one of the ions of water and liberating the other (cf. Chapter XIII, paragraphs 23 *ff*). All of this is adequate for the treatment of aqueous solutions both qualitatively and quantitatively, and, in the opinion of many teachers, provides the most satisfactory approach to the subject for elementary students of chemistry. It is desirable, nevertheless, at a somewhat later stage, to become familiar with several other although more or less related systems, each of which offers certain advantages in dealing with certain types of acidic and basic substances or with reactions in certain solvents. The remainder of this chapter was written for that purpose.

4. The Ammonia System. Liquid ammonia is one of the best electrolytic solvents after water (cf. Chapter VIII, paragraph 17). Many salts dissolve in it to give electrically conducting, ionized solutions. Acids react with it to give NH_4^+, ammonium ion, far more strongly than they do to give OH_3^+, "hydronium ion," in water as a solvent. Moreover, we can have far more confidence in the correctness of the formula NH_4^+ than we can in the formula OH_3^+. The molecules in both liquid ammonia and water are connected to each other through hydrogen bonds or bridges (cf. Chapter XX, paragraph 12) but the bonds are much stronger in the case of water. The approximately right-angled molecules of water tend to unite with each other indefinitely to form the ice structure, except as interfered with by thermal agitation, which may be indicated in two dimensions as follows:

$$\begin{array}{c}
\text{H} \\
\text{H} : \overset{\cdot\cdot}{\text{O}} : \text{H} : \overset{\cdot\cdot}{\underset{\cdot\cdot}{\text{O}}} : \quad \text{H} \qquad\qquad \text{H} \\
\overset{\cdot\cdot}{\text{H}} \qquad\quad \overset{\cdot\cdot}{\text{H}} \; : \overset{\cdot\cdot}{\underset{\cdot\cdot}{\text{O}}} : \text{H} : \overset{\cdot\cdot}{\text{O}} : \quad \text{etc.} \\
\text{H}
\end{array}$$

An extra hydrogen ion can add onto a pair of unoccupied electrons of a water molecule, but unless that molecule were thereby detached from the neighbors to which it is already bound by strong dipole forces, we would hardly be justified in writing OH_3^+ while excluding $O_2H_5^+$, etc. In the case of ammonia, however, the bonds uniting NH_3 to NH_3 are so much weaker, and the bond between NH_3 and H^+ so much stronger that NH_4^+ is fully justified.

5. Pure liquid ammonia is a definite, if feeble, conductor, about 0.1 as good as water, but its ions, for the reasons given above, cannot be considered as H^+ and NH_2^-, by analogy with water, but rather NH_4^+ and NH_2^-. In this solvent, therefore, a salt such as NH_4NO_3 is an acid and KNH_2, potassium amide, is a base. These and analogous compounds can be titrated against each other with phenolphthalein, just as HNO_3 and KOH can be titrated in aqueous solution with the same indicator. The neutralization equation can be written:

$$NH_4^+ + NH_2^- = 2\ NH_3.$$

6. Amides can be changed to imides and nitrides by losing ammonia just as hydroxides can be dehydrated in one or more steps to form oxides:

$$2\ KNH_2 = K_2NH + NH_3.$$
$$3\ KNH_2 = K_3N + 2\ NH_3.$$

By pursuing the analogy between the ammonia system and the water system, an extensive chemistry of reactions in liquid ammonia has been developed and systematized. These studies have yielded occasional by-products of significance for "aquo-chemistry." One of the most interesting is an explanation of compounds such as $HgNH_2Cl$, whose nature was formerly very puzzling. It is now regarded as "ammono-basic mercuric chloride," the NH_2 being analogous to OH in $MgOHCl$.

7. Other systems based on the ions of the solvent, like the water and ammonia systems, suggest themselves for solvents having a sufficiently high dielectric constant to

give ionized solutions but which are themselves so weakly ionized as to be formed by "neutralization" reactions. An acid would be defined as a substance giving the positive ion of the solvent, a base, one giving the negative ion. This has never proven to be a useful point of view, however, largely because it is too restricted, and overemphasizes the role of the solvent.

8. The Proton-Donor-Acceptor System. The majority of substances deserving to be called acids contain ionizable hydrogen. There are, consequently, a great many molecular species in addition to OH^- which can unite with and therefore more or less neutralize H^+. This has encouraged the development of a system in which OH^- loses its special role as a

TABLE 1

Relative Strength of Inorganic Acids and Bases

Acid	=	Proton	+	Base
$HClO_4$	=	H^+	+	ClO_4^-
HCl	=	H^+	+	Cl^-
H_3O^+	=	H^+	+	H_2O
HSO_4^-	=	H^+	+	SO_4^{--}
CH_3COOH	=	H^+	+	CH_3COO^-
H_2CO_3	=	H^+	+	HCO_3^-
NH_4^+	=	H^+	+	NH_3
HCO_3^-	=	H^+	+	CO_3^{--}
H_2O	=	H^+	+	OH^-
OH^-	=	H^+	+	O^{--}

Increasing strength (left margin, upward)   *Increasing strength* (right margin, downward)

base and H_2O its unique significance as a solvent and in which the sole criterion of acid and basic character is considered to be the gain or loss of a proton, unsolvated H^+. According to this point of view, an acid is a substance having the chemical property of losing a proton, H^+, to another substance, and a base is a substance, conversely, which is capable of adding a proton. These definitions hold regardless of whether the particular molecular species in question is an ion or a neutral molecule. The examples in Table 1 should make these terms clear.

9. Since unsolvated protons do not exist in water and most other solvents, most actual acid-base reactions consist in a transfer of the proton from the stronger acid to the conjugate base of the weaker acid, illustrated by the examples in Table 2.

TABLE 2
Acid-Base Exchange Reactions

Acid A	+	Base B	=	Base A	+	Acid B
$HClO_4$	+	H_2O	=	ClO_4^-	+	H_3O^+
NH_4^+	+	OH^-	=	NH_3	+	H_2O
H_3O^+	+	CH_3COO^-	=	H_2O	+	CH_3COOH
HSO_4^-	+	HCO_3^-	=	SO_4^{--}	+	H_2CO_3

The greater the disparity in strengths the larger the equilibrium concentrations of the species on the right.

10. This method of regarding acidic and basic properties does not require the concept of hydrolysis to explain either the acidic character of NH_4^+ or the basic character of CO_3^{--}. Furthermore, it emphasizes the basic character of NH_3 in its own right as due to the reaction, $H^+ + NH_3 = NH_4^+$. It does not limit that character to its aqueous solution as due liberating OH^- by the reaction, $NH_3 + H_2O = NH_4OH = NH_4^+ + OH^-$. At the same time, it permits us to write the equation, $NH_4^+ + H_2O = NH_3 + H_3O^+$, practically identical with the hydrolysis equation as ordinarily written, $NH_4^+ + H_2O = NH_4OH + H^+$, where the H^+ is understood to be $H^+(aq.)$, equivalent to H_3O^+. The fact that only a very little NH_3 is formed, in the one case, or NH_4OH in the other, is explained by saying with respect to the former, either that H_3O^+ is a much stronger acid than NH_4^+, or, what amounts to the same thing, NH_3 is a much stronger base than H_2O, and this is really equivalent to what we have been accustomed to say with respect to the small hydrolysis of NH_4^+, that H_2O is less ionized than NH_4OH to form OH^-.

11. There is a complete terminology for this system[1] of which the following definitions are samples.

AMPHIPROTIC SUBSTANCE—a substance which can act either as an acid or as a base. Example: HCO_3^-.

[1] Cf. *Journal of Chemical Education*, Vol. 16, page 535 (1939).

APROTIC SOLVENT—a solvent which will neither lose a proton to the solute, nor gain a proton from the solute. Example: C_6H_6.

LYOLYSIS—or Solvolysis (also Hydrolysis, Ammonolysis, and so forth)—a protolytic reaction between a cation acid or an anion base and the solvent (water, ammonia, and so forth). Example: $NH_4^+ + H_2O \rightleftarrows NH_3 + H_3O^+$;
$$CN^- + H_2O \rightleftarrows HCN + OH^-.$$

MONOPROTIC ACID—an acid which has only one proton to lose to a base. Examples: HCl; HSO_4^-. Also Diprotic Acid, etc., and Polyprotic Acid.

PROTOLYSIS, PROTOLYTIC REACTION—a reaction in which a proton is transferred from an acid to a base. Example: $A_1 + B_2 \rightarrow A_2 + B_1$; as in $HCl + CH_3COO \rightarrow CH_3COOH + Cl^-$.

SALT—an ionic compound. Example: $NaCl$.

12. The chief advantage of this system is that it ascribes acidic and basic strength to the substance itself, and not to its behavior in a particular solvent. This is particularly helpful to the organic chemist, who finds it necessary to change from one to another of his ordinary solvents, such as ether, alcohol, benzene, toluene, or mixtures of them. All experienced chemists would agree, for example, that acid strength decreases in the order $HClO_4$, HCl, CH_3COOH, H_2O, regardless of solvent and, similarly, that basic strength decreases in the order $Ba(OH)_2$, NH_3, H_2O.

13. The order given in Table 1 would doubtless be regarded as a completely satisfactory representation of the relative strengths of these species as acids and bases, divorced from the specific influences of solvents by referring each conjugate pair to unsolvated proton. The effect of a particular solvent is then introduced by considering its own reaction with the proton. To illustrate, let us compare the results of dissolving HCl gas in an excess of (*a*) water, and (*b*) liquid ammonia. The former is a slightly stronger base and the latter a much stronger base than Cl^-, hence, while both react with HCl, as follows:

(a) $\quad$ HCl (gas) + H$_2$O (liquid, excess) = H$_3$O$^+$ + Cl$^-$.

(b) $\quad$ HCl (gas) + NH$_3$ (liquid, excess) = NH$_4$$^+$ + Cl$^-$.

Reaction (b) proceeds much farther than (a) as shown by the fact that HCl gas escapes from concentrated HCl(aq.) but not from equally concentrated NH$_4$Cl in liquid NH$_3$.

But in spite of the fact that the effects of different solvents on the H$^+$ are adequately accounted for in this way, it should be realized that the equilibria in Tables 1 and 2 are still not independent of the nature of the solvent, because the forces acting upon the acids and bases themselves are different in different solvents. A set of equilibrium constants derived from aqueous solutions could not be applied unchanged to solutions of the same species in alcohol, ether, or benzene. The users of the system must be content with approximate predictions only when changing solvents. A solvent is not simply space in which molecules are free to wander unaffected as they do in the gaseous state.

14. The substances listed in Table 1 are chiefly those used in aqueous solutions, selected so as to set forth the new point of view in terms of species whose behavior is already familiar in the "water system." The proton-donor-acceptor system is chiefly valuable, however, in organic chemistry, and therefore a tabulation consisting mainly of typical organic acids and bases as in Table 3, should prove more useful. The arrangement brings out certain general rules familiar to organic chemists, such as that acid strength is increased by substituting H for CH$_3$, C$_6$H$_5$ for CH$_3$, Cl for H, C$_6$H$_5$ for H, CH$_3$ for C$_2$H$_5$.

15. The Electron-Donor-Acceptor System. While the acid-base system described in the paragraphs immediately preceding escapes from the restriction of OH$^-$ as the criterion of basic character, it limits the definition of acids to substances capable of splitting off protons, as illustrated by the lists in Tables 1 and 3. Now there is still another point

of view, one which escapes this restriction also, and which has proven its value for over a century, particularly in interpreting combinations between oxides. Berzelius, long before the discovery of electrons and protons, explained combinations such as $CaO + CO_2$ as due to attraction between +

TABLE 3

Relative Strengths of Organic Acids and Bases

Acids		Bases
HCl	=	$H^+ + Cl^-$
H_3O^+	=	$H^+ + H_2O$
$CH_3OH_2^+$	=	$H^+ + CH_3OH$ Methanol
$C_2H_5OH_2^+$	=	$H^+ + C_2H_5OH$ Ethyl alcohol
$(CH_3)_2OH^+$	=	$H^+ + (CH_3)_2O$ Dimethyl ether
$(C_6H_5)_2NH_2^+$	=	$H^+ + (C_6H_5)_2 NH$ Diphenyl amine
$C_6H_5NH_3^+$	=	$H^+ + C_6H_5NH_2$ Aniline
$ClCH_2COOH$ Chloroacetic acid	=	$H^+ + ClCH_2COO^-$
CH_3COOH Acetic acid	=	$H^+ + CH_3COO^-$
C_6H_5COOH Benzoic acid	=	$H^+ + C_6H_5COO^-$
NH_4^+	=	$H^+ + NH_3$
C_6H_5OH Phenol	=	$H^+ + C_6H_5O^-$
$CH_3NH_3^+$	=	$H^+ + CH_3NH_2$ Methyl amine
H_2O	=	$H^+ + OH^-$
CH_3OH Methanol	=	$H^+ + CH_3O^-$
NH_3	=	$H^+ + NH_2^-$

(Left margin: increasing strength ↑) *(Right margin: Increasing strength ↓)*

and — parts of molecules, and regarded oxygen, the "acid-generator," rather than hydrogen as responsible for acid character. It was recognized that there is no great distinction between two such reactions as

$$Ca(OH)_2 + H_2SO_3 = CaSO_3 + H_2O \text{ and}$$

$$CaO + SO_2 = CaSO_3.$$

It is but natural, therefore, to designate CaO as a basic oxide and SO_2 as an acid oxide. Again, since H_2O, CO_2, SO_2, and SO_3 are evolved with increasing difficulty in that order from their solid compounds with CaO, it is consistent to explain this as due to their increasing acidity. The relative basic characters of MgO, CaO, and BaO can be inferred as increasing in that order from the decomposition temperatures of their combinations with any one of the relatively acid oxides, H_2O, CO_2, or SO_2. It is thus possible to arrange the following series of oxides, from the most basic to the most acid, in such a way that the farther apart two of them are in the series, the more stable is their combination.

Most basic K_2O, Na_2O, BaO, CaO, MgO, ZnO,

           FeO, CuO, H_2O, CO_2, SO_2, SO_3 *Most acidic*

The increase in stability as compounds are chosen from oxides farther apart in the list is illustrated in Table 4.

TABLE 4

Decomposition Temperatures of Hydroxides and Carbonates

	CuO	MgO	CaO	BaO
H_2O	<100	184	547	988
CO_2	—	553	897	1361

The series is a perfectly good acid-base series in spite of the fact that H^+ is nowhere involved. Similar compounds are formed between halides, as illustrated by

$$KAlCl_4 = KCl \cdot AlCl_3, \qquad K_2PtCl_6 = PtCl_4 \cdot 2\,KCl,$$

$$K_2SnCl_6 = SnCl_4 \cdot 2\,KCl.$$

16. Another characteristic of acid-base reaction, the color changes of indicators, can also occur in systems from which H^+ is absent. Pyridine,

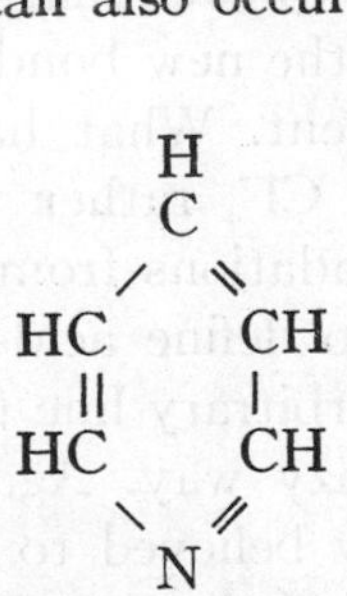

$$
\begin{array}{c}
\text{H} \\
\text{C} \\
\diagup \quad \diagdown \\
\text{HC} \qquad \text{CH} \\
\| \qquad\quad | \\
\text{HC} \qquad \text{CH} \\
\diagdown \quad \diagup \\
\text{N}
\end{array}
$$

and triethylamine, $(C_2H_5)_3N$ can act as bases, and SO_2,

BCl_3, and $SnCl_4$ as acids in CCl_4 or dioxane,

$$
\begin{array}{ccc}
 & O & \\
 & \diagup \quad \diagdown & \\
HC & & CH \\
\| & & \| \\
HC & & CH \\
 & \diagdown \quad \diagup & \\
 & O &
\end{array}
$$

giving color changes with suitable indicators on neutralization like ordinary acids and bases. It is therefore an exaggeration to claim that H^+ is the crux of acid-base neutralization. The reason why it is responsible for acid character in so many cases is that it is an "electron acceptor" in the sense that it can unite with unoccupied electron pairs of other ions or molecules in rapidly reversible equilibrium, as illustrated by cases 1, 2, 3, in Table 5. But SO_3 and $AlCl_3$, in cases 4, 5, and 6, are also acceptors, and can behave as acids towards the bases, CaO and KCl, due to their ions, O^{--} and Cl^-. In case 7, H_2O is an acceptor on account of the ability of its hydrogen to form "hydrogen bonds" (cf. Chapter XX, paragraph 12) between the atoms N, O, and F. Ag^+ is an acceptor to NH_3 due to its ability to form two more or less covalent bonds. Case 9, pyridine and BCl_3, is a neutralization reaction that is quite "aprotic," which can be carried out in an "aprotic" solvent, with an indicator to mark the end point.

It must be admitted however that in several of the above cases, notably 5 and 6, the new bonds formed are doubtless ionic rather than covalent. What has been "accepted" is a negative ion, O^{--} or Cl^-, rather than an electron pair. Indeed, there are all gradations from one to the other, and it would seem absurd to define acid-base reactions in such a way as to require an arbitrary line to be drawn somewhere along this somewhat hazy way. Again, the union of NH_3 and H_2O, case 7, is now believed to be due to their strong dipoles and closeness of their approach rather than to the formation of two covalent bonds by hydrogen. That fact should not, however, exclude this reaction from the category of acid-base reaction, where it certainly belongs from the point of view of actual chemical behavior. We are thus led back to the all-inclusive view of chemical union, held a century and a half ago by such master minds as Lavoisier and Berzelius, that the positive part of one molecule is attracted to the negative part of another with a strength depending on the difference in electric character, and we need not differentiate between the several sources of this difference, whether ionic charge, permanent dipoles, or unoccupied electron pairs.

17. The donor-acceptor concept of acid-base reactions must not be confused with the electron transfers involved in oxidation-reduction reactions. The former consists in a more or less unequal sharing, the latter in a complete transfer. The distinction may be illustrated by comparing the reduction of SO_3 to SO_3^{--} by acquiring the electrons of Ca with the neutralization of SO_3 by addition of O^{--} from CaO to form SO_4^{--}.

$$SO_3 \text{ as oxidizing agent} \qquad Ca\,(:) \longrightarrow \begin{matrix} :\overset{\cdot\cdot}{O}: \\[2pt] \overset{\cdot\cdot}{S} : \overset{\cdot\cdot}{\underset{\cdot\cdot}{O}}: \\[2pt] :\overset{\cdot\cdot}{O}: \end{matrix}$$

$$SO_3 \text{ as acid} \qquad Ca\left(:\overset{\cdot\cdot}{\underset{\cdot\cdot}{O}}:\right) \longrightarrow \begin{matrix} :\overset{\cdot\cdot}{O}: \\[2pt] \overset{\cdot\cdot}{S} : \overset{\cdot\cdot}{\underset{\cdot\cdot}{O}}: \\[2pt] :\overset{\cdot\cdot}{\underset{\cdot\cdot}{O}}: \end{matrix}$$

18. Relative Values of the Different Systems. There is a temptation, when dealing with rival points of view, such as these systems of acids and bases, to assume that one of them is "right" and the others "wrong," forgetting that they are only convenient, altogether artificial schemes for classifying reactions. No one of them is either true or false. The distinctions between them are not at all like the difference between the phlogiston theory of combustion and the "oxygen theory" (cf. Chapter I, paragraph 19). The choice

TABLE 5

Electron-Donor-Acceptor System

	Ordinary formulas			Electron formulas	
	Base	Acid		Donor	Acceptor
1.	OH^- +	H^+	= H_2O		
2.	NH_3 +	H^+	= NH_4^+		
3.	ClO^- +	H^+	= $ClOH$		
4.	CaO +	SO_3	= $CaSO_4$		
5.	KCl +	$AlCl_3$	= $KAlCl_4$		

6. $2 \text{ KCl} + \text{SnCl}_4 = \text{K}_2\text{SnCl}_6$

$$2 \text{ K} \; \overset{\displaystyle ..}{\underset{\displaystyle ..}{\text{Cl}}} : \; + \; \overset{\displaystyle :\overset{..}{\text{Cl}}:}{\underset{\displaystyle :\overset{..}{\text{Cl}}:}{\text{Cl} : \text{Sn} : \text{Cl}}} \; = \; \text{K}_2 \left[\; \overset{\displaystyle :\overset{..}{\text{Cl}}:}{\underset{\displaystyle :\overset{..}{\text{Cl}}:}{\overset{\displaystyle :\overset{..}{\text{Cl}}:}{\underset{\displaystyle :\overset{..}{\text{Cl}}:}{\text{Cl} : \text{Sn} : \text{Cl}}}} \; \right]^{-}$$

7. $\text{NH}_3 + \text{H}_2\text{O} = \text{NH}_4\text{OH}$

$$\text{H} : \overset{\displaystyle \text{H}}{\underset{\displaystyle \text{H}}{\text{N}}} : \; + \; \text{H} : \overset{\displaystyle ..}{\underset{\displaystyle ..}{\text{O}}} : \text{H} \; = \; \text{H} : \overset{\displaystyle \text{H}}{\underset{\displaystyle \text{H}}{\text{N}}} : \overset{\displaystyle ..}{\underset{\displaystyle ..}{\text{O}}} : \text{H}$$

8. $2 \text{ NH}_3 + \text{Ag}^+ = \text{Ag}(\text{NH}_3)_2^+$

$$2 \text{ H} : \overset{\displaystyle \text{H}}{\underset{\displaystyle \text{H}}{\text{N}}} : \; + \; [\text{Ag}]^+ \; = \; \left[\; \text{H} : \overset{\displaystyle \text{H}}{\underset{\displaystyle \text{H}}{\text{N}}} : \text{Ag} : \overset{\displaystyle \text{H}}{\underset{\displaystyle \text{H}}{\text{N}}} : \text{H} \; \right]^+$$

9. $\text{C}_5\text{H}_5\text{N} + \text{BCl}_3 = \text{C}_5\text{H}_5\text{N}\cdot\text{BCl}_3$

between them should depend solely upon the region of chemistry in which one is operating, like the choice between the different clefs in music for recording the part for a particular instrument. Violin parts are usually written in the treble clef, viola parts in the alto clef, and violoncello parts in the bass clef because these best correspond to the ranges of the respective instruments, not because it would be either wrong or impossible to write a given part in another clef. Just as a trained musician can read from any clef, so an intelligent chemist can select whichever system of acids and bases best suits his particular purpose. The "water system" is perfectly adapted to aqueous solutions; the ammonia system to reactions in that solvent; the proton system is preferable to the preceding ones for dealing with the variety of solvents and bases encountered in organic chemistry, but it is inadequate for dealing with the cases continually coming to light, even in organic chemistry, of acid behavior in the absence of H^+. A particularly striking case is offered by the substitution of BF_3 for H_2SO_4 as an acid catalyst in the production of high octane gasoline. And the mineral chemist is scarcely likely to agree to definitions which would deny him the right to refer to an igneous rock as acidic or basic. It is desirable that the chemist retain sufficient elasticity of mind to avoid definitions which are so rigid as to act as shackles rather than serve as tools.

CHAPTER XXIII

STRUCTURES OF INORGANIC COMPOUNDS

1. Crystal Structures. When a narrow beam of X-rays passes through a crystal onto a photographic plate, a diffraction pattern of spots (cf. Chapter II, paragraph 13) is obtained whose arrangement depends upon the arrangement of atoms or ions in the crystal lattice. A sample pattern is illustrated in Fig. 1. The type and dimensions of the X-ray pattern usually serves to identify the type of lattice and to permit the calculation of the interatomic distances. Errors of identification are sometimes made in the case of complicated crystal lattices.

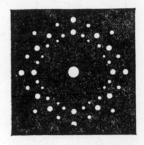

Fig. 1. Typical X-ray diffraction pattern.

2. The crystal systems[1] are based upon their axes of symmetry, shown in Fig. 2. Additional faces usually appear, and some faces generally outgrow others, distorting ideal shapes of the crystals. The relative lengths of these axes and the angles between them are as follows:

	Cubic	Tetrag-onal	Rhombic	Mono-clinic	Tri-clinic	Hexagonal
Relative length of axes	3 equal	2 equal	None equal			3 equal
Angles between axes	all 90.	all 90.	all 90.	2 at 90.	None at 90.	90. and 120.

3. Lattices. Different kinds of lattices may conform to a single system, thus the cubic system includes the following:

[1] Cf. Latimer and Hildebrand, *Reference Book of Inorganic Chemistry*, New York, The Macmillan Company, 1940, Appendix V.

Lattice	*Examples*	
Simple cubic	Halides of Li, Na, K	Fig. 3
Body-centered	MgO, CaO, AgCl, PbS, Li, Na, K, Cr, α-Fe, W	Fig. 4
Face-centered	Ag, Al, Au, Ca, Cu, γ-Fe, Ni, Pb, Pt, A	Fig. 5
Diamond	Si, Sn (grey)	Fig. 7

4. Close Packing. In the case of elements, whose atoms are all alike, there are two arrangements which represent the closest possible packing, the face-centered cubic (Fig. 5) and the hexagonal (Fig. 6). Both of these may be considered

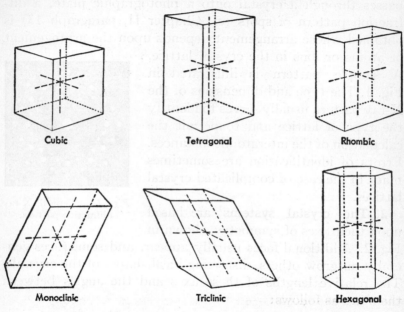

Cubic   Tetragonal   Rhombic

Monoclinic   Triclinic   Hexagonal

Fig. 2. Crystal systems.

as built up of close-packed layers (shown in Fig. 7) where all the spheres are in contact, making triangular and hexagonal patterns in which every sphere is surrounded by six others. A second identical layer is placed on top of this first one, its spheres fitting into pockets formed by three spheres in the first. A third close-packed layer is next placed on top of the second in the same way, but there are two sets of pockets in which to place it: one in which each sphere in the third layer is directly over a sphere in the first, forming the hexagonal close-packed lattice (Fig. 6); the other in which the spheres in the third layer are over holes in the first, forming the face-centered cubic close-packed lattice

Fig. 3. Sodium chloride lattice, simple cubic. The large spheres represent chloride ions, radius 1.81 Ångstroms; the small ones, sodium ions, radius 0.95 Ångstroms.

(Fig. 5), where only one ball of the third layer has been placed in position in order better to reveal the cubic faces containing one at the four corners and one in the center of

Fig. 4. Body-centered cubic lattice.

Fig. 5. Face-centered cubic lattice.

each. The elements of a hexagonal prism are clearly seen in Fig. 6, where the hexagonal arrangement occurs only in the horizontal plane. In the face-centered cubic lattice, the hexagonal arrangement is found in each plane cutting the diagonals of the cube.

It is obvious that these two lattices have the same density, since there is no difference in the relation of adjacent close-packed layers.

5. It is interesting to note that the changes in the physical properties of iron and steel caused by rapid versus slow cooling (annealing) are connected with the change between the body-centered and face-centered structures. Also, the presence in Fe of Ni, naturally face centered, stabilizes that

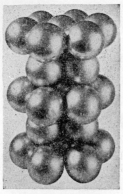

Fig. 6. Hexagonal close-packed lattice.

Fig. 7. Close-packed layer.

structure, permitting the necessarily slow cooling of large masses of nickel-steel armor plate without the loss of "temper."

6. In **diamond,** Fig. 8, the atomic arrangement is less easily described, but is such that each carbon atom can attach itself by an electron pair to its 4 nearest neighbors. The 4 chemical bonds of carbon are thus all called into play, and since the carbon atoms are very small, and can get very close together, so that the forces between them are very large, diamond is the hardest of all known substances. It is possible to see in the diamond lattice the main structures of organic chemistry, viz., the tetrahedron, the zigzag chain, and the hexagon. The lattice of graphite, shown in Fig. 9, retains the chain and the hexagon, now flat, but has lost the tetrahedron. The flat planes are far apart and can slide over each other; hence graphite is a lubricant, in striking contrast to diamond. It is also an electric conductor, due to the loosening of the electrons between the planes, and is much less dense than diamond.

In the crystal of an un-ionized substance, such as benzene, the molecules do not lose their identity, so that the same molecule which builds up a crystal comes off when the crystal

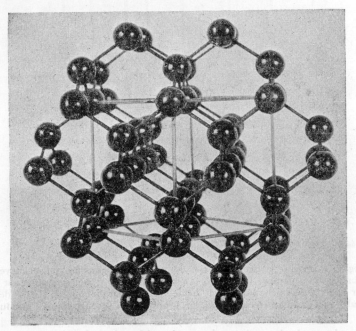

Fig. 8. Diamond lattice. This lattice exhibits various arrangements of carbon atoms found in saturated hydrocarbons: the zig-zag "straight chain," the tetrahedron, and the hexagon.

dissolves or evaporates, unlike the NaCl crystal, where a sodium ion, in leaving the surface, might go off with any one of the surrounding chloride ions.

7. The equal spacing of the ions in crystals of the NaCl type offers the strongest kind of evidence that there are no permanent molecules of NaCl present. Each Na^+ is surrounded at equal distances by 6 Cl^- and vice versa. Similarly, in a crystal of calcite, $CaCO_3$, the lattice (shown in Fig. 10) is made up of the ions Ca^{++} and CO_3^{--}. Moreover, the $C-O$ distances are all the same, showing that the CO_3^{--} is a flat

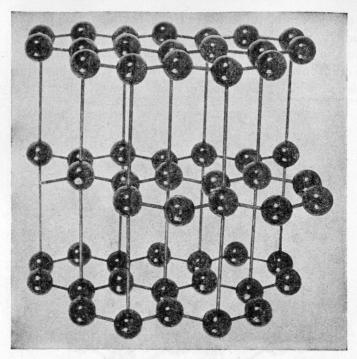

Fig. 9. Graphite lattice. Here the chains and hexagons remain, but layers of the latter are separated from each other so much that they can slip past each other and the electrons are loosely held; hence while diamond is the hardest of all substances and an electric insulator, graphite is a lubricant and a conductor.

triangle and that there is no justification for regarding the Ca as bonded to O-atoms, as implied by the formula

$$Ca\begin{array}{c} O \\ \diagup \quad \diagdown \\ \quad \quad C=O \\ \diagdown \quad \diagup \\ O \end{array}$$

that used to appear in textbooks. Similarly, the structure of NH_4Cl shows it to be made up of the ions, $(NH_4)^+Cl^-$, and that there is no basis for assuming pentavalent nitrogen, as used to be done before the various types of valence (cf. Chapter IX) were clearly distinguished.

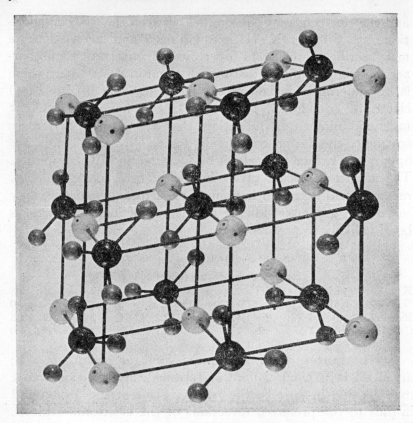

Fig. 10. Lattice of $CaCO_3$ and $NaNO_3$.

8. It is found, in general, that the polyatomic ions, such as SO_4^{--}, ClO_3^-, $Fe(CN)_6^{---}$, $Cu(NH_3)_4^{++}$, $Cr(NH_3)_6^{+++}$ are quite symmetrical in their crystals. This leaves open, however, the question whether the surrounding atoms or groups are bound to the central atom by electron-pair bonds or only by electrostatic attraction. Thus, SO_4^{--} may be represented either by

$$\begin{bmatrix} & :\!\overset{\cdot\cdot}{O}\!: & \\ :\!\overset{\cdot\cdot}{O}\!:\!\overset{\cdot\cdot}{\underset{\cdot\cdot}{S}}\!:\!\overset{\cdot\cdot}{O}\!: \\ & :\!\overset{\cdot\cdot}{\underset{\cdot\cdot}{O}}\!: & \end{bmatrix}^{--} \quad \text{or by} \quad \begin{bmatrix} & O^{--} & \\ O^{--}\ S^{+6}\ O^{--} \\ & O^{--} & \end{bmatrix}^{--}$$

and the electrons may "resonate" between the two configurations (cf. Chapter XVIII, paragraphs 9 and 23) so that we may ascribe to the bond a certain percentage of each character. It is possible to distinguish them in cases where there is a difference in magnetic moment, due to unpaired electrons. Thus $Fe(CN)_6^{---}$ and FeF_6^{---} have very different magnetic moments, indicating that the former is largely covalent, the latter completely ionic. Covalent bonds are apparently rather general with NO_2, CN, and CO complexes. The negativity scale given in Chapter V, paragraph 14, repeated and extended here in Table 1 for convenience, may serve as a guide to indicate the degree of ionic character a bond is likely to possess.

TABLE 1

Electronegativity Scale (after Pauling)

K	0.8	Li	1.0	Ti	1.6	B	2.0	I	2.4	Br	2.8
Na	0.9	Mg	1.2	Sn	1.8	As	2.0	Se	2.4	N	3.0
Ba	0.9	Be	1.5	Si	1.8	H	2.1	C	2.5	O	3.5
Ca	1.0	Al	1.5	Sb	1.8	P	2.1	S	2.5	F	4.0

9. The four surrounding atoms, ions, or groups may be arranged in a plane square or tetrahedrally. The difference may be due in part to the relative sizes of the atoms and in part to the preferred directions of the electronic orbitals. The following are examples of the two types:

Square grouping	*Tetrahedral grouping*
$Ni(CN)_4^{--}$	SiO_4^{--}
$PtCl_4^{--}$	PO_4^{---}
$PdCl_4^{--}$	SO_4^{--}
$CuCl_2(H_2O)_2$	ClO_4^{---}
	$Ni(CO)_4$
	Tetrahalides
	CH_4
	NH_4^+

10. A coordination number of five, as in $Fe(CO)_5$, and PCl_5, corresponds to a trigonal bipyramid; one of six to an octagon, examples of which include $Fe(CN)_6^{----}$, $Fe(CN)_6^{---}$, $Co(NH_3)_6^{+++}$, $PtCl_6^{--}$, SF_6. The latter structure allows

isomers when two different substituents are present, as in $Co(NH_3)_4(NO_2)_2{}^+$, where the two NO_2 groups may be either adjacent or opposite.

11. The tetrahedral structure of CH_4 and $NH_4{}^+$ cannot be verified by X rays because the hydrogen atom does not scatter sufficiently to reveal its position in any of its compounds. We must rely upon such evidence as is furnished by the absorption spectra, which show that their modes of vibration are those of a tetrahedron.

TABLE 2

Bond Angles and Dipole Moments

	Bond angles	Dipole moments $\times 10^{18}$ electrostatic units
$O=C=O$	180°	0
$S=C=S$	180°	0
$N=N=O$	180°	0
$H-O-H$	105°	1.85
$H-S-H$	92°	0.95
$O-S-O$	129°	1.61
$O-O-O$	127°	
$O-N-O$	141°	
$F-O-F$	100°	
$Cl-O-Cl$	115°	
$Cl-N-O$	116°	
$Br-N-O$	117°	

12. Gaseous Molecules. Triatomic molecules may be either linear, bent, or triangular. The bent molecules are most numerous due to the tendency of the electron pairs of the middle atom to approach a tetrahedral arrangement except as distorted by the end molecules. Table 2 gives bond angles for triatomic molecules, calculated from vibrations of the molecules as revealed by spectroscopic data or from the interatomic distances determined by the diffractions of electrons, which have an associated wave length and can serve for this purpose with gaseous molecules where X-ray diffraction is not sufficiently intense. The bond angle for a regular tetrahedron is 109° C.

13. The dipole moments furnish additional evidence serving to distinguish bent and linear structures. If, for example,

H_2O were linear, $H-O-H$, it would not have a dipole moment, and CO_2 cannot be unsymmetrical, for then it would have a moment since the $-CO$ group has one.

14. In view of the natural tendency of bonds to approach tetrahedral angles, we find linear triatomic molecules only where double or triple bonds are formed, as in $O=C=O$, indeed, linear molecules are strong evidence of multiple bonds. They are largely limited to the first row elements, C, N, O.

15. Polyatomic Molecules. The molecules of active phosphorus, P_4, and arsenic, As_4, have the 4 atoms at the corners of a regular tetrahedron. The angles $X-P-X$ in the trihalides of P, As, and Sb, are all close to $100°$, showing them to be flat pyramids. This is confirmed by dipole moments, which show them to be unsymmetrical (cf. Chapter V, Table 6).

APPENDIX I

SAMPLE FINAL EXAMINATION QUESTIONS
FOR THE FIRST SEMESTER

1. Which solution in the following list:
   (a) 0.01 M-HCl
   (b) 0.5 M-Na$_2$CO$_3$
   (c) 0.001 M-Ba(OH)$_2$
   (d) 0.01 M-NH$_3$
   (e) 0.01 M-NaCl
   (f) 0.001 M-KOH
   (g) 0.01 M-(NH$_4$)$_2$SO$_4$
   (h) 0.1 M-NaHCO$_3$
   (i) 0.01 M-H$_2$SO$_4$
   (j) 0.5 M-NaOH

   has a molal concentration of OH$^-$ nearest to (indicate by writing the corresponding letter)
   (1) 10^{-2} (4) 10^{-8} (7) 10^{-13}
   (2) 10^{-3} (5) 10^{-6}
   (3) 10^{-11} (6) 10^{-7}

2. The atoms R, X, Y, and Z have, respectively, one, two, two, and seven valence electrons. Their atomic numbers increase in the order, X, Y, Z, R. Atoms X and R have 8 electrons immediately below their valence electrons and atoms Y and Z have 18. Which are atoms of metallic elements?.......... Write the formula of the simplest ion of Z ......; of X ....; of the complex ammonia ion most likely to form ....; of the hydroxide that is the strongest base ....; of a probable compound between X and Z ....

3. 0.2 mole of BaCO$_3$ weighs .... grams; will give .... grams, or .... moles of CO$_2$ gas. This gas will occupy .... liters at 273° C. and 0.2 atmosphere. The BaO left on strongly heating the 0.2 mole of BaCO$_3$ will react with 5 liters of water to give .... molal or .... normal Ba(OH)$_2$. The concentration of OH$^-$ in this solution will be .... molal. 100 cc. of this solution will neutralize .... cc. of 0.5 M-HCl.

4. If the hypothetical ion, M$^+$, shows the following reactions:
   (a) MCl + Na$_2$CO$_3$ (aq.) gives a ppt. which, after filtration, easily dissolves in HNO$_3$ (aq.).
   (b) M$_2$SO$_4$ dissolves in KCN (aq.).

425

(*c*) M_2SO_4 ppt. $+$ H_2S gives M_2S ppt.

(*d*) The product obtained on treating M_2SO_4 with Na_2CO_3 (aq.) and filtering out is insoluble in HNO_3 (aq.).

State, in words, two reactions that you can predict with certainty from these observations.

5. State the effect, quantitatively where you can, of each of the following changes upon (*a*) the number of molecular impacts per second per square centimeter upon the containing walls and (*b*) the force of each impact.

(1) Gas in a cylinder with a movable piston, immersed in a large water bath, is compressed from 3 liters to 2 liters.

Ans. (*a*)................   (*b*).......................

(2) The air pressure in an automobile tire is slowly pumped up from 25 lbs. per sq. in. to 30 lbs. per sq. in.

Ans. (*a*)................   (*b*).......................

(3) H_2S gas is kept in a closed vessel at constant temperature until it has all decomposed into H_2 and liquid sulfur.

Ans. (*a*)................   (*b*).......................

6. Which of the substances, $NaOH$, Al_2O_3, $Al_2(SO_4)_3$, Na_2CO_3, $CaSO_4 \cdot 2\,H_2O$, K_2SO_4, ZnS, $ZnSO_4$, $Na_2B_4O_7$, $CaCl_2$, $CaSO_4$, $CaSO_4 \cdot \frac{1}{2}\,H_2O$, MgO, $(NH_4)_2SO_4$, is most appropriate for each of the following uses:

(*a*) Water softener.......   (*e*) Cleaning metals for welding
(*b*) White paint.........   or hard soldering........
(*c*) Abrasive...........   (*f*) Making plaster casts.......
(*d*) Making soap from fat.   (*g*) Fertilizer...............
                                     (*h*) Avoiding dust on roads....

7. Give the formulas of the solids remaining after evaporating to dryness solutions of the following:

(*a*) 0.1 mole $AgCl$ and 1 mole HNO_3.....................
(*b*) 0.02 mole NH_4Cl and 0.05 mole of $NaOH$...............
(*c*) 0.02 mole $Zn(NO_3)_2$ and 1 mole HCl...................
(*d*) 0.1 mole $Zn(NO_3)_2$ and 0.01 mole H_2SO_4..............
(*e*) 0.02 mole $CuSO_4$ and 0.2 mole HNO_3...................

8. Given that the elements A, B, C, D, and E have atomic numbers (nuclear charges) of 6, 9, 13, 19, and 30 respectively, underline correct answers below.

(*a*) The compound of A and B will have the formula AB, AB_2, A_2B, AB_4, A_4B.

(*b*) Which of the following complex ions are stable? $C(NH_3)_4^{++}$, $D(NH_3)_2^+$, $E(NH_3)_6^{+++}$, $E(NH_3)_4^{++}$.

(c) Which of the elements are ordinarily gases with diatomic molecules? A, B, C, D, E.

(d) The compound of B and D will be essentially ionic, electron pair bonded.

(e) Which of the elements are metals? A, B, C, D, E.

(f) The compound of B and C will have the formula CB, CB_2, CB_3, CB_4, C_4B, C_2B.

9. Which solution in the following list:

(a) 0.1 M-HAc   (d) 0.05 M-Ba(OH)$_2$ (g) 1 M-NH$_4$Ac
(b) 1 M-NaAc   (e) 1 M-NaOH   (h) 1 M-HCl
(c) 0.5 M-Na$_2$CO$_3$ (f) 0.1 M-HCl

has a molal concentration of OH$^-$ nearest to (indicate by writing the corresponding letter)

(a) 10^{-7}. . . . .   (c) 10^{-5}. . . . .
(b) 10^{-1}. . . . .   (d) 10^{-11}. . . . .

10. Underline the formula of that substance in each of the following groups which has the property stated in the highest degree:

(a) Solubility in water: $CaCO_3$, $BaSO_4$, $CaSO_4$, CaC_2O_4
(b) Density (all gases): N_2O, H_2, NH_3, C_2H_6
(c) Conc. of OH$^-$:   0.5 M-Na$_2$CO$_3$, 1 M-NaHCO$_3$, 0.05 M-Ba(OH)$_2$, 1 M-NH$_4$-OH, 0.05 M-KOH

(d) Conc. of H$^+$:   0.01 M-H$_2$SO$_4$, 1 M-HAc, 1 M-NH$_4$NO$_3$, 0.04 M-HCl

(e) Atomic number: K, Mg, Al, Li, Ag, Cu
(f) Acidic nature: Zn(OH)$_2$, Cu(OH)$_2$, Ca(OH)$_2$, LiOH

(g) Degree of hydrolysis: 0.1 M-KAc, 0.1 M-NH$_4$Ac, 0.1 M-NH$_4$NO$_3$

(h) Effect on the freezing point of 1 liter of water: 0.02 mole of KCl, 0.01 mole of K$_2$SO$_4$, 0.03 mole of HAc, 0.01 mole of BaCl$_2$

(i) Ionizing potential of the gaseous atom: Na, Ca, Al, Ag

(j) Insolubility in water: $CaSO_4$, Ca(OH)$_2$, CaC_2O_4, Ca(NO$_3$)$_2$

11. Some solid Ca(OH)$_2$ is in equilibrium with its saturated solution. How will the amount of solid Ca(OH)$_2$ be affected (indicate by writing +, − or 0 for increase, decrease or practically no effect, respectively) by adding small amounts of the following:

(a) KOH.........   (d) HAc........   (g) $(NH_4)_2C_2O_4$....
(b) $Ca(NO_3)_2$.....   (e) $CaCO_3$.......   (h) $ZnSO_4$........
(c) NH_4Cl........   (f) KNO_3.......

12. Give the concentration of OH^- in each of the following solutions as accurately as you can. Some latitude will be allowed in certain cases:

(a) 1 M-NH_4OH ....   0.1 M-$Ba(OH)_2$ and 100
(b) 0.01 M-NH_4OH .....   cc. of 0.05 M-HCl......
(c) 0.5 M-Na_2CO_3 ......   (h) A molal solution of the
(d) 0.01 M-NH_4Ac ......   sodium salt of an acid
(e) CO_2 at 1 atm........   whose degree of dissocia-
(f) Saturated $Ca(OH)_2$...   tion is 0.01 of that of
(g) A solution resulting   HAc when both are in
from mixing 100 cc. of   molal solution........

13. The following are mixed in 1 liter of water in the order given. Write the formula of the precipitate finally present. 0.05 mole of $CaCl_2$, 1 mole of HCl, 0.1 mole of Na_2SO_4, 0.1 mole of NH_3, 0.2 mole of Na_2CO_3.

SAMPLE FINAL EXAMINATION QUESTIONS FOR THE SECOND SEMESTER

Questions 1–4 represent hypothetical "unknowns," made by selecting one or more of the substances listed in each case. The amounts are not necessarily equivalent but are always more than mere traces.

On the basis of the observations given, write, in the space immediately following the formula, + for each substance known to be present, − for each substance known to be absent, and a question mark (?) for each substance whose presence is in doubt.

1. $Pb(NO_3)_2$..............   Treatment with hot water gives
$CuSO_4$.................   a white residue and a colorless
$HgCl_2$.................   solution, which, after filtration,
$ZnCl_2$..................   gives a white ppt. on addition
$(NH_4)_2SO_4$............   of ammonia, insoluble in excess.
K_2CrO_4................
$NaNO_3$................

2. Zn..................   Treatment with 0.1 M-H_2SO_4
Cu...................   gives effervescence, and leaves
Ag..................   a residue, which, after separa-

Fe....................
Al....................

tion from the solution, dissolves in 2 M-HNO$_3$ to give a colorless solution. The sulfuric acid solution gives no ppt. on addition of H$_2$S but a black ppt. upon subsequent addition of NaOH.

3. SnCl$_2$.................
Fe$_2$(SO$_4$)$_3$..............
KHSO$_4$...............
K$_2$Cr$_2$O$_7$...............
Hg$_2$Cl$_2$...............
FeSO$_4$................
Ba(NO$_3$)$_2$.............
ZnCl$_2$.................

Treatment with water gives a green solution and leaves a white residue, which is filtered out. The green solution, upon addition of 6 M-NaOH, gives a ppt., soluble in excess. The white residue is not visibly affected by ammonia.

4. K$_2$SO$_4$................
ZnS.................
Al$_2$(OH)$_4$..............
BaCO$_3$................
CuO..................
HgCl$_2$................
Pb(NO$_3$)$_2$.............

Treatment with 0.3 M-HCl gives a solution and a dark gray residue which is filtered out. The solution, upon addition of ammonia, remains colorless, but gives a white ppt. The dark gray residue turned white and partly dissolved when treated with hot 2 M-HNO$_3$. This white residue is insoluble in 6 M-NaOH.

5. Answer the following by underlining the symbol or formula of the substance having the characteristic called for:

(a) The highest melting point

Fe, Zn, W, Ni, Bi

(b) The greatest hardness

SnO$_2$, SiO$_2$, PbO$_2$, SO$_2$

(c) The greatest affinity for electrons

Cl$_2$, Fe^{+++}, H$^+$, I$_2$, Zn

(d) The largest number of valence electrons

Sb, Sn, Si, Al, Ag

(e) The highest oxidation number of vanadium

VO^{++}, NH$_4$VO$_3$, V$_2$(SO$_4$)$_3$, VS$_2$, V(CN)$_6^{----}$

(f) The largest degree of hydrolysis

KAsO$_3$, KPO$_3$, KNO$_3$, KNO$_2$, KAsO$_2$

(g) The largest atomic number

B, Br, Ba, Bi

(h) The largest solubility   HgS, CuS, FeS, PbS, SnS
in water

6. State the colors of the following:

(a) Fe_2O_3.........   (f) HgS.........   (k) I_2 vapor.......
(b) Cr_2O_3.........   (g) $Cr_2O_7^{--}$.....   (l) Cu^{++}..........
(c) Al_2O_3.........   (h) Fe^{++}........   (m) $Fe_2Fe(CN)_6$....
(d) Pb_3O_4........   (i) Fe^{+++}.......   (n) PbO_2..........
(e) $PbCrO_4$.......   (j) Cl_2..........   (o) $CoSiO_3$........

7. Underline the two substances in each of the following series which most closely resemble each other in chemical behavior:

(a) Al^{+++}, Bi^{+++}, Cr^{+++}, Fe^{+++} (d) SO_4^{--}, ClO_4^-, SiO_4^{----},
(b) BaO_2, SO_2, MnO_2, PbO_2 CrO_4^{--}
(c) K^+, Ag^+, Hg_2^{++}, Cu^{++} (e) HgS, PbS, FeS, ZnS

8. Answer the following by underlining the substance having the characteristic called for:

The greatest hardness MgO, As_2O_3, Al_2O_3, CaO
The greatest affinity for Ag^+, Hg^{++}, Cl_2, Br_2, Fe^{+++}
electrons
The largest number of   Br, B, Ba, Bi, Be
valence electrons
The highest atomic number   Ag, Hg, Mg, Mn, Al
The lowest oxidation num- Na_2MoO_4, MoF_6, Mo_3O_8, Mo-
ber of molybdenum $(OH)_3$, MoS_2, MoO_3
The largest atomic radius   Na, Cr, Ca, K, Br
The lowest melting point   C, Si, Ni, Fe, Sn
The strongest reducing I^-, F^-, Cl^-, Br^-
power

9. An electric cell consists of an electrode of silver coated with silver chloride, and another of zinc, both immersed in a solution of 0.01 M-$ZnCl_2$.
As the cell discharges, electrons flow in the external circuit from the .... electrode. The oxidizing agent is .... and the reducing agent is .... The half-reaction occurring at the silver-silver chloride electrode is .... If the concentration of the $ZnCl_2$ were increased the electromotive force of the cell would be .... The cell evolves heat while discharging, hence the electromotive force would be .... by lowering the temperature.

10. How many moles of each of the following oxidizing agents would be required to oxidize 0.1 mole of Ti^{+++} to TiO^{++} and how

many moles of H^+ would be used (denote by $-$), or liberated (denote by $+$), in each case.

Oxidizing agent Fe^{+++} Hg^{++} Cl_2 MnO_4^- to Mn^{++}

No. of moles . . .   .

No. of moles of H^+ .   ...

11. The atoms X, Y, and Z have atomic weights increasing in that order. X has 2, 8, 8, 2 electrons outside its nucleus. The atomic number of Y is 11 greater than that of X and the atomic number of Z is 15 greater than that of X. The simplest ions of these elements are .... The strongest reducing agent is .... The least metallic element is ....

Questions 12–15 represent "unknowns" made by selecting one or more of the substances listed in each case. The amounts are not necessarily equivalent but are always more than mere traces. Mark $+$ for those known to be present, $-$ for those known to be absent, and ? for those which are undetermined.

12. $KHSO_4$................   The unknown dissolves in water
     $Pb(NO_3)_2$..............   to give a clear orange-colored
     $NaNO_3$................   solution.
     $(NH_4)_2CrO_4$............
     $BaCO_3$.................
     KCl...................

13. $AgNO_3$................   The unknown is partially sol-
     Hg_2Cl_2................   uble in water, but leaves a white
     KNO_3.................   residue. When the residue is
     NH_4Cl................   treated with NH_4OH, a solution
     Na_2SO_4...............   and a black residue are obtained.
     $HgCl_2$.................   Acidifying the ammoniacal solu-
       tion with 1 M-HNO_3 gives a
       white precipitate. The gradual
       addition of NaOH solution to
       the original aqueous solution
       gives a white precipitate in-
       soluble in excess NaOH solution.

14. FeS..................   The unknown is partially sol-
     $Cr(OH)_3$..............   uble in cold water. When the
     $BaCO_3$................   residue is treated with 6 M-
     $NaCl$.................   NaOH, a green solution is ob-
     KNO_3................   tained, and a dark residue which
     NH_4Cl................   dissolves in 1 M-HCl with ef-
       fervescence. The addition of
       NaAc and Na_2CrO_4 solution

to the boiled HCl solution gives a yellow precipitate. The original aqueous solution imparts a violet color to the flame which can be seen without the use of a cobalt glass. The addition of NaOH to this solution gave no odor.

15. What is the color of (a) SnS............ (b) PbCrO$_4$........
   (c) HgNH$_2$Cl...... (d) Fe$_2$Fe(CN)$_6$.....(e) Fe(OH)$_3$.......

16. Which solvent in the following list:
   (a) CS$_2$,   (b) Cl$_2$(aq.),   (c) 6 M-NH$_4$OH,   (d) 6 M-NaOH,
   (e) 0.3 M-HCl,   (f) 0.3 N-H$_2$SO$_4$,   (g) NH$_4$SH(aq.)
   would be most effective in dissolving (answer each simply by writing in the corresponding letter from the above list)
   (a) PbSO$_4$..............   (e) BaCrO$_4$.................
   (b) AgCl...............   (f) CaC$_2$O$_4$.................
   (c) Hg$_2$Cl$_2$..............   (g) SnS$_2$....................
   (d) Sulfur..............   (h) CuHAsO$_3$...............

17. The following reactions are observed, using 0.1 molal solutions and approximately equivalent amounts:
   $$UO_2^{++} + 4 H^+ + Sn^{++} = Sn^{++++} + U^{++++} + 2 H_2O$$
   $$Cd + 2 TiO^{++} + 4 H^+ = Cd^{++} + 2 Ti^{+++} + 2 H_2O$$
   $$2 Ti^{++} + Sn^{++++} = 2 Ti^{+++} + Sn^{++}$$
   $$Fe^{+++} + Ti^{+++} + H_2O = TiO^{++} + Fe^{++} + 2 H^+$$
   $$UO_2^{++} \text{ does not oxidize } Fe^{++}.$$

   On the basis of these observations, select (a) the strongest oxidizing agent, ..., (b) the strongest reducing agent, ... If the data are insufficient to permit a decision, write in the word "undetermined."

   Questions 18, 19, 20, and 21 represent hypothetical "unknowns" made by selecting one or more of the substances listed in each case. The amounts are not necessarily equivalent but are always more than mere traces. On the basis of the observations given, mark − all substances known to be absent, mark + those known to be present, and mark ? those whose presence is in doubt.[1]

18. BaCO$_3$,   Na$_2$SO$_4$,   CaCl$_2$,   Al(NO$_3$)$_3$,   (NH$_4$)$_2$SO$_4$,   KOH

   Treatment with water gives a white residue, A, and a solution, B. The residue, A, filtered out and washed, is insoluble in dilute HCl. The solution, B, shows a violet flame test without

[1]See Appendix II for answers.

using cobalt glass, and upon treatment with dilute HCl it gives effervescence, and a white ppt. soluble in excess of the acid.

19. ZnS,   PbCl$_2$,   FeCl$_3$,   CrCl$_3$,   KHSO$_4$,   HgS

    Treatment with 0.3 M-HCl gives a black ppt., A, and a solution, B. The ppt., A, after filtration and washing, dissolves in hot 2 M-HNO$_3$, except for a small dirty yellow residue. The solution, B, treated with excess of 6 M-NaOH, gives a green solution and no ppt.

20. AlCl$_3$,   NH$_4$NO$_3$,   Na$_2$CO$_3$,   CaO,   K$_2$Cr$_2$O$_7$,   Pb(NO$_3$)$_2$, CuSO$_4$,   SnCl$_2$,   Hg$_2$Cl$_2$

    Treatment with water gives an odorless, yellow solution, and a white ppt., which, after filtration and washing, is not visibly affected by either H$_2$S or NH$_3$.

21. Zn,   Sn,   Fe,   Hg,   Ag,   PbO$_2$

    When treated with hot 2 M-HCl, the unknown gives a pungent gas, a yellow solution and a white residue. The yellow solution yields a black ppt. on passing in H$_2$S.

22. Atom X has an atomic number of 10. Atom Y has 7 valence electrons, with 2 electrons in the group below the valence group. Atom Z has 11 more extra nuclear electrons than Y. Atom Q has 2 valence electrons, with 18 in the underlying level. On the basis of these figures, supply the following information. The formula of: (a) the most stable ion of Y.........., (b) of Z.........., (c) the moelcule of the free element X.........., (d) the molecule of the element Y ...., (e) the most basic hydroxide ...., (f) the most stable binary compound with hydrogen ...., (g) the most probable ammonia complex ion ...., (h) the hydroxide most likely to be amphoteric...........

23. Which solvent in the following list:

    (a) 0.3 N-H$_2$SO$_4$ (c) 6 M-NaOH   (e) CCl$_4$ (g) Br$_2$(aq.)
    (b) 0.3 N-HCl   (d) 6 M-NH$_4$OH   (f) NH$_4$SH(aq.)

    would be most effective (answer by writing only the letter, a, b, c, etc.) for dissolving each of the following

    (a) CaC$_2$O$_4$.......   (d) PbCrO$_4$......   (g) C$_{24}$H$_{50}$.........
    (b) Ag$_2$CO$_3$.......   (e) HgS..........   (h) Hg$_2$Br$_2$........
    (c) HgO..........   (f) SnS$_2$........   (i) Pb(OH)$_2$.......

24. How many valence electrons are there in each of the following?

    (a) Na.....   (d) Cl$^-$......   (g) NH$_3$.....   (j) SO$_4^{--}$.....
    (b) H$^+$.....   (e) F$_2$........   (h) NH$_4^+$....
    (c) H$_2$......   (f) HCl.....   (i) CaO.....

25. 112 cc. of Cl_2 at 1 atmosphere and 0° C. is passed into 100 cc. of 0.2 M-$FeCl_2$. Supply the numbers called for in the following table.

	Before passing in Cl_2		After passing in Cl_2	
	No. of moles	*Conc.*	*No. of moles*	*Conc.*
Fe^{++}	....	....	....	....
Fe^{+++}	....	....	....	....
Cl^-	....	....	....	....
Cl_2	....	.... in gas	....	....

26. An electric cell consists of an electrode of platinum in contact with gaseous hydrogen and another of PbO_2, both electrodes dipping into 0.1 M-H_2SO_4. Write equations for

(a) The reaction at the hydrogen electrode..................

(b) The reaction at the PbO_2 electrode.....................

(c) The total cell reaction...............................

The voltage of the cell would be increased, decreased, unaffected by   (cross out two) substituting 0.2 M-H_2SO_4. The oxidizing agent is.........., the reducing agent is.............

ANSWERS TO EXERCISES
AT THE ENDS OF CHAPTERS

Chapter II

Exercises	Answers
5.	2 atoms
6.	6 g.-atoms
7.	⅔ g.-atoms
8.	34.9 lb.
9.	2 g.-atoms
10.	0.126 g.
11.	38 g.
12.	53%

Exercises	Answers
13.	0.31 kg.
14.	2.49 lb.
15.	36 g.
16.	6.67 kg.
17. (a)	48.0 g.
(b)	3 g.-atoms
18.	1 lb.-atom
	contains 2.73×10^{26} atoms

Chapter III

Exercises	Answers
2.	5 atm.
3.	14.9 g.
4.	$-33°$ C.
5.	35.5 lbs./sq. in.
6.	0.118
7.	$-53°$ C.
8.	$-73°$ C.
9.	77° C.
10.	41 (1 atm. left)
11.	0.84 g.
12.	142 g.
13.	2.16 g./1
14.	3 atm.
15.	739 mm.
18.	(a) (b)
(1)	⅔ same
(2)	44.7/34.7 same
(3)	Increase ($\sqrt{17}$) decrease

Exercises	Answers
19. (a)	$s_1 < s_2$
(b)	$n_1 = n_2$
(c)	$v_1 < v_2$
(d)	$T_1 < T_2$
(e)	$p_1 \; ? \; p_2$
21. (a)	H_2
(b)	CO_2
(c)	Water vapor
22. (a)	He = Ne
(b)	$O_2 >$ Ne
23.	5×10^{10}
24. (a)	A = Ne
(b)	$CO_2 <$ A
25.	0.03 mm.

435

Chapter IV

Exercises	Answers	Exercises	Answers
3.	P_4	18.	C_2H_2
4.	4.5 1	20. (b)	$ScCl_3$
7.	1.25 moles	21.	C_2N_2
8. (a)	0.5 mole	22.	$v = 0.82TW/Mp$.
(b)	11.2 1.	23.	H_2O_2
9. (a)	2 atm.	24. (a)	1, (b) 1.5,
(b)	2⅔ atm.	(c)	1.75, (d) 1.5
10.	0.97, 1.11, 0.97 etc.	25.	Diffusion rate de-
11.	33.6 1.		creases with increas-
12.	26.8 to 24.8 to 12.8		ing molecular weight.
14. (b)	C_2H_6	26.	10^{-4}
15. (b)	48.4 1.	27.	1.004
16.	74.6　*76.4*	28.	4.8 cc.　*3.11 cc*
17.	58.4 1.	29.	1390 cals.
		30.	.24 g.

Chapter VI

Exercises	Answers	Exercises	Answers
4.	2 moles	11.	62.5 cc.
5. (a)	0.01 M; (b) 0.02 N.	12. (a)	100 cc.;
6. (a)	0.01 M; (b) 0.02 N.	(b)	200 cc.
7. (a)	0.02 mole *equi*	13.	2.34 l.
(b)	0.01 mole		
(c)	0.02 equiv.	14.	125 g.
(d)	0.73 g.	15.	1 equiv.; 0.5 mole;
8. (a)	2 N; (b) 1 M;		0.80 g.
(c)	98 g./1.	16.	2 M.
9.	0.00 S equiv.,	17.	$BaCl_2$, 0.0015 mole
	0.20 g.; 0.185 g.		$Ba(OH)_2$, 0.0035
10.	0.1 N.		mole

Chapter VII

Exercises	Answers	Exercises	Answers
2.	42.0 k cal.	5.	0.013 ¢
3.	114 k cal.	6.	1.1 ¢
4. (a)	22.9 k cal.	7.	0.44 ¢
(b)	Less		

Chapter VIII

Exercises	Answers	Exercises	Answers
12. (a)	0.02 equiv./1	17. (2)	(a) 0.034 f.;
(b)	0.34 g./1		(b) 3290 coul.
15.	0.004 or 0.4%		(c) 55 min.
16. (a)	(b) 0.012 M.	18.	(f)(d)(b)(e)(c)(a).
(c)	1.988 M.	19.	(a) 0.05 M-Zn^{++}
			0.1 M-Cl$^-$

Chapter XII

Exercises	Answers	Exercises	Answers
6.	10^{-3}	18. (a)	(b) increase
	5.5×10^{-5}	(c)	no effect
	1.5×10^{-4}	(d)	decrease
	7×10^{-5}	17.	10^{-11} 13
	4.5×10^{-6}	18.	10^{-7} 5
8. (a)	$10^{-3} M$	19.	4.7×10^{-8} 3
(b)	25 cc.		

Chapter XIII

Exercises	Answers	Exercises	Answers
28.	(OH) = $\sqrt{MK_w/K_a}$	30.	0.027
29.	3×10^{-3}	31.	5.6×10^{-8}

Chapter XXI

Exercises	Answers	Exercises	Answers
9.	5.6 l. 2.8 l		
10.	Increase, (d), (b), (a) = (e), (c).		
14.	0.003		
15.	0.005		
16.	2.4×10^{-4}		
17	8×10^{-5}		
18.	7×10^{-7}		
19.	0.1		

ANSWERS TO SAMPLE FINAL EXAMINATION
QUESTIONS FOR THE SECOND SEMESTER

Question	Page	
1	428	$Pb(NO_3)_2$ +, $CuSO_4$ −, $HgCl_2$ +, $ZnCl_2$?, $(NH_4)_2SO_4$ +, K_2CrO_4 −, $NaNO_3$?
2	428	Zn ?, Cu −, Ag +, Fe +, Al ?
3	428	$SnCl_2$ +, $Fe_2(SO_4)_3$ −, $KHSO_4$ +, $K_2Cr_2O_7$ +, Hg_2Cl_2 −, $FeSO_4$ −, $Ba(NO_3)$ +, $ZnCl_2$?
4	428	K_2SO_4 +, ZnS +, $Al_2O(OH)_2$ +, $BaCO_3$ +, CuO ?, $HgCl_2$ −, $Pb(NO_3)_2$?
12	431	$KHSO_4$ +, $Pb(NO_3)_2$ −, $NaNO_3$? $(NH_4)_2CrO_4$ +, $BaCO_3$ −, KCl ?
13	431	$AgNO_3$ +, Hg_2Cl_2 +, KNO_3 ?, NH_4Cl +, Na_2SO_4 ?, $HgCl_2$ +
14	431	FeS +, $Cr(OH)_3$ +, $BaCO_3$, $NaCl$ −, KNO_3 +, NH_4Cl ?
18	432	$BaCO_3$ +, Na_2SO_4 −, $CaCl_2$ −, $Al(NO_3)_3$ +, $(NH_4)_2SO_4$ +, KOH +
19	433	ZnS +, $PbCl_2$ +, $FeCl_3$ −, $CrCl_3$ +, $KHSO_4$?, HgS −
20	433	$AlCl_3$ +, NH_4NO_3 −, Na_2CO_3 ?, CaO ? or −, $K_2Cr_2O_7$ +, $Pb(NO_3)_2$ −, $CuSO_4$ −. $SnCl_2$ −, Hg_2Cl_2 −
21	433	Zn ?, Sn ?, Fe +, Hg ?, Ag +, PbO_2

INDEX

439